George Facer

EDEXCEL A LEVEL
CHEMISTRY

YEAR 2

HODDER
EDUCATION
AN HACHETTE UK COMPANY

Cover photo: leszekglasner/Fotolia; p. 1 Zahoor Ul-Haq, p. 20 Zahoor Ul-Haq, p. 24 J. Pinkston and L. Stern/US Geological Survey, p. 42 Zahoor Ul-Haq, p. 48 Andrew Lambert Photography/Science Photo Library, p. 49 (top and middle) Zahoor Ul-Haq, p. 50 Andrew Lambert Photography/Science Photo Library, p. 71 Philip Allan Updates, p. 101 Zahoor Ul-Haq, p. 111 Philip Allan Updates, p. 113 TopFoto, p. 119 Zahoor Ul-Haq, p. 137 Zahoor Ul-Haq, p. 139 Andrew Lambert Photography/Science Photo Library, p. 145 Andrew Lambert Photography/Science Photo Library, p. 149 Nigel Evans, p. 160 Zahoor Ul-Haq, p. 190 Philip Allan Updates, p. 191 Zahoor Ul-Haq, p. 230 Science Photo Library, p. 258 Charles D. Winters/Science Photo Library, p. 267 Dr Stanley Flegler, Visuals Unlimited/Science Photo Library, p. 280 Garry Watson/Science Photo Library, p. 297 (top) Andrew Lambert Photography/Science Photo Library, p. 297 (bottom) Jerry Mason/Science Photo Library

Although every effort has been made to ensure that website addresses are correct at time of going to press, Hodder Education cannot be held responsible for the content of any website mentioned in this book. It is sometimes possible to find a relocated web page by typing in the address of the home page for a website in the URL window of your browser.

Hachette UK's policy is to use papers that are natural, renewable and recyclable products and made from wood grown in sustainable forests. The logging and manufacturing processes are expected to conform to the environmental regulations of the country of origin.

Orders: please contact Bookpoint Ltd, 130 Milton Park, Abingdon, Oxon OX14 4SB. Telephone: +44 (0)1235 827720. Fax: +44 (0)1235 400454. Lines are open 9.00 a.m.–5.00 p.m., Monday to Saturday, with a 24-hour message answering service. Visit our website at www.hoddereducation. co.uk

© George Facer 2015
First published in 2015 by
Hodder Education,
An Hachette UK Company
Carmelite House
50 Victoria Embankment
London EC4Y 0DZ

Impression number   10 9 8 7 6

Year   2021 2020 2019

Typeset in Bembo 11/13 pt by Aptara, Inc.

Printed in Dubai

A catalogue record for this title is available from the British Library.

ISBN 978 1 4718 0743 5

Contents

Introduction

About this book

This textbook covers the specification for the second year of the Edexcel chemistry A level course. The order of topics follows that of the specification. To give students a better understanding of — and feel for — some topics, the content of the book occasionally goes beyond the confines of the A level specification.

Margin comments are provided throughout the book. These comprise valuable reminders and snippets of information, and include tips that clarify what you need to know and common sources of confusion.

This book is not a guide to the practical chemistry that all A level students will study. However, many of the reactions that will be met in the laboratory are detailed throughout.

At the back of the book (p. 324), there is a periodic table that gives relative atomic masses to one decimal place. This should be referred to for atomic numbers, atomic masses and symbols of the elements. The table is similar to the one printed on the back of the examination papers.

Online resources

Each chapter includes 'Test yourself' questions. The answers to these are available at https://www.hoddereducation.co.uk/FacerChemistry2. At the end of every chapter are a number of practice questions, including some typical exam-style questions. Answers to the end-of-chapter questions are available as part of George Facer's Edexcel A Level Chemistry Teaching and Learning Resources. Go to www.hoddereducation.co.uk/dynamiclearning to sign up for a free trial. A practice exam-style paper and multiple-choice tests to print off for students to complete are also available.

Required previous knowledge and skills

All students should be:

- familiar with the use of a calculator
- able to change the subject of an algebraic equation
- able to draw straight-line and curved graphs from supplied data and to extrapolate graphs
- able to draw tangents to curves and to calculate the slope of the tangent and of straight-line graphs
- confident in the use of scientific (standard) notation, for example that the number 1234 can be written as 1.234×10^3 and that 1.234×10^{-3} is the same as 0.001234

Scheme of assessment

Students take three theory papers:

- Paper 1 lasts for 1 hour 45 minutes and has a maximum mark of 90. The questions are based on the **inorganic and physical** chemistry topics in years 1 and 2 of the course.
- Paper 2 also lasts for 1 hour 45 minutes and has a maximum mark of 90. The questions are based on the **organic and physical** chemistry topics in years 1 and 2 of the course.

Topics 1–10 are in Book 1

Paper 1	Paper 2
Topic 1 Atomic structure and the periodic table	Topic 1 Atomic structure and the periodic table
Topic 2 Bonding and structure	Topic 2 Bonding and structure
Topics 3 and 14 Redox I and II	Topic 3 Redox I
Topic 4 Inorganic chemistry and the periodic table	Topic 4 Inorganic chemistry and the periodic table
Topic 5 Formulae, equations and amounts of substance	Topic 5 Formulae, equations and amounts of substance
Topics 8 and 13 Energetics I and II	Topics 6, 17 and 18 Organic chemistry I, II and III
Topics 10 and 11 Equilibrium I and II	Topics 7 and 19 Modern analytical techniques I and II
Topic 12 Acid–base equilibria	Topics 9 and 16 Kinetics I and II
Topic 15 Transition metals	

Both papers 1 and 2 will have at least 10 multiple-choice questions embedded in longer questions.

- Paper 3 lasts for 2 hours 30 minutes and has a maximum mark of 120. It draws on the entire specification and includes synoptic questions and questions that require recall and understanding of experimental procedures, especially with reference to the core practicals listed in the specification.

Hazard and risk

This book is not intended to be a laboratory manual. All experiments described in this book should be risk assessed by a qualified chemistry teacher before being performed either as a demonstration or as a class practical. Safety goggles and a laboratory coat or apron must be worn in all experiments.

Exam technique

Mark allocation

In all the A level papers the marks for each part of the question are given in brackets. This is a much better guide as to how much to write than the number of dotted lines provided for the answer. If there are 2 marks, two statements must be made.

For example, if the question asks for the conditions for a particular reaction and there are 2 marks available, two different conditions must be given, such as solvent, temperature or catalyst.

Alternative answers

Do *not* give alternative answers. If one of them is wrong, the examiner will not award any marks for this part of the question. If both answers are correct, you *would* score the mark. However, there is no point in risking one answer being wrong. Beware also of contradictions, such as giving the reagent as concentrated sulfuric acid and then writing $H_2SO_4(aq)$ in an equation.

Writing your answers

In Edexcel A level chemistry exams, the answers are written in the spaces on the question paper. If part of your answer is written elsewhere on the page, alert the examiner by writing, for example, 'see below' or 'continued on page 5'. Exam papers will be marked online, so question papers and answers will be electronically scanned. For this reason, it is *essential not to write outside the borders* marked on the page.

Multiple-choice questions

You must put a cross in the box corresponding to your chosen answer. If you change your mind, put a horizontal line through the cross and then mark your new answer with a cross. Be aware that some questions are expressed as negatives — for example, 'Which of the following is **not**...?'

In numerical multiple-choice questions, you should just work out the answer and then look to see which option is the same as your answer. Otherwise, read *all* the options. This will help avoid being misled by a half-correct response.

Writing a tick or cross after the end of each response could help to focus your mind. If you find that you have two ticks, then think about which is really the correct answer.

If you are having difficulty with a question, put a large ring around the question number, leave it and go on to the next question. If you have time, come back when you have finished sections B and C. Remember that you should not spend more than 30 minutes on the multiple-choice section, i.e. one question every 90 seconds. Some questions will take less time than this and others will take longer, especially if a calculation is involved.

Correction fluid, red pens or pencils

Do not use any of these. Mistakes should be crossed out neatly before writing a new answer. Red ink and pencil will not show up when the paper is scanned electronically.

Equations

- Equations must always be balanced. Word equations never score any marks.
- Ionic equations and half-equations must also balance for charge.
- State symbols must be included:
  - if the question asks for them
  - in all thermochemical equations
  - if a precipitate or a gas is produced
- The use of the symbols [O] and [H] in organic oxidation and reduction reactions, respectively, is acceptable. Equations using these symbols must be properly balanced.
- Organic formulae used in equations must be written in such a way that their structures are unambiguous.

Stability

'A secondary carbocation is stable' has no meaning. 'Stability' must be used only when comparing two states or two sets of compounds. You have to know and understand the difference between thermodynamic stability (ΔS and E_{cell}) and kinetic stability (activation energy and rate of reaction).

Graphs

Normally, there is a mark for labelling the axes. When sketching a graph, make sure that any numbers on the axes are on a linear scale. The graph should start at the right place, have the correct shape and end at the right place. An example is the Maxwell–Boltzmann distribution, which starts at the origin, rises in a curve to a maximum and tails off as an asymptote to the x-axis.

Diagrams of apparatus

Make sure that a flask and condenser are not drawn as one continuous piece of glassware. The apparatus must work. There must be an outlet to the air somewhere in the apparatus. In distillation, the top should be closed and the outlet should be at the end of the condenser. For heating under reflux, the top of the condenser must be open. Never draw a Bunsen burner as the heater. It is always safer to draw an electrical heater, in case one of the reagents is flammable.

Read the question

Questions are often very similar to, but slightly different from, those previously asked. Make sure that you answer this year's question, not last year's! Look for the words 'using your answer to…' or 'hence…'. For example, if you have been asked to calculate oxidation numbers and are then asked to 'hence explain why this is a redox reaction', your answer must be in terms of changes in oxidation number and not in terms of loss or gain of electrons.

Quality of written communication

The most important thing is for you to convey the meaning clearly, accurately and in a logical order. Minor spelling and punctuation errors will not be penalised as long as they do not distort the meaning. Note the subtle difference between 'more successful collisions' (a total number) and 'more of the collisions are successful' (a proportion of the number).

1 Equilibrium II (Topic 11)

Some reactions go to completion, and others do not. The latter type of reaction is called a **reversible** reaction. Physical changes, such as evaporation, are also reversible, for example:

$$Br_2(l) \rightleftharpoons Br_2(g)$$

When liquid bromine is mixed with air in a sealed container, a dynamic equilibrium between the liquid and gaseous bromine is reached. Gaseous bromine molecules condense into the liquid at exactly the same rate as bromine molecules evaporate from the surface of the liquid.

Consider the gaseous reaction:

$$H_2(g) + I_2(g) \rightleftharpoons 2HI(g)$$

When hydrogen and iodine are mixed in a sealed container at a temperature, T, and left, dynamic equilibrium is eventually reached. At this point, there is no further change in the concentrations of the reactants and products but the reactions have not stopped. The forward and backward reactions are continuing at the same rate.

The reaction between hydrogen and iodine was studied by Guldberg and Waage in 1864. They mixed different amounts of hydrogen and iodine and allowed the mixtures to reach equilibrium at 480°C. They then measured the concentration of the three substances at equilibrium and tried to find a mathematical relationship between these concentrations. Typical results for this are shown in Table 1.1.

Liquid bromine in equilibrium with gaseous bromine

Square brackets around the symbol of a species mean the concentration, in $mol\,dm^{-3}$, of that substance.

Table 1.1 Reaction between hydrogen and iodine

Initial [H₂]	Initial [I₂]	[H₂] at equilibrium	[I₂] at equilibrium	[HI] at equilibrium	$\dfrac{[HI]}{[H_2][I_2]}$	$\dfrac{[HI]^2}{[H_2][I_2]}$
0.040	0.040	0.0089	0.0089	0.062	783	49
0.080	0.040	0.0426	0.0026	0.0748	675	51
0.080	0.080	0.018	0.018	0.124	383	47
0.020	0.080	0.0005	0.0605	0.0389	1286	50

The values in the final column are constant to within experimental error so, from these results, it appears that:

$$\frac{[HI]^2_{eq}}{[H_2]_{eq}[I_2]_{eq}} = \text{a constant}$$

Key term

In a **dynamic equilibrium**, the rates of the forward and reverse reactions are the same. Therefore, there is no further change in the concentrations of the reactants and products.

Required year 1 knowledge

The equilibrium constant, K_c

Law of mass action and K_c

The results given in Table 1.1, and those of other equilibrium reactions, enabled Guldberg and Waage to formulate the **law of mass action**. This states that when reactions reach equilibrium, the equilibrium concentrations of the products multiplied together and divided by the equilibrium concentrations of the reactants also multiplied together, with the concentration of each substance raised to the power appropriate to the reaction stoichiometry, are a constant at a given temperature.

For example, for the reaction:

$$N_2(g) + 3H_2(g) \rightleftharpoons 2NH_3(g)$$

$$\frac{[NH_3]_{eq}^2}{[N_2]_{eq}[H_2]_{eq}^3} = \text{a constant}$$

where $[NH_3]_{eq}$ is the concentration, in $mol\,dm^{-3}$, of ammonia at *equilibrium*.

The constant is called the **equilibrium constant** (measured in terms of concentrations) and has the symbol K_c.

The value of the equilibrium constant depends on:

- the nature of the reaction
- the stoichiometry of the equation written
- the temperature at equilibrium

The value of the equilibrium constant does *not* change when the concentration of a species or the pressure is altered or if a catalyst is added.

In general, for a reaction:

$$xA + yB \rightleftharpoons nC + mD$$

where x, y, n and m are the stoichiometric amounts in the equation, the value of K_c is given by:

$$K_c = \frac{[C]_{eq}^n[D]_{eq}^m}{[A]_{eq}^x[B]_{eq}^y}$$

The right-hand side of this expression is called the **reaction quotient** and given the symbol Q.

It is important to realise that the equilibrium constant only equals quotient, Q, when the system it at equilibrium.

- If $Q = K$, the system is in equilibrium and there will be no further change in concentration of the reactants and products.
- If $Q > K$, the system is not in equilibrium and will react to reduce the value of the numerator. Thus products will be converted into reactants (the position of equilibrium will shift to the left).

> **Tip**
>
> Remember that, in an equilibrium constant expression, the products are on top and the reactants are on the bottom.

- If $Q < K$, the system is not in equilibrium and will react to increase the value of the numerator. Thus, reactants will be converted into products (the position of equilibrium will shift to the right).

Tip

The numerator is the term on the top of a fraction.

The chemical equation and the expression for K

Equilibrium constant in terms of concentration, K_c

This is defined in terms of the equilibrium concentrations of the reactants and products of the reversible reaction.

An equilibrium constant has no meaning unless it is linked to a chemical equation. Consider the equilibrium reaction of sulfur dioxide and oxygen reacting reversibly to form sulfur trioxide. This reaction can be represented by two equations and hence by two expressions for the equilibrium constant, K_c. The values given below are at 727°C (1000 K).

$$2SO_2(g) + O_2(g) \rightleftharpoons 2SO_3(g)$$

$$K_c = \frac{[SO_3]_{eq}^2}{[SO_2]_{eq}^2[O_2]_{eq}} = 2800\, mol^{-1}dm^3$$

or

$$SO_2(g) + \frac{1}{2}O_2(g) \rightleftharpoons SO_3(g)$$

$$K_c' = \frac{[SO_3]_{eq}}{[SO_2]_{eq}[O_2]_{eq}^{1/2}} = 52.9\, mol^{1/2}dm^{3/2}$$

Note that $K_c' = \sqrt{K_c}$ and that $52.9 = \sqrt{2800}$

The reaction can also be written in the other direction, giving a third expression for K:

$$2SO_3(g) \rightleftharpoons 2SO_2(g) + O_2(g)$$

$$K_c'' = \frac{[SO_2]_{eq}^2[O_2]_{eq}}{[SO_3]_{eq}^2} = 3.57 \times 10^{-4}\, mol\, dm^{-3}$$

Note that $\dfrac{1}{2800} = 3.57 \times 10^{-4}$

The three equilibrium constants are connected by the expression:

$$K_c = (K_c')^2 = \frac{1}{K_c''}$$

The reactions above are all examples of **homogeneous** reactions.

Gases always mix, so reactions involving only gases are homogeneous. Reversible reactions in solution are also examples of homogeneous equilibria. In such reactions, the concentration terms of all the reactants and products appear in the expression for the equilibrium constant. For example, for the homogeneous reaction:

Key term

A **homogeneous** reaction is one in which all the reactants and products are in the same phase.

$$CH_3COOH(l) + C_2H_5OH(l) \rightleftharpoons CH_3COOC_2H_5(l) + H_2O(l)$$

$$K_c = \frac{[CH_3COOC_2H_5]_{eq}[H_2O]_{eq}}{[CH_3COOH]_{eq}[C_2H_5OH]_{eq}}$$

Test yourself

1 Write the expression for K_c for the reaction:

$$NO(g) + \tfrac{1}{2}O_2(g) \rightleftharpoons NO_2(g)$$

[H₂O] in equilibrium expressions

- When water is a reactant but not the solvent, the term $[H_2O]$ must always appear in the expression for the equilibrium constant.
- When water is in the gaseous state, $[H_2O]$ must appear in equilibrium constant expressions.
- When water is the solvent, even if it is also a reactant or product, $[H_2O]$ does *not* appear in the expression for the equilibrium constant. This is because its concentration remains constant.

Worked example 1

Write the expression for the equilibrium constant, K_c, for the reaction:

$$CH_3COOCH_3(l) + H_2O(l) \rightleftharpoons CH_3COOH(l) + CH_3OH(l)$$

Answer

$$K_c = \frac{[CH_3COOH]_{eq}[CH_3OH]_{eq}}{[CH_3COOCH_3]_{eq}[H_2O]_{eq}}$$

> Water is a reactant but not the solvent, so $[H_2O]_{eq}$ appears in the equilibrium expression.

Worked example 2

Write the expression for the equilibrium constant, K_c, for the reaction:

$$Cr_2O_7{}^{2-}(aq) + H_2O(l) \rightleftharpoons 2CrO_4{}^{2-}(aq) + 2H^+(aq)$$

Answer

$$K_c = \frac{[CrO_4{}^{2-}]_{eq}[H^+]_{eq}^2}{[Cr_2O_7{}^{2-}]_{eq}}$$

> Water is a reactant *and* the solvent, so $[H_2O]_{eq}$ is omitted from the equilibrium expression.

Solids in an equilibrium expression

The concentration of a solid cannot alter and so it is left out of an equilibrium expression.

Worked example

Write the expression for the equilibrium constant, K_c, for:

$$3Fe(s) + 4H_2O(g) \rightleftharpoons Fe_3O_4(s) + 4H_2(g)$$

Answer

$$K_c = \frac{[H_2]^4}{[H_2O]^4}$$

Test yourself

2 Write the expression for K_c for the following reaction:

$$CaCO_3(s) \rightleftharpoons CaO(s) + CO_2(g)$$

Year 2 equilibrium

Calculation of K_c from experimental data

A typical question would give the starting amounts of the reactants, the total volume and the percentage that reacted and ask you to calculate the equilibrium constant. The calculation requires the use of a table, as in the worked example below.

- Write the chemical equation.
- Construct a suitable table and write in the following:
  - the initial amounts (in moles) of the reactants and of the products if their initial amounts were not zero
  - the amounts by which the reactants and the products change in reaching equilibrium — use the stoichiometry of the equation
  - the amount, in moles, of each substance at equilibrium
  - the equilibrium concentration in mol dm^{-3} — divide the equilibrium number of moles by the total volume
- Below the table, write the expression for the equilibrium constant.
- Substitute the equilibrium concentrations into the expression and calculate its value. At the same time, determine the units of K_c and include them in your answer.

Worked example 1

When 0.0200 mol of sulfur trioxide is placed in a flask of volume 1.50 dm³ and allowed to reach equilibrium at 600°C, 29% of it decomposes into sulfur dioxide and oxygen. Calculate the value of the equilibrium constant, K_c, at 600°C.

Answer

The equation is:

$$2SO_3(g) \rightleftharpoons 2SO_2(g) + O_2(g)$$

	SO_3	SO_2	O_2
Initial moles	0.0200	0	0
Change (moles)	$(-29/100) \times 0.0200$ $= -0.0058$	$+0.0058$	$+\frac{1}{2} \times 0.0058$ $= +0.0029$
Moles at equilibrium	$0.0200 - 0.0058$ $= 0.0142$	$0 + 0.0058$ $= 0.0058$	$0 + 0.0029$ $= 0.0029$
Concentration at equilibrium/ mol dm^{-3}	$0.0142/1.50$ $= 0.00947$	$0.0058/1.50$ $= 0.00387$	$0.0029/1.50$ $= 0.00193$

Note that as 0.0058 mol of sulfur trioxide reacts, 0.0058 mol of sulfur dioxide and $\frac{1}{2}$ of 0.0058 = 0.0029 mol of oxygen are produced. This is because the ratio of the three substances in the chemical equation is 2:2:1 or $1:1:\frac{1}{2}$.

$$K_c = \frac{[SO]_{eq}^2[O_2]_{eq}}{[SO_3]_{eq}^2} = \frac{\left(0.00387 \, \text{mol dm}^{-3}\right)^2 \times \left(0.00193 \, \text{mol dm}^{-3}\right)}{\left(0.00947 \, \text{mol dm}^{-3}\right)^2}$$

$$= 3.2 \times 10^{-4} \, \text{mol dm}^{-3}$$

The same method is used when some product, as well as the reactants, is initially present. In this type of question the equilibrium moles of reactants will be less than the initial amounts, but the equilibrium moles of the product will be more than the initial amount.

The units are determined as in worked examples 1 and 2 on p. 8.

Note that if 0.048 mol of methane reacts, then 0.048 mol of steam also reacts and 0.048 mol of carbon monoxide and 3 × 0.048 mol of hydrogen are produced. This is because the reaction stoichiometry is 1:1:1:3.

Worked example 2

A vessel of volume 2.0 dm^3 was filled with 0.060 mol of methane, CH_4, 0.070 mol of steam and 0.010 mol of hydrogen and allowed to reach equilibrium at a temperature of T°C. 80% of the methane reacted. Calculate the value of the equilibrium constant, K_c, at this temperature.

Answer
The equation is:

$$CH_4(g) + H_2O(g) \rightleftharpoons CO(g) + 3H_2(g)$$

	CH_4	H_2O	CO	H_2
Initial moles	0.060	0.070	0	0.010
Change (moles)	−0.80 × 0.060 = −0.048	−0.048	+0.048	+3 × 0.048 = +0.144
Moles at equilibrium	0.060 − 0.048 = 0.012	0.070 − 0.048 = 0.022	0 + 0.048 = 0.048	0.144 + 0.010 = 0.154
Concentration at equilibrium/ mol dm^{-3}	0.012/2.0 = 0.0060	0.022/2.0 = 0.011	0.048/2.0 = 0.024	0.154/2.0 = 0.077

$$K_c = \frac{[CO]_{eq}[H_2]_{eq}^3}{[CH_4]_{eq}[H_2O]_{eq}}$$

$$= \frac{0.024 \times (0.077)^3}{0.0060 \times 0.011} - 0.17 \, mol^2 \, dm^6$$

Worked example 3

Iron(II) sulfate, $FeSO_4$, and silver nitrate, $AgNO_3$, react according to the equation:

$$Ag^+(aq) + Fe^{2+}(aq) \rightleftharpoons Fe^{3+}(aq) + Ag(s)$$

To find the equilibrium constant K_c for this reaction, 25.0 cm^3 of 0.100 mol dm^{-3} solutions of iron(II) sulfate, $FeSO_4$, and silver nitrate, $AgNO_3$, were mixed and allowed to reach equilibrium.

The unreacted silver ions were then titrated using a 0.0600 mol dm^{-3} potassium thiocyanate solution. The titre was 21.00 cm^3.

In the titration, the Ag^+ ions react in a 1:1 ratio with the thiocyanate ions to form a precipitate of silver thiocyanate. The titration is self indicating — an intense red colour forms with one drop of excess potassium thiocyanate and the iron(III) ions present in the equilibrium mixture.

Calculate:

a the initial amount (moles) of Ag^+ and Fe^{2+}

b the final amount (moles) of Ag^+ and hence the equilibrium amounts of Ag^+, Fe^{2+} and Fe^{3+}

c the final concentrations of all three ions and hence K_c

Answer

a initial amount (moles) of Ag^+ = $0.100\,mol\,dm^{-3} \times 0.0250\,dm^3 = 0.00250\,mol$ = initial amount (moles) of Fe^{2+}

b amount (moles) of thiocyanate in titre = $0.060\,mol\,dm^{-3} \times 0.02100\,dm^3$
= $0.00126\,mol$ = amount of Ag^+ at equilibrium = amount of Fe^{2+} at equilibrium

amount Ag^+ reacted = $0.0025 - 0.00126 = 0.00124\,mol$ = amount Fe^{3+} formed

c volume of solution at equilibrium = $0.050\,dm^3$ so:

$$[Ag^+] = [Fe^{2+}] = \frac{0.00126}{0.050} = 0.0252\,mol\,dm^{-3}$$

$$[Fe^{3+}] = \frac{0.00124}{0.050} = 0.0248\,mol\,dm^{-3}$$

$$K_c = \frac{[Fe^{3+}(aq)]}{[Ag^+(aq)][Fe^{2+}(aq)]}$$

$$= \frac{0.0248}{0.0252 \times 0.0252} = 39.1\,mol^{-1}\,dm^3$$

This method assumes that the position of equilibrium does not move to the left as the silver ions are removed in the titration. One way to tell would be to repeat the experiment, but pause for 1 minute halfway through the titration and see if the titre alters.

> **Tip**
>
> $[Ag(s)]$ does not appear in the expression for K_c because it is a solid in a heterogeneous reaction (see p. 4).

Test yourself

3 Hydrogen and iodine react reversibly to form hydrogen iodide:

$$H_2(g) + I_2(g) \rightleftharpoons 2HI(g)$$

The value of the equilibrium constant, K_c, at 420°C = 49.

Calculate the percentage of hydrogen that reacts when 1.0 mol of hydrogen and 1.0 mol of iodine reach equilibrium at 420°C in a vessel of volume 50 dm³.

Units of K_c

Care must be taken when evaluating the units of K_c. The simplest way is to look at the equilibrium constant expression and work out the resultant power (dimension) of the concentration, the unit of which is $mol\,dm^{-3}$. For example, for the expression:

$$K_c = \frac{[SO_2]_{eq}^2[O_2]_{eq}}{[SO_3]_{eq}^2}$$

the dimension of the top line is (concentration)³ and that of the bottom line is (concentration)². Therefore, the resultant dimension is (concentration)¹ which has units of $mol\,dm^{-3}$. Therefore, K_c has units of $mol\,dm^{-3}$.

Worked example 1

Calculate the units of the equilibrium constant, K_c, for the following equilibrium reaction:

$$N_2(g) + 3H_2(g) \rightleftharpoons 2NH_3(g)$$

Answer

$$K_c = \frac{[NH_3]^2_{eq}}{[N_2]_{eq}[H_2]^3_{eq}}$$

$$\text{dimensions} = \frac{(\text{concentration})^2}{(\text{concentration})^4} = \text{concentration}^{-2}$$

units of $K_c = (\text{mol dm}^{-3})^{-2} = \text{dm}^6\,\text{mol}^{-2}$

Worked example 2

Calculate the units of the equilibrium constant, K_c, for the following equilibrium reaction:

$$CH_4(g) + H_2O(g) \rightleftharpoons CO(g) + 3H_2(g)$$

Answer

$$K_c = \frac{[CO]_{eq}[H_2]^3_{eq}}{[CH_4]_{eq}[H_2O]_{eq}}$$

$$\text{dimensions} = \frac{(\text{concentration})^4}{(\text{concentration})^2} = (\text{concentration})^2$$

units of $K_c = (\text{mol dm}^{-3})^2 = \text{mol}^2\,\text{dm}^{-6}$

Tip

The marks awarded in questions that ask for the value of K_c to be calculated are for:

- calculating the moles of each substance at equilibrium
- dividing these values by the volume to find the equilibrium concentrations
- correctly stating the expression for the equilibrium constant
- correctly substituting equilibrium concentrations into the expression and calculating the value of K_c
- working out the units (if there are no units, you must state this)

For some reactions the equilibrium constant has no units. This happens when there are an equal number of moles on each side of the equation. In examples like this, you may not be told the total volume, as it will cancel when the value of K_c is calculated.

Worked example

1.00 mol of ethanol and 2.00 mol of ethanoic acid were mixed in a sealed flask at 35°C and formed a homogeneous mixture. They were left to reach equilibrium.

$$C_2H_5OH(l) + CH_3COOH(l) \rightleftharpoons CH_3COOC_2H_5(l) + H_2O(l)$$

The equilibrium mixture contained 1.15 mol of ethanoic acid. Calculate the value of the equilibrium constant, K_c, at 35°C.

Answer

initial amount (moles) of ethanoic acid = 2.00 mol

number of moles at equilibrium = 1.15 mol

number of moles that reacted = (2.00 − 1.15) = 0.85 mol

	C_2H_5OH	CH_3COOH	$CH_3COOC_2H_5$	H_2O
Initial moles	1.00	2.00	0	0
Change	−0.85	−0.85	+0.85	+0.85
Moles at equilibrium	0.15	1.15	0.85	0.85
Concentration at equilibrium	0.15/V	1.15/V	0.85/V	0.85/V

where V = the total volume

$$K_c = \frac{[CH_3COOC_2H_5][H_2O]}{[C_2H_5OH][CH_3COOH]}$$
$$= \frac{0.85/V \times 0.85/V}{0.15/V \times 1.15/V} = 4.2$$

K_c has no units, as the volume, V, cancels.

> ### Tip
> If the volume is not given, divide the moles by V, which will later cancel out when the concentration values are substituted into the expression for K_c.

Test yourself

4 Calculate the units of K_c for the equilibrium:
$$CH_4(g) + 2H_2O(g) \rightleftharpoons CO_2(g) + 4H_2(g)$$

The equilibrium constant in terms of partial pressure, K_p

The molecules of a gas are in constant and random motion. The pressure of a gas is caused by the frequency and momentum of the collisions of its molecules with the container walls.

In a mixture of gases, every gas molecule contributes to the overall pressure. The sum of the individual contributions equals the total pressure. The contribution of one gas to the total pressure is called the **partial pressure** of that substance.

The partial pressure of a gas A in a mixture of gases is the pressure that the gas A would exert if it were alone in the container at that particular temperature.

This definition is better expressed as:

The partial pressure of a gas A, $p(A)$, is equal to the mole fraction of gas A multiplied by the total pressure.

$$p(A) = \frac{\text{moles of A}}{\text{total number of moles}} \times P$$

The sum of the partial pressures of the gases in a mixture equals the total pressure. For a mixture of three gases A, B and C:

$$p(A) + p(B) + p(C) = P$$

The symbol for partial pressure is a lower case p with the identity of the gas in brackets, $p(A)$, or as a subscript, p_A. The total pressure is an upper case P.

Dry air is a mixture of 78% nitrogen, 21% oxygen and 1% argon (plus small amounts of CO_2 and other gases). The partial pressure of nitrogen when the total air pressure is 1.0 atm is:

$$\frac{78}{100} \times 1.0\,\text{atm} = 0.78\,\text{atm}$$

When a diver descends to a depth of 10 m, the pressure of the air doubles. The partial pressure of nitrogen is now:

$$\frac{78}{100} \times 2.0\,\text{atm} = 1.56\,\text{atm}$$

At this higher partial pressure, nitrogen dissolves in the blood. When the diver returns to the surface, the nitrogen comes out of solution. This causes pain and could even result in the death of the diver. This condition is called the 'bends'. To minimise the problem of the bends, experienced sports divers use an air mixture called 'nitrox', which has a lower mole fraction of nitrogen, equal to two-thirds instead of the four-fifths found in ordinary air.

The partial pressure of a gas is a measure of its concentration in the mixture. Therefore, partial pressures can be used to calculate equilibrium constants. The units are those of pressure and not $mol\,dm^{-3}$, so the value of the equilibrium constant will be different. The equilibrium constant in terms of pressures is given the symbol K_p.

The relation between the equilibrium constant, K_p, and partial pressures is similar to that for K_c and concentrations. For a reaction:

$$xA(g) + yB(g) \rightleftharpoons mR(g) + nS(g)$$

$$K_p = \frac{p(R)^m\, p(S)^n}{p(A)^x\, p(B)^y}$$

The units of K_p are $(\text{atm})^{m+n-x-y}$.

Test yourself

5 Write the expression for K_p and give its units for:

$$SO_2Cl_2(g) \rightleftharpoons SO_2(g) + Cl_2(g)$$

To get the correct thermodynamic value of K_p, the total pressure, and hence the partial pressures, must be measured in atmospheres (atm). The reason for this is beyond A level.

The units for K_p can be worked out easily because the dimensions of K_p are obtained from the equilibrium expression.

For the reaction $N_2(g) + 3H_2(g) \rightleftharpoons 2NH_3(g)$:

$$K_p = \frac{p(NH_3)^2}{p(N_2)\,p(H_2)^3}$$

and so the dimensions are:

$$\frac{(pressure)^2}{(pressure) \times (pressure)^3} = \frac{1}{(pressure)^2} = (pressure)^{-2}$$

Hence, the unit is atm^{-2}.

For the reaction:

$$H_2(g) + I_2(g) \rightleftharpoons 2HI(g)$$

$$K_p = \frac{p(HI)^2}{p(H_2)\,p(I_2)}$$

K_p has no units in this reaction, as the top line is in atm^2 and the bottom line $atm \times atm$. The units cancel, leaving K_p as a dimensionless number.

The quotient equals the value of K_p only when the system is in equilibrium, so equilibrium partial pressures must always be used in K_p calculations.

Calculation of K_p from experimental data

The calculation of K_p from experimental data is carried out in a similar way to the calculation of K_c. However, there is an extra step, which is the calculation of the total number of moles at equilibrium. The calculation requires the use of a table, as in the worked example below.

- Write the chemical equation.
- Construct a suitable table and write in the following:
  - the initial amounts (in moles) of the reactants and of the products if their initial amounts were not zero
  - the amounts by which the reactants and the products change in reaching equilibrium — use the stoichiometry of the equation
  - the amount (in moles) of each substance at equilibrium; then add these values to find the total number of moles
  - the **mole fraction** of each gas — divide the equilibrium number of moles by the total number of moles
  - the partial pressure of each gas — multiply the mole fraction of each substance by the total pressure
- Below the table, write the expression for the equilibrium constant.
- Substitute the equilibrium concentrations into the equilibrium constant expression and calculate its value. At the same time, work out the units of K_p and include them in your answer.

> **Tip**
>
> Never use square brackets in K_p expressions. Square brackets around a formula mean the concentration, in $mol\,dm^{-3}$, of that substance and so must be used only in K_c expressions.

Worked example 1

Phosphorus pentachloride decomposes on heating:

$$PCl_5(g) \rightleftharpoons PCl_3(g) + Cl_2(g)$$

When some phosphorus pentachloride was heated to 250°C in a flask, 69% of it dissociated and the total pressure in the flask was 2.0 atm. Calculate the value of the equilibrium constant, K_p.

Answer

Assume that the initial volume of $PCl_5(g)$ contains 1 mol.

	PCl_5	PCl_3	Cl_2
Initial moles	1	0	0
Change	−0.69	+0.69	+0.69
Equilibrium moles	1 − 0.69 = 0.31	0 + 0.69 = 0.69	0 + 0.69 = 0.69
Total number of moles at equilibrium = 0.31 + 0.69 + 0.69 = 1.69			
Mole fraction	0.31/1.69 = 0.183	0.69/1.69 = 0.408	0.69/1.69 = 0.408
Partial pressure/atm	0.18 × 2.0 = 0.366	0.408 × 2.0 = 0.816	0.408 × 2.0 = 0.816

$$K_p = \frac{p(PCl_3)\,p(Cl_2)}{p(PCl_5)} = \frac{0.816 \times 0.816}{0.366} = 1.8 \text{ atm at } 250°C$$

Tip

When there is only one reactant, you might not be told its initial amount. You must assume that it is 1 mol. You will be told the percentage or the fraction that reacts.

Tip

Always check that the mole fractions add up to 1.

Worked example 2 is more complicated because the stoichiometry is not 1:1.

Worked example 2

One of the reactions by which the gaseous fuel methane, CH_4, can be produced is:

$$3H_2(g) + CO(g) \rightleftharpoons CH_4(g) + H_2O(g)$$

Hydrogen and carbon monoxide were mixed in a 3:1 ratio and allowed to reach equilibrium at a temperature of 1000 K. 65% of the hydrogen reacted and the total pressure was 1.2 atm. Calculate the value of the equilibrium constant, K_p.

Answer

Assume that the initial volume of gas is such that there are 3 mol of H_2 and 1 mol of CO.

	$3H_2$	CO	CH_4	H_2O
Initial moles	3	1	0	0
Change	−0.65 × 3 = −1.95	−1.95/3 = −0.65	+0.65	+0.65
Equilibrium moles	3 − 1.95 = 1.05	1 − 0.65 = 0.35	0 + 0.65 = 0.65	0 + 0.65 = 0.65

Total number of moles at equilibrium = 1.05 + 0.35 + 0.65 + 0.65 = 2.7

Mole fraction	1.05/2.7 = 0.389	0.35/2.7 = 0.130	0.65/2.7 = 0.241	0.65/2.7 = 0.241
Partial pressure/atm	0.389 × 1.2 = 0.467	0.130 × 1.2 = 0.156	0.241 × 1.2 = 0.289	0.241 × 1.2 = 0.289

$$K_p = \frac{p(CH_4)\,p(H_2O)}{p(H_2)^3\,p(CO)} = \frac{0.289 \times 0.289}{(0.467)^3 \times 0.156} = 5.3\,atm^{-2}$$

$$dimensions = \frac{(pressure)^2}{(pressure)^4} = (pressure)^{-2}$$

units of $K_p = atm^{-2}$

Test yourself

6 At 35°C and at a pressure of 1.2 atm, dinitrogen tetroxide, N_2O_4, is 15% dissociated.

$$N_2O_4(g) \rightleftharpoons 2NO_2(g)$$

Calculate the value of the equilibrium constant, K_p.

Finding the percentage converted using a given value of K_c

This type of calculation is difficult. It is required when two reactant molecules react reversibly to form two product molecules. The calculation involves letting the fraction of one substance that reacts equal an unknown, z. A table is used as in the calculation of an equilibrium constant. The value of z is found by taking the square root of the equilibrium expression.

Worked example

The esterification of ethanol with ethanoic acid is represented by the equation:

$$C_2H_5OH + CH_3COOH \rightleftharpoons CH_3COOC_2H_5 + H_2O$$

The equilibrium constant K_c at 25°C is 4.0.

Calculate the percentage of ethanol that is converted to ester when 1.0 mol of ethanol is mixed with 1.0 mol of ethanoic acid in a propanone solvent of volume 1.0 dm³ and allowed to reach equilibrium.

Answer

	C_2H_5OH	CH_3COOH	$CH_3COOC_2H_5$	H_2O
Initial moles	1.0	1.0	0	0
Change	−z	−z	+z	+z
Equilibrium moles	(1 − z)	(1 − z)	+z	+z
Equilibrium concentration/mol dm⁻³	(1 − z)/1.0 = 1 − z	(1 − z)/1.0 = 1 − z	z/1.0 = z	z/1.0 = z

$$K_c = \frac{[CH_3COOC_2H_5][H_2O]}{[C_2H_5OH][CH_3COOH]}$$

$$= \frac{z \times z}{(1-z)(1-z)}$$

$$= \frac{z^2}{(1-z)^2} = 4.0$$

Taking the square root of both sides:

$$\frac{z}{(1-z)} = \sqrt{4.0} = 2.0$$

$$z = 2.0 - 2z$$

$$3z = 2.0$$

$z = 0.67$, so 67% of the ethanol reacted.

Tip

Technically the square root of 4.0 is ±2, but negative values of moles are meaningless.

Heterogeneous equilibria

In all the examples so far, the reactants and products have been in the same phase. Some reversible reactions involve reactants and products in different phases.

There are three physical states — solid, liquid and gas.

- All gases mix completely. Therefore, a mixture of gases always forms a single phase in which any one part is identical with any other part.
- A solution of several solutes in water exists in a single phase, also forming a homogeneous mixture.
- Two liquids mix to form either a single phase or, if they are immiscible, two layers — two liquid phases.
- Solids that dissolve in a solvent form a single liquid phase.
- A mixture of a solid and a gas forms two distinct phases.
- Mixtures of solids are usually in two different solid phases.

Key term

A **heterogeneous** mixture is one that exists in two or more different phases.

In a heterogeneous equilibrium reaction at least one substance is in a different phase from the others. An example of this is the reaction between carbon and steam to form carbon monoxide and hydrogen:

$$C(s) + H_2O(g) \rightleftharpoons CO(g) + H_2(g)$$

The three gases are in the same phase but carbon is in a different phase. The concentration of a solid, such as carbon, is constant and so is left out in the expression for K_c. For the reaction above, the equilibrium constant, K_c, is given by the expression:

$$K_c = \frac{[CO]_{eq}[H_2]_{eq}}{[H_2O]_{eq}}$$

Involatile solids have no vapour pressure and so they do not appear in the expression for the equilibrium constant, K_p. For the reaction:

$$3Fe(s) + 4H_2O(g) \rightleftharpoons Fe_3O_4(s) + 4H_2(g)$$

$$K_p = \frac{p[H_2]^4}{p[H_2O]^4}$$

where all partial pressures are equilibrium values.

Worked example 1

Ammonium hydrogensulfide, NH_4HS, decomposes when heated, according to the equation:

$$NH_4HS(s) \rightleftharpoons NH_3(g) + H_2S(g) \qquad K_p = 0.142 \, atm^2 \text{ at } 50°C$$

a State the expression for K_p.

b Calculate the partial pressure of both gases at 50°C and hence the total pressure.

Answer

a $K_p = p(NH_3)p(H_2S) = 0.142$

b As the reaction produces NH_3 and H_2S in a 1:1 ratio, $p(H_2S) = p(NH_3)$

$$K_p = p(NH_3)^2 = 0.142$$

$$p(NH_3) = \sqrt{0.142} = 0.377 \, atm$$

$$p(H_2S) = 0.3770 \, atm$$

total pressure = sum of partial pressures = $0.377 + 0.377 = 0.7540 \, atm$

Another heterogeneous equilibrium is that between solid calcium hydroxide and aqueous calcium ions and hydroxide ions:

$$Ca(OH)_2(s) + aq \rightleftharpoons Ca^{2+}(aq) + 2OH^-(aq)$$

The solid calcium hydroxide is in one phase and the dissolved ions and the solvent are in another. The expression for the equilibrium constant is:

$$K_c = [Ca^{2+}]_{eq} [OH^-]^2_{eq}$$

> The product of the concentrations of the aqueous ions formed from a sparingly soluble solid is called the solubility product and given the symbol K_{sp}.

Worked example 2

The value of K_c for dissolving calcium hydroxide is $5.5 \times 10^{-5} \, mol^3 \, dm^{-9}$ at 25°C. Calculate:

a the concentration of OH^- ions in a saturated solution

b the number of OH^- ions in $1 \, dm^3$ of solution

Answer

a $K_c = [Ca^{2+}]_{eq}[OH^-]_{eq}^2 = 5.5 \times 10^{-5}$

Let $[Ca^{2+}] = z$

Ratio of OH^- to $Ca^{2+} = 2:1$, so $[OH^-] = 2z$. $\qquad K_c = z \times (2z)^2 = 5.5 \times 10^{-5}$

$$4z^3 = 5.5 \times 10^{-5}$$

$$z = 0.024$$

$$[OH^-] = 2z = 0.048 \, mol \, dm^{-3}$$

b number of OH^- ions = $[OH^-] \times$ the Avogadro constant = $0.048 \times 6.012 \times 10^{23}$
$= 2.89 \times 10^{22}$

Effect of a change in temperature

A change in temperature will always cause a change in the value of K, unless ΔH for the reaction is zero. It is the only variable condition that alters the value of the equilibrium constant for a given reaction.

Exothermic reactions: ΔH negative

- If the temperature is increased, the value of K decreases.
- This means that the quotient Q is now larger than the new K, so the position of equilibrium moves to the left until the Q and K are once again equal.

Endothermic reactions: ΔH positive

- If the temperature is increased, the value of K increases.
- This means that the quotient Q is now smaller than the new K, so the position of equilibrium moves to the right until the Q and K are once again equal.

The explanation of the change in the value of the equilibrium constant, K, as the temperature is altered is given in Chapter 3 on p. 84.

Table 1.2 Effect of temperature on K

Reaction	$\Delta H/$ $kJ\,mol^{-1}$	$T/°C$	K_p	K_c
Exothermic: $N_2(g) + 3H_2(g) \rightleftharpoons 2NH_3(g)$	−92	25	$6.8 \times 10^5\,atm^{-2}$	$4.2 \times 10^{12}\,dm^6\,mol^{-2}$
		125	$43\,atm^{-2}$	$4.7 \times 10^8\,dm^6\,mol^{-2}$
		225	$3.7 \times 10^{-2}\,atm^{-2}$	$9.1 \times 10^5\,dm^6\,mol^{-2}$
		325	$1.7 \times 10^{-3}\,atm^{-2}$	$5.7 \times 10^4\,dm^6\,mol^{-2}$
		425	$7.8 \times 10^{-5}\,atm^{-2}$	$3.4 \times 10^3\,dm^6\,mol^{-2}$
Endothermic: $N_2O_4(g) \rightleftharpoons 2NO_2(g)$	+58	25	$0.24\,atm$	$9.7 \times 10^{-5}\,mol\,dm^{-3}$
		80	$4.0\,atm$	$0.0014\,mol\,dm^{-3}$
		100	$46\,atm$	$0.015\,mol\,dm^{-3}$
		150	$350\,atm$	$0.10\,mol\,dm^{-3}$

Remember that the value of the equilibrium constant is *not* altered by any change in concentration, pressure or the addition of catalyst. Its value, for a given reaction, depends solely on the temperature.

Effect on the rate of reaching equilibrium

An increase in temperature always results in an increase in the rate of reaction. This is true whether the reaction is exothermic or endothermic. It happens because the molecules possess greater average kinetic energy, so more collisions have energy that is greater than the activation energy. This means that a greater proportion of the collisions result in a reaction.

In a reversible reaction, an increase in temperature increases the rate of the forward and back reactions, but does not do so equally. The endothermic reaction has higher activation energy and so its rate is increased more than that of the exothermic reaction. This is one reason why the position of equilibrium shifts in the endothermic direction when the temperature of the system is raised.

Because the rates of both reactions are increased, equilibrium is reached more rapidly.

Test yourself

8 State the effect of decreasing the temperature on the equilibrium constant, K_p for:

$$N_2(g) + O_2(g) \rightleftharpoons 2NO(g) \qquad \Delta H = +180 \, \text{kJ mol}^{-1}$$

Effect of change of pressure or volume of the container on gaseous reactions

Effect on the equilibrium constant

Altering the pressure of a gaseous system or the volume of the container has *no* effect on the value of the equilibrium constant.

Effect on the position of equilibrium

This depends on the number of gas molecules on each side of the equation.

In all the examples below assume that the pressure has been doubled by halving the volume of the container. This will cause the concentrations of all species to double.

The equilibrium involving hydrogen, iodine and hydrogen iodide is an example of a reaction in which the number of gas moles on the left equals the number on the right:

$$H_2(g) + I_2(g) \rightleftharpoons 2HI(g)$$

$$K_c = \frac{[HI]^2_{eq}}{[H_2]_{eq}[I_2]_{eq}}$$

- An increase in pressure (caused by a decrease in the volume of the container) has *no* effect on the value of K_c.
- The concentration of HI rises by a factor of 2, and so $[HI]^2$ increases by a factor of 4.
- The concentrations of both H_2 and I_2 rise by a factor of 2. Therefore, $[H_2]$ multiplied by $[I_2]$ increases by a factor of 4.
- Both the top and the bottom lines of the quotient rise by the same factor. Therefore, its value does not change.

- Neither K_c nor the quotient has altered, thus K_c still equals the quotient. This means that the system is still in equilibrium, so there is no change to the position of equilibrium.

The equilibrium between nitrogen, hydrogen and ammonia is an example of a reaction in which the number of gas moles on the left is more than the number on the right:

$$N_2(g) + 3H_2(g) \rightleftharpoons 2NH_3(g)$$

$$K_c = \frac{[NH_3]_{eq}^2}{[N_2]_{eq}[H_2]_{eq}^3}$$

Assume that the total pressure is doubled (or the volume of the container is halved):

- An increase in pressure has *no* effect on the value of K_c.
- The concentration of ammonia doubles, so $[NH_3]^2$ rises by a factor of 4.
- $[N_2]$ multiplied by $[H_2]^3$ rises by a factor of 2×2^3. This is a greater increase than that of the top line of the quotient.
- The quotient becomes smaller. Therefore, it no longer equals K_c, and the system is no longer in equilibrium.
- The system reacts to make the quotient bigger until it once again equals the unaltered value of K_c. It does this by hydrogen reacting with nitrogen to make more ammonia, so the position of equilibrium shifts to the right.

An increase in pressure does not alter K_c, but the quotient is lowered as there are fewer gas moles on the right. Therefore, the system reacts to make more ammonia, until the quotient equals K_c once more.

> **Tip**
>
> An increase in pressure will drive the position of equilibrium to the side with the *fewer* moles of gas.

Test yourself

9 State whether the position of equilibrium below moves to the left or right when the pressure of the system is increased. Justify your answer.
$$4NH_3(g) + 5O_2(g) \rightleftharpoons 4NO(g) + 6H_2O(g)$$

> **Tip**
>
> If a syringe is filled with an equilibrium mixture of these two gases and then the plunger is pushed in, the colour at first darkens and then gets lighter. The reason is that the brown NO_2 molecules are in a smaller volume, but as equilibrium is slowly re-established the colour of the mixture gets lighter.

Explanation in terms of K_p

The equilibrium between dinitrogen tetroxide and nitrogen dioxide is an example of a reaction in which the number of gas moles on the left is less than the number on the right:

$$N_2O_4(g) \rightleftharpoons 2NO_2(g)$$

$$K_p = \frac{p(NO_2)^2}{p(N_2O_4)}$$

Assume that the volume of the container is halved, thus doubling the total pressure. This has no effect on the value of K_p but causes the partial pressures of *both* gases to double and so the quotient increases by a factor of $2^2/2 = 2$ times. It is now greater than K_p and therefore some NO_2 reacts to form N_2O_4 until the quotient regains the value of the unchanged K_p. The position of equilibrium moves to the left.

Addition of an inert gas

When pressure is increased by the addition of an inert gas at constant volume, there is no effect on the concentrations of the reactants or products. This is because the number of moles of the reacting species has not been altered and neither has the volume. Concentration is the number of moles divided by the volume. As neither has altered, the concentration remains the same.

The effect can also be explained in terms of K_p. The mole fractions decrease because addition of inert gas increases the number of total moles, but the total pressure increases by the same factor, so the quotient is unaltered. Since neither the value of K nor the value of the quotient changes, the system is still in equilibrium. The position of equilibrium does not change, even though the pressure has been increased.

Le Châtelier would predict otherwise but he would be wrong!

Effect on the rate of reaching equilibrium

If the reaction is homogeneous, the rate of collision increases when the pressure is increased. This causes an increase in the rates of the forward and back reactions and so equilibrium is reached sooner.

This is not the case for gaseous reactions catalysed by a solid catalyst. The rate is determined by the number of **active sites** on the catalyst surface, so an increase in pressure does not alter the rate. The active sites are always occupied unless the pressure falls to an extremely low value. A typical mechanism is:

reactant gases + free active sites $\rightleftharpoons$ adsorbed reactants   fast step

adsorbed reactants $\rightleftharpoons$ adsorbed products   slow step

adsorbed products $\rightleftharpoons$ gaseous products + free active sites   fast step

Biological reactions catalysed by enzymes have similar mechanisms — extra substrate does not increase the rate of the reaction. Eating a chocolate bar will not make you run faster, but getting 'psyched up' will, as this causes you to produce adrenaline, which triggers the production of more enzyme.

Effect of change of concentration of one species

Effect on the equilibrium constant

Altering the concentration of a reactant or product has no effect on the value of the equilibrium constant.

Effect on the position of equilibrium

The equilibrium involving sulfur dioxide, oxygen and sulfur trioxide is represented by the equation:

$$2SO_2(g) + O_2(g) \rightleftharpoons 2SO_3(g)$$

$$K_c = \frac{[SO_3]^2_{eq}}{[SO_2]^2_{eq}[O_2]_{eq}}$$

The percentage conversion of sulfur dioxide to sulfur trioxide can be increased by adding more oxygen. Addition of extra oxygen to the system in equilibrium does not alter the value of K_c but causes the quotient, Q, to become smaller. Therefore, it no longer equals K_c. The system reacts, making more SO_3, until equality is regained. This means that a greater proportion of sulfur dioxide is converted to sulfur trioxide.

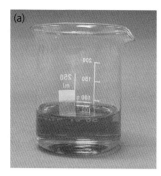

Acidified potassium dichromate (a) before and (b) after the addition of alkali

Effect of adding a catalyst

- A catalyst has no effect on either the value of the equilibrium constant or the quotient and so has no effect on the position of equilibrium.
- A catalyst speeds up both the forward and the back reactions equally. Therefore, equilibrium is reached more quickly.

Catalysts are used in exothermic industrial processes so that a faster rate can be obtained at a lower temperature. For an exothermic reaction this results in an increased yield, compared with the same reaction carried out at the same rate but at a higher temperature in the absence of a catalyst.

The cost of heating to a high temperature can always be partially recovered by the use of heat exchangers. High pressure is expensive, not only in the energy costs of compression, but also in the extra cost of a plant that will withstand the high pressure.

Industrial and pharmaceutical processes

The aim is to:

- maximise the percentage conversion of reactants to products (increase the equilibrium yield)
- make this amount of product as quickly as possible (fast rate of reaction)
- keep the costs as low as possible
- have as high an atom economy as possible

The chemical industry frequently uses a **continuous flow** method of production. The reactants are added continuously at one end of the plant and the products are removed continuously at the other. It is not truly an equilibrium system because it is not closed, but the reactants are in the presence of the catalyst for long enough for the principles of equilibrium to be useful when deciding on optimum conditions. This type of process is particularly effective when gases react in the presence of a solid catalyst.

The pharmaceutical industry uses a **batch process** — the reactants are added together in a reaction vessel. When the reaction is complete, the products are separated from any catalyst, the solvent and any unused reactants. The catalyst is often bonded to resin particles so that it can be removed easily from the reaction mixture and re-used.

The Haber process

The chemical reaction is:

$$N_2(g) + 3H_2(g) \rightleftharpoons 2NH_3(g) \qquad \Delta H = -92\,\text{kJ}\,\text{mol}^{-1}$$

$$K_p = \frac{p(NH_3)^2_{eq}}{p(N_2)_{eq}\,p(H_2)^3_{eq}}$$

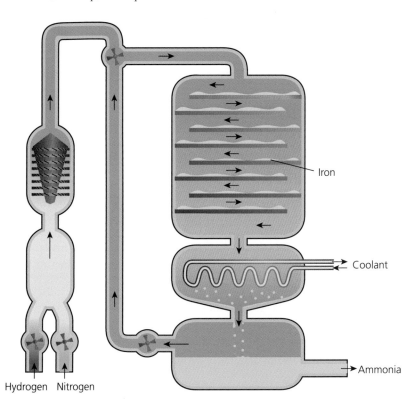

Iron

Coolant

Ammonia

Hydrogen   Nitrogen

Figure 1.1 Schematic diagram of the Haber process. Hydrogen and nitrogen are mixed and compressed. The mixture cycles through the reaction tower over trays of iron

The conditions are:

- temperature of 400°C to 450°C (673 K to 723 K)
- pressure of 200 atm
- catalyst — iron promoted by traces of aluminium and potassium oxides

Effect of temperature

The reaction is exothermic. Any increase in temperature reduces the value of the equilibrium constant, K, and hence the yield. Figure 1.2 shows how the value of $\ln K_p$ and hence K_p falls dramatically as the temperature is increased.

At first sight, it would appear that the Haber process should be carried out at room temperature, but then the rate would be so slow as to be effectively zero and almost no product would be formed. A high temperature would result in a low yield being achieved quickly; the rate at a lower temperature would be so slow that the reaction would not approach equilibrium. To overcome these problems, an iron catalyst is used. This allows the

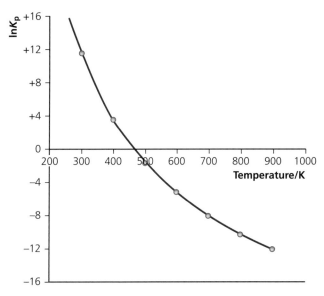

Figure 1.2 Plot of $\ln K_p$ against temperature for the Haber process equilibrium

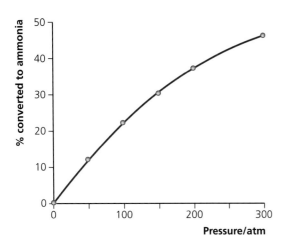

Figure 1.3 Graph showing the effect of pressure on the percentage of reactants converted to ammonia at a temperature of 400°C

reaction to take place at a reasonable rate at a temperature of 700 K, which is a compromise temperature of a reasonable yield at an economically acceptable rate.

Effect of pressure

At 400°C, the equilibrium constant, K_p, is 3.9×10^{-4} atm^{-2}, so the yield at 1 atm pressure is low. Fritz Haber understood the principles of equilibrium and realised that high pressure would increase the yield (Figure 1.3). His co-worker, Carl Bosch, designed apparatus that could work at 200 atm pressure.

An increase in pressure does not alter the value of the equilibrium constant, but it causes the partial pressure expression to become smaller. This means that K_p no longer equals the partial pressure expression (the quotient), so the system reacts making more ammonia until the quotient once again equals the value of the equilibrium constant. This means that the position of equilibrium shifts to the right.

The rate of reaction is not altered by increasing the pressure, as the rate is controlled by the availability of the active sites on the surface of the catalyst (see p. 177).

As there are more molecules on the left-hand side of the equation, the bottom line of the partial pressure expression increases more than the top line. This makes the quotient, Q, smaller and temporarily less than K_p.

The choice of optimum conditions based on an understanding of the principles of kinetics and equilibrium is an example of 'How Science Works'.

Even under these conditions only about 30% of the hydrogen is converted to ammonia. This is because the rate of reaction is still too slow for equilibrium to be reached in the catalyst chamber.

To obtain an economic overall yield, the ammonia is removed by cooling the gases leaving the catalyst chamber. The ammonia liquefies and is separated from the unreacted nitrogen and hydrogen, which are then recycled through the catalyst chamber. In this way almost all the hydrogen is eventually converted to ammonia.

The process enables nitrogenous fertilisers to be manufactured cheaply. Haber and Bosch were awarded the Nobel prize for their work.

The Contact process

The crucial step in the manufacture of sulfuric acid is:

$$2SO_2(g) + O_2(g) \rightleftharpoons 2SO_3(g) \qquad \Delta H = -196 \text{ kJ mol}^{-1}$$

$$K_p = \frac{p(SO_3)^2_{eq}}{p(SO_2)^2_{eq}\, p(O_2)_{eq}}$$

The conditions are:

- temperature of 425°C (698 K)
- pressure of 2 atm
- catalyst — vanadium(v) oxide, V_2O_5

Effect of temperature

The reaction is exothermic, so an increase in temperature decreases the value of K_p.

Figure 1.4 shows how $\ln K_p$ varies with temperature.

K_p at 298 K = 3×10^{24} atm^{-1}

K_p at 698 K = 6×10^{4} atm^{-1}

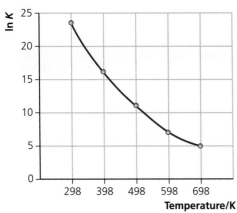

Figure 1.4

The value of K_p for this reaction, under the conditions of the Contact process, is about a billion times larger than that of the reaction in the Haber process.

To ensure that the reaction is fast enough to be economic at a temperature of 698 K, a catalyst of vanadium(V) oxide is used. A higher temperature would mean a lower yield and a lower temperature would mean an uneconomic rate. The temperature used is a compromise that produces a high yield quickly.

At a pressure of 2 atm and a temperature of 698 K, the equilibrium mixture contains 95% sulfur trioxide.

Effect of pressure

As there are more molecules on the left-hand side of the equation, an increase in pressure would drive the equilibrium to the right.

However, the yield is high anyway and the use of high pressure is expensive in terms of both the energy required to compress the gases and the extra cost involved in making the plant able to withstand the high pressure. It does not make economic sense to increase the yield further by using high pressure.

The reason for this is the same as for the Haber process.

However, a pressure greater than 1 atm must be used in order to drive the gases through the plant, so the air and sulfur dioxide are compressed to about 2 atm. Under these conditions, the equilibrium yield is over 95%.

Final yield and pollution

It would be a waste of raw materials if unreacted sulfur dioxide were released into the atmosphere and it would also cause considerable atmospheric pollution. A higher final yield is obtained by passing the gases from the catalyst chamber into concentrated sulfuric acid, which absorbs the sulfur trioxide from the equilibrium mixture. The unreacted sulfur dioxide and air are then passed back through another bed of catalyst where a further 95% conversion takes place. The result is that the gases released into the environment contain only slight traces of sulfur dioxide.

The gases are passed through the first catalyst bed at a temperature of 698 K (Figure 1.5). As the reaction is exothermic, the gases heat up to about 900 K and the conversion is only 60%. The gases are then cooled to 700 K and passed back through another bed of catalyst. The conversion is now 95% and the mixture of sulfur trioxide, sulfur dioxide and oxygen is passed through a tower containing concentrated sulfuric acid. The sulfur trioxide forms oleum, $H_2S_2O_7$, and the remaining gases are passed through another catalyst bed. The overall conversion of sulfur dioxide is 99.5%.

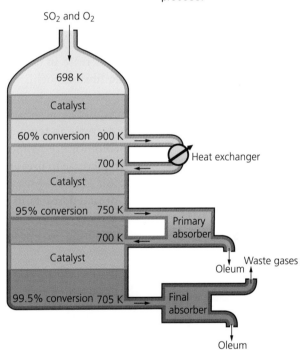

Figure 1.5 A schematic representation of the Contact process

The sulfur trioxide reacts with the concentrated sulfuric acid to form oleum, $H_2S_2O_7$. Water is added carefully and sulfuric acid is formed.

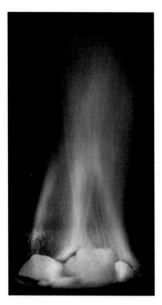

Solid methane hydrate burning

The extraction of methane from methane hydrate

A possible future source of methane is deposits of methane hydrate (see p. 183 of the year 1 student book). These are found either in the oceans on some continental shelves or in permafrost in the polar regions. Methane can be extracted by bringing the solid methane hydrate to room temperature and pressure. It has been estimated that the total oceanic methane hydrate reservoirs contain about eight times that in the known deposits of natural gas.

$$CH_4 \cdot 6H_2O(s) \rightleftharpoons CH_4(g) + 6H_2O(l) \qquad \Delta H \text{ positive}$$

It can be seen from the equation that either a reduction in pressure or an increase in temperature will drive this equilibrium to the right, releasing methane gas from the solid methane hydrate.

The extraction of methane from shale deposits

The shale in many deposits contains adsorbed methane. This can be extracted by drilling down to the shale and then pumping in water and sand under high pressure. The water forces out the methane and the sand keeps the cracks in the shale open.

Summary

- An increase in temperature of an exothermic reaction will result in a decrease in equilibrium yield.
- An increase in temperature of an endothermic reaction will result in an increase in equilibrium yield.
- A decrease in temperature will result in a lower rate of reaction, so a catalyst and a compromise temperature may be used to optimise rate and yield.
- An increase in pressure will drive the equilibrium to the side of the equation with fewer gas molecules. However, the use of high pressure is expensive.
- Unreacted reactants are recycled to improve the final yield, to conserve raw materials and to reduce environmental pollution.
- Many industrial processes are not true equilibrium systems because the products are removed.

Summary tasks

Make sure that you:

- can define dynamic equilibrium
- can write expressions for the equilibrium constant given the chemical equation
- know when to include $[H_2O]$ in an expression for K_c
- regard [solid] in a heterogeneous equilibrium as a constant and so omit it from expressions for K
- can define mole fraction and partial pressure

Make sure that you can calculate:

- K_c and K_p from experimental data
- the units of K

Make sure that you can explain the effect on K (if any) and the position of equilibrium when:

- the temperature is altered
- the pressure is increased
- the concentration of a reactant or product is altered
- a catalyst is added

Questions

1 $K_c = 40\,mol^{-1}\,dm^3$ at 250°C for the reaction:

$$PCl_3(g) + Cl_2(g) \rightleftharpoons PCl_5(g)$$

Calculate the value of K_c, at 250°C, for the reaction:

$$PCl_5(g) \rightleftharpoons PCl_3(g) + Cl_2(g)$$

2 Sulfur trioxide was heated to 700°C in a vessel of volume $10\,dm^3$ and allowed to reach equilibrium:

$$2SO_3(g) \rightleftharpoons 2SO_2(g) + O_2(g)$$

The equilibrium mixture was found to contain 0.035 mol sulfur trioxide, 0.044 mol sulfur dioxide and 0.022 mol oxygen. Calculate the value of the equilibrium constant, K_c, at 700°C.

3 Partition experiments can be used to find the formula of the deep blue ammonia/copper(II) complex ion.

$100\,cm^3$ of a solution of copper sulfate containing 0.010 mol of $Cu^{2+}(aq)$ ions was added to $100\,cm^3$ of a solution of ammonia containing 0.100 mol of ammonia. The following reaction took place:

$$Cu^{2+}(aq) + nNH_3(aq) \rightarrow [Cu(NH_3)_n]^{2+}(aq)$$

This solution was shaken with $100\,cm^3$ of ethoxyethane and the dissolved ammonia became distributed between the aqueous and the organic layers. The partition constant of ammonia between water and ethoxyethane is 30.

$$\frac{[NH_3]\ in\ water}{[NH_3]\ in\ ethoxyethane} = 30$$

The organic layer was found to have an ammonia concentration of $0.0194\,mol\,dm^{-3}$.

Calculate:

a) the concentration of ammonia in the aqueous layer

b) the amount (in moles) of ammonia in each layer and hence the total amount (in moles) of free dissolved ammonia

c) the amount (in moles) of ammonia that reacted with the copper ions

d) the ratio of reacted ammonia to copper ions and hence the formula of the ammonia/copper(II) complex ion

4 1.00 mol of methane, CH_4, and 2.00 mol of steam were mixed in a vessel of volume $10\,dm^3$ and allowed to reach equilibrium at 1200 K:

$$CH_4(g) + H_2O(g) \rightleftharpoons CO(g) + 3H_2(g)$$

Analysis of the equilibrium mixture showed that 0.25 mol of methane was present.

a) Write the expression for the equilibrium constant, K_c.

b) Calculate the value of the equilibrium constant, K_c, at a temperature of 1200 K.

5 The ester dimethyl ethanedioate is hydrolysed by water:

$$CH_3OOCCOOCH_3 + 2H_2O \rightleftharpoons$$
$$HOOCCOOH + 2CH_3OH$$

11.8 g of dimethyl ethanedioate were mixed with 5.40 g of water and allowed to reach equilibrium. 75% of the ester reacted and the total volume was $15.0\,cm^3$. Calculate the value of the equilibrium constant, K_c, at the temperature of the experiment.

6 Write the expression for K_p for the following reaction:

$$H_2O(g) + C(s) \rightleftharpoons CO(g) + H_2(g)$$

7 Silver carbonate decomposes according to the equation:

$$Ag_2CO_3(s) \rightleftharpoons Ag_2O(s) + CO_2(g)$$
$$K_p = 1.48\,atm\ at\ 500°C$$

Calculate the partial pressure of carbon dioxide at 500°C.

Exam practice questions

1 a) Hydrogen is manufactured from methane by the reaction:

$$CH_4(g) + H_2O(g) \rightleftharpoons 3H_2(g) + CO(g)$$
$$\Delta H = +212\,kJ\,mol^{-1}$$

i) The expression for K_c for this reaction is:

A $\dfrac{[H_2]^3[CO]}{[CH_4]}$ **C** $\dfrac{[CH_4]}{[H_2]^3[CO]}$

B $\dfrac{[H_2]^3[CO]}{[CH_4][H_2O]}$ **D** $\dfrac{[CH_4][H_2O]}{[H_2]^3[CO]}$ (1)

ii) When 1 mol of methane and 1 mol of steam were allowed to reach equilibrium in a vessel of volume 50 dm³ and at a temperature T, 76% of the methane was converted. Calculate the value of K_c at this temperature. Include units in your answer.   (5)

b) Explain the effect on the values of the equilibrium constant, K, and on the yield, of an increase in:
i) pressure   (3)
ii) temperature   (3)

(Total 12 marks)

2 a) i) Methanol, CH_3OH, can be made by passing carbon monoxide and hydrogen over a heated zinc oxide and chromium(III) oxide catalyst:

$$CO(g) + 2H_2(g) \rightleftharpoons CH_3OH(g)$$

When 0.100 mol of carbon monoxide and 0.300 mol of hydrogen were heated to 400°C in a vessel of volume 10 dm³, equilibrium was reached after 30% of the carbon monoxide had reacted. Calculate the value of the equilibrium constant, K_c.   (4)

ii) The expression for K_c for the reaction

$$CO(g) + 2H_2(g) \rightleftharpoons CH_3OH(g)$$ (1)

is:

A $\dfrac{[CH_3OH(g)]}{[CO(g)]\,[H_2(g)]}$

B $\dfrac{[CH_3OH(g)]}{[CO(g)]\,[H_2(g)]^2}$

C $\dfrac{[CO(g)]\,[H_2(g)]}{[CH_3OH(g)]}$

D $\dfrac{[CO(g)]\,[H_2(g)]^2}{[CH_3OH(g)]}$

b) $K_c = 1.0$ at 1100 K for the reaction:

$$CO(g) + H_2O(g) \rightleftharpoons CO_2(g) + H_2(g)$$

1.5 mol of carbon monoxide and 1.5 mol of steam at 1100 K are mixed with 3.0 mol of carbon dioxide and 1.0 mol of hydrogen in a container of volume 100 dm³. Calculate whether the system is in equilibrium. If it is not, explain in which direction the system will move in order to reach equilibrium.   (3)

(Total 8 marks)

3 a) The expression for K_p for the reaction

$$2NO(g) + O_2(g) \rightleftharpoons 2NO_2(g)$$

is $K_p =$ (1)

A $\dfrac{[NO_2(g)]^2}{[NO(g)]^2\,[O_2(g)]}$

B $\dfrac{[NO(g)]^2\,[O_2(g)]}{[NO_2(g)^2]}$

C $\dfrac{p(NO_2)^2}{p(NO)^2 p(O_2)}$

D $\dfrac{p(NO)^2 p(O_2)}{p(NO_2)^2}$

b) Nitrogen and hydrogen were mixed in a 1:3 ratio and heated to 400°C over an iron catalyst at a pressure of 30 atm until equilibrium was reached. 15% of the nitrogen was converted to ammonia:

$$N_2(g) + 3H_2(g) \rightleftharpoons 2NH_3(g)$$

i) Write the expression for K_p.   (1)
ii) Calculate its value under these conditions.   (6)

(Total 8 marks)

2 Acid–base equilibria (Topic 12)

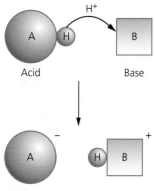

Acid

Base

Figure 2.1

Acids were first defined in terms of their sour taste. When indicators such as litmus were discovered, an acid was thought of as any substance that turned litmus red. Later, the understanding of acidity led Arrhenius to define an acid as a substance that produces an excess of H^+ ions in aqueous solution. This definition is limited to aqueous solutions and was extended by Lowry and Brønsted to include non-aqueous solvents. Their definitions of acids and bases are given below.

An acid is a substance that gives a proton (H^+ ion) to a base.

A base is a substance that accepts a proton (H^+ ion) from an acid.

This is illustrated in Figure 2.1.

For an acid–base equilibrium, the changes are:

$$\text{acid} \underset{\text{gain of proton}}{\overset{\text{loss of proton}}{\rightleftharpoons}} \text{base}$$

Acid–base conjugate pairs

The reaction of an acid with a base can be written as the chemical equation:

$$HA + B \rightarrow BH^+ + A^-$$

For many acids this is a reversible reaction:

$$HA + B \rightleftharpoons BH^+ + A^-$$

- For the left-to-right reaction, HA is the acid and B is the base.
- For the right-to-left reaction, the acid is BH^+ and A^- is the base.

The acid, HA, and the base, A^-, derived from it by loss of a proton, are called an acid–conjugate base pair. The base, B, and the acid, BH^+, derived from it by acceptance of a proton, are a base–conjugate acid pair.

The acid HCl reacts with the base H_2O (Figure 2.2).

Figure 2.2

Cl^- is the conjugate base of the acid HCl; the conjugate acid of the base H_2O is H_3O^+.

Ammonia is a base and reacts with water, which acts as an acid giving a proton to the ammonia molecule (Figure 2.3).

Figure 2.3

The relationship between conjugate pairs is:

- acid − H^+ → conjugate base
- base + H^+ → conjugate acid

Test yourself

1 Write the formula of:

  a) the conjugate acid of NH_3

  b) the conjugate base of NH_3

Worked example

Concentrated sulfuric acid reacts with concentrated nitric acid:

$$H_2SO_4 + HNO_3 \rightarrow H_2NO_3^+ + HSO_4^-$$

Mark the acid–base conjugate pairs.

Answer

See Figure 2.4.

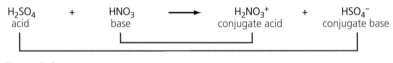

H_2SO_4 + HNO_3 ⟶ $H_2NO_3^+$ + HSO_4^-
acid   base   conjugate acid   conjugate base

Figure 2.4

Conjugate means joined together, here by the loss or gain of a proton.

In this reaction, nitric acid is acting as a base, as it is protonated by the sulfuric acid, which is a stronger acid.

Some acid–base conjugate pairs are listed in Table 2.1 in order of decreasing acid strength and increasing base strength.

Table 2.1 Acid–conjugate base pairs

	Acid		Base	
	Name	Formula	Formula	Name
Strong acids	Sulfuric acid	H_2SO_4	HSO_4^-	Hydrogensulfate ion
	Hydroiodic acid	HI	I^-	Iodide ion
	Hydrobromic acid	HBr	Br^-	Bromide ion
	Hydrochloric acid	HCl	Cl^-	Chloride ion
	Nitric acid	HNO_3	NO_3^-	Nitrate ion
	Hydronium ion	H_3O^+	H_2O	Water
Weak acids	Hydrogensulfate ion	HSO_4^-	SO_4^{2-}	Sulfate ion
	Hydrofluoric acid	HF	F^-	Fluoride ion
	Ethanoic acid	CH_3COOH	CH_3COO^-	Ethanoate ion
	Carbonic acid	H_2CO_3	HCO_3^-	Hydrogencarbonate ion
	Ammonium ion	NH_4^+	NH_3	Ammonia
	Hydrogencarbonate ion	HCO_3^-	CO_3^{2-}	Carbonate ion
	Water	H_2O	OH^-	Hydroxide ion

Strong and weak acids and bases

A strong acid is an acid that is totally ionised in aqueous solution forming hydrated hydrogen ions, H_3O^+.

For example, hydrochloric acid, $HCl(aq)$, is a strong acid:

$$HCl(aq) + H_2O(l) \rightarrow H_3O^+(aq) + Cl^-(aq)$$

A weak acid is an acid that is only *very slightly* ionised in aqueous solution.

For example, ethanoic acid is a weak acid:

$$CH_3COOH(aq) + H_2O(l) \rightleftharpoons H_3O^+(aq) + CH_3COO^-(aq)$$

A $0.1\,mol\,dm^{-3}$ solution of ethanoic acid is only 1.3% ionised.

A strong base is totally ionised in aqueous solution, forming hydroxide ions, OH^-.

For example, sodium hydroxide is a strong base:

$$NaOH(aq) \rightarrow Na^+(aq) + OH^-(aq)$$

A weak base is protonated to only a small degree in solution and so only forms a small proportion of hydroxide ions.

For example, ammonia is a weak base:

$$NH_3(aq) + H_2O(l) \rightleftharpoons NH_4^+(aq) + OH^-(aq)$$

> **Tip**
>
> Do not say that a weak acid is only partially ionised because this could mean that the ionisation is considerable but less than complete. Even HF, which is one of the strongest 'weak' acids, is only 5.7% ionised in a $0.1\,mol\,dm^{-3}$ solution.

> **Tip**
>
> State symbols need not be written in equations in this topic, as all the substances are in solution.

Acid and base equilibrium constants

Acid dissociation constant, K_a

A weak acid is in equilibrium with its conjugate base in aqueous solution. Consider a weak acid, HA:

$$HA + H_2O \rightleftharpoons H_3O^+ + A^-$$

The expression for the equilibrium constant (known in this context as the **acid dissociation constant, K_a**) is:

$$K_a = \frac{[H_3O^+][A^-]}{[HA]}$$

$[H_2O]$ is not included in this expression as the concentration of water, in aqueous solutions, is constant.

The equation for a weak acid is sometimes written as $HA \rightleftharpoons H^+ + A^-$. So the expression for K_a is:

$$K_a = \frac{[H^+][A^-]}{[HA]}$$

where $[H^+]$ can be regarded as being shorthand for $[H_3O^+]$.

> **Tip**
>
> Never include $[H_2O]$ in the expression for K_a.

Base dissociation constant, K_b

An aqueous solution of a weak base is in equilibrium with its conjugate acid, for example:

$$NH_3 + H_2O \rightleftharpoons NH_4^+ + OH^-$$

The expression for the **base dissociation constant, K_b**, is:

$$K_b = \frac{[NH_4^+][OH^-]}{[NH_3]}$$

As with weak acids, $[H_2O]$ is omitted from the expression because its value is constant in aqueous equilibria involving weak bases.

Auto-ionisation of water and the pH scale

Water is amphoteric. It can act as either a base, as in its reaction with hydrogen chloride, or as an acid, as in its reaction with ammonia.

The amphoteric nature of water is even evident in the absence of another acid or base. One molecule of water can protonate another molecule of water (Figure 2.5).

$$\underset{\text{acid}}{H_2O} \quad + \quad \underset{\text{base}}{H_2O} \quad \rightleftharpoons \quad \underset{\text{conjugate acid}}{H_3O^+} \quad + \quad \underset{\text{conjugate base}}{OH^-}$$

Figure 2.5

The equilibrium constant for this reaction is given the symbol K_w. The equilibrium expression does not include the term $[H_2O]$ because its value is constant.

$$K_w = [H_3O^+][OH^-]$$

This is often written as $K_w = [H^+][OH^-]$.

K_w is also called the **ionic product** of water. Its value at 25°C is $1.0 \times 10^{-14}\,mol^2\,dm^{-6}$.

In any aqueous solution at 25°C the value of $[H^+] \times [OH^-]$ always equals K_w, the value of which is $1.0 \times 10^{-14}\,mol^2\,dm^{-6}$.

Thus:

$$[OH] = \frac{1.0 \times 10^{-14}}{[H^+]}$$

For an acidic solution containing $1.0 \times 10^{-3}\,mol\,dm^{-3}$ of $H^+(aq)$ ions:

$$[OH^-] = \frac{1.0 \times 10^{-14}}{1.0 \times 10^{-3}} = 1.0 \times 10^{-11}\,mol\,dm^{-3}$$

pH scale

Hydrogen ion concentration varies over a huge range of values (by a factor of about a trillion), so a logarithmic scale of measurement was devised. To avoid negative numbers in most cases, the scale was defined as:

$$pH = -\log_{10}[H^+] \text{ (this is often written as } -\log[H^+] \text{ or } -\lg[H^+])$$

Hence:

$$[H^+] = 10^{-pH}$$

pH equals the negative logarithm to the base 10 of the hydrogen ion (hydronium ion) concentration.

In practice, the pH scale runs from about −1 to just over 14.

Tip

You should report all pH values to two decimal places.

Worked example

Calculate the pH of a solution in which $[H^+]$ is equal to:

a) $10\,mol\,dm^{-3}$

b) $1.0\,mol\,dm^{-3}$

c) $0.10\,mol\,dm^{-3}$

d) $1.23 \times 10^{-4}\,mol\,dm^{-3}$

e) $4.56 \times 10^{-9}\,mol\,dm^{-3}$

f) $7.89 \times 10^{-15}\,mol\,dm^{-3}$

Answer

a) $pH = -\log 10 = -1.00$

b) $pH = -\log 1.0 = 0.00$

c) $pH = -\log 0.10 = 1.00$

d) $pH = -\log 1.23 \times 10^{-4} = 3.91$

e) $pH = -\log 4.56 \times 10^{-9} = 8.34$

f) $pH = -\log 7.89 \times 10^{-15} = 14.10$

The hydrogen ion concentration can be calculated from the pH, using the expression:

$$[H^+] = 10^{-pH}$$

Worked example

Calculate the hydrogen ion concentration in solutions of pH:

a) 3.50 b) 7.00 c) 12.85

Answer

a) $[H^+] = 10^{-3.50} = 3.16 \times 10^{-4}\,mol\,dm^{-3}$

b) $[H^+] = 10^{-7.00} = 1.0 \times 10^{-7}\,mol\,dm^{-3}$

c) $[H^+] = 10^{-12.85} = 1.41 \times 10^{-13}\,mol\,dm^{-3}$

Test yourself

3 Calculate the concentration of hydrogen ions in solutions of pH = 13.67.

Neutrality

A neutral solution is one in which the concentrations of H^+ and OH^- ions are the same:

$$K_w = [H^+][OH^-] = 1.0 \times 10^{-14}\,mol^2\,dm^{-6} \text{ at } 25°C$$

$$[H^+] = [OH^-]$$

$$[H^+]^2 = 1.0 \times 10^{-14} \quad or \quad [H^+] = \sqrt{1.0 \times 10^{-14}} = 1.0 \times 10^{-7}\,mol\,dm^{-3}$$

$$pH = -\log 1.0 \times 10^{-7} = 7.00$$

In all aqueous solutions at 25°C, $[H^+] \times [OH^-] = 1.0 \times 10^{-14}$.

An acidic solution has $[H^+] > [OH^-]$. Therefore $[H^+] > 1.0 \times 10^{-7}$ and the solution has $pH < 7$.

An alkaline solution has $[H^+] < [OH^-]$. Therefore $[H^+] < 1.0 \times 10^{-7}$ and the solution has pH > 7.

At 25°C: neutral pH = 7; acidic pH < 7; alkaline pH > 7.

The ionisation of water is endothermic, so the value of K_w increases with temperature. At 37°C (normal blood temperature), the value of K_w is $2.4 \times 10^{-14}\,mol^2\,dm^{-6}$, hence:

$$[H^+] = \sqrt{2.4 \times 10^{-14}} = 1.549 \times 10^{-7}\,mol\,dm^{-3}$$

$$\text{neutral pH at } 37°C = -\log_{10}(1.549 \times 10^{-7}) = 6.81$$

At 100°C $K_w = 5.13 \times 10^{-13}\,mol^2\,dm^{-6}$. Therefore at 100°C, neutral pH is 6.14.

pK_w, pOH and pK_a

The prefix 'p', in this context, means 'the negative log of'.

$$pK_w = -\log K_w$$

$$\text{At } 25°C,\ pK_w = -\log(1.0 \times 10^{-14}) = 14.0$$

$$pOH = -\log[OH^-]$$

As $K_w = [H^+][OH^-]$ and since $\log(a \times b) = \log a + \log b$:

$$\log K_w = \log[H^+] + \log[OH^-]$$

$$pK_w = pH + pOH$$

At 25°C: $\qquad$ pH + pOH = 14 $\qquad$ and $\qquad$ pOH = 14 − pH

Worked example

Calculate the concentration of hydroxide ions in a solution of pH 1.23.

Answer 1
Method 1, which uses pH + pOH = 14.

$$pOH = 14 - pH = 14 - 1.23 = 12.77$$

$$[OH^-] = 10^{-12.77} = 1.70 \times 10^{-13}\ mol\,dm^{-3}$$

Answer 2
Method 2, which uses $[OH^-] = \dfrac{K_w}{[H^+]}$.

$$[H^+] = 10^{-1.23} = 0.0589\,mol\,dm^{-3}$$

$$[OH^-] = \frac{1.00 \times 10^{-14}}{0.0589} = 1.70 \times 10^{-13}\,mol\,dm^{-3}$$

Test yourself

4 Calculate:

a) the $[OH^-]$ of a solution with $[H^+] = 3.3 \times 10^{-10}\,mol\,dm^{-3}$

b) the pH of a solution in which $[OH^-] = 6.6 \times 10^{-2}\,mol\,dm^{-3}$

The acid dissociation constant, K_a, and pK_a are related by the expression:

$$pK_a = -\log K_a \quad \text{or} \quad K_a = 10^{-pK_a}$$

Worked example

a) Calculate the value of K_a of a weak acid with $pK_a = 5.45$.

b) Calculate the value of pK_a of a weak acid with $K_a = 2.17 \times 10^{-6}\,mol\,dm^{-3}$.

Answer

a) $K_a = 10^{-pK_a} = 10^{-5.45} = 3.55 \times 10^{-6}\,mol\,dm^{-3}$

b) $pK_a = -\log K_a = -\log(2.17 \times 10^{-6}) = 5.66$

The pH of acids, bases and salts

The pH of strong acids

A **strong acid**, such as nitric acid, HNO_3, is totally ionised in aqueous solution. Thus, for example, a nitric acid solution of concentration $0.123\,mol\,dm^{-3}$ has a hydrogen ion concentration of $0.123\,mol\,dm^{-3}$.

$$pH = -\log 0.123 = 0.91$$

Worked example 1

Calculate the pH of a solution of HCl made by dissolving 4.56 g of hydrogen chloride, HCl (or $3.00\,dm^3$ of HCl gas where the molar volume of a gas under these conditions is $24.0\,dm^3\,mol^{-1}$) in water and making the solution up to a volume of $250\,cm^3$.

Answer

$$\text{amount of HCl} = \frac{4.56\,g}{36.5\,g\,mol^{-1}} = 0.125\,mol$$

$$\left(\text{or } \frac{3.00\,dm^3}{24.0\,dm^3\,mol^{-1}}\right) = 0.125\,mol$$

$$[HCl] = \frac{mol}{volume} = \frac{0.125\,mol}{0.250\,dm^3} = 0.500\,mol\,dm^{-3}$$

$$pH = -\log 0.500 = 0.30$$

Worked example 2

Calculate the pH of a $2.00\,mol\,dm^{-3}$ solution of hydrochloric acid.

Answer

$$[H^+] = 2.00\,mol\,dm^{-3}$$

$$pH = -\log 2.00 = -0.30$$

Tip

Note that if a strong acid has a concentration greater than $1.00\,mol\,dm^{-3}$, it will have a negative pH.

The pH of strong bases

A **strong base** is totally ionised in aqueous solution. For example, a solution of a soluble base MOH of concentration $0.123\,mol\,dm^{-3}$ has a hydroxide ion concentration of $0.123\,mol\,dm^{-3}$.

A solution of a strong base $M(OH)_2$ of concentration $0.123\,mol\,dm^{-3}$ has a hydroxide ion concentration of $0.246\,mol\,dm^{-3}$, as there are two moles of OH^- ions per mole of base.

The pH can be worked out in one of two ways.

Method 1

Using the expression $pH + pOH = 14$, calculate pOH and hence pH.

If $[OH^-] = 0.123\,mol\,dm^{-3}$:

$$pOH = -\log[OH^-] = -\log 0.123 = 0.91$$

$$pH = 14 - pOH = 14 - 0.91 = 13.09$$

Method 2

Using the expression $[H^+] \times [OH^-] = 1.0 \times 10^{-14}\,mol^2\,dm^{-6}$, calculate $[H^+]$ and hence the pH.

In the example above:

$$[OH^-] = 0.123\,mol\,dm^{-3}$$

$$[H^+] = \frac{1.0 \times 10^{-14}}{[OH^-]} = \frac{1.0 \times 10^{-14}}{0.123} = 8.13 \times 10^{-14}\,mol\,dm^{-3}$$

$$pH = -\log[H^+] = -\log 8.13 \times 10^{-14} = 13.09$$

Worked example

Calculate the pH of a $0.0444\,mol\,dm^{-3}$ solution of barium hydroxide, $Ba(OH)_2$.

Answer using method 1

1 mol of $Ba(OH)_2$ produces 2 mol of OH^- ions.

$$[OH^-] = 2 \times 0.0444 = 0.0888\,mol\,dm^{-3}$$

$$pOH = -\log 0.0888 = 1.05$$

$$pH = 14 - pOH = 14 - 1.05 = 12.95$$

Answer using method 2

1 mol of $Ba(OH)_2$ produces 2 mol of OH^- ions.

$$[OH^-] = 2 \times 0.0444 = 0.0888\,mol\,dm^{-3}$$

$$[H^+] = \frac{1.0 \times 10^{-14}}{0.0888} = 1.13 \times 10^{-13}$$

$$pH = -\log[H^+] = -\log 1.13 \times 10^{-13} = 12.95$$

Tip

You should always check your calculation of pH to ensure it makes sense. An acid solution at 298 K cannot have a pH > 7; an alkaline solution cannot have a pH < 7. If you have obtained an impossible answer as a result of a calculation, then you should do the calculation again.

Test yourself

5 Calculate the pH of $0.200\,mol\,dm^{-3}$ lithium hydroxide, LiOH, which is a strong base.

The pH of weak acids

A weak acid is in equilibrium with its conjugate base:

$$HA + H_2O \rightleftharpoons H_3O^+ + A^-$$

The rates of the forward and back reactions are so rapid, that the system is always in equilibrium. The equilibrium constant (the acid dissociation constant, K_a) is given by:

$$K_a = \frac{[H_3O^+][A^+]}{[HA]}$$

The reaction is sometimes simplified to:

$$HA \rightleftharpoons H^+ + A^-$$

$$K_a = \frac{[H^+][A^-]}{[HA]}$$

$[H_2O]$ is omitted from these expressions, as its concentration is effectively constant.

The pH of a solution of a weak acid can be calculated using the same method as for K_c calculations.

Consider a $0.10\,mol\,dm^{-3}$ solution of a weak acid with $K_a = 1.0 \times 10^{-5}\,mol\,dm^{-3}$. Let $x\,mol$ of HA ionise per dm^3:

	HA	H₃O⁺	A⁻
Initial concentration	0.10	0	0
Equilibrium concentration	(0.10 – x)	x	x

$$K_a = \frac{[H_3O^+][A^-]}{[HA]} = \frac{x^2}{0.10 - x} = 1.0 \times 10^{-15}\,mol\,dm^{-3}$$

This can be solved only by using the formula for a quadratic equation, which is outside the A level chemistry specification. However, for most weak acids even in very dilute solutions, the percentage ionisation is less than 5%. This means that the value of x is much less than the initial concentration of the weak acid, and so the term $(0.10 - x)$ can be approximated to 0.10. The value of x can now be solved easily:

$$\frac{x^2}{0.10} = 1.0 \times 10^{-5}$$

$$x = \sqrt{(1.0 \times 10^{-5} \times 0.10} = 1.0 \times 10^{-3}\,mol\,dm^{-3}$$

Thus,

$$[H_3O^+] = 1.0 \times 10^{-3}\,mol\,dm^{-3}$$

$$pH = -\log 1.0 \times 10^{-3} = 3.000$$

In calculations involving weak acids, the following assumptions are made:

- $[H_3O^+] = [A^-]$ (because there is no other source of A^- ions)
- $[HA]$ at equilibrium is equal to the concentration of the acid HA given in the question, which is also called $[HA]_{initial}$ (only about 1% of the weak acid molecules are ionised, so this is a fair assumption)

A level students studying maths can use the formula for quadratic equations. This gives the pH = 3.002 which to 2 decimal places is the same.

These assumptions allow the expression for K_a to be simplified:

$$K_a = \frac{[H_3O^+][A^-]}{[HA]} = \frac{[H_3O^+]^2}{[HA]_{initial}}$$

This simplified expression can be used to calculate the pH of a solution of a weak acid, given its concentration and the value of K_a.

Tip

The subscript in [weak acid]$_{initial}$ is the value as if none of the acid had dissociated. It is the value given in the question.

Tip

Always use the equilibrium constant expression in these and buffer solution calculations. It is safer than trying to remember a formula such as pH = $\frac{1}{2}pK_a - \frac{1}{2}\log c$ (where c = the concentration of the acid).

Worked example

Calculate the pH of a 0.135 mol dm^{-3} solution of ethanoic acid. (K_a for ethanoic acid = 1.8×10^{-5} mol dm^{-3} at 25°C)

Answer

Ethanoic acid ionises in water:

$$CH_3COOH + H_2O \rightleftharpoons H_3O^+ + CH_3COO^-$$

$$K_a = \frac{[H_3O^+][CH_3COO^-]}{[CH_3COOH]}$$

$$= \frac{[H_3O^+]^2}{0.135}$$

$$= 1.8 \times 10^{-5} \text{ mol dm}^{-3}$$

$$[H_3O^+]^2 = 0.135 \times 1.8 \times 10^{-5}$$

$$= 2.43 \times 10^{-6} \text{ mol}^2 \text{ dm}^{-6}$$

$$[H_3O^+] = \sqrt{(2.43 \times 10^{-6})}$$

$$= 0.00156 \text{ mol dm}^{-3}$$

$$pH = -\log[H_3O^+] = -\log 0.00156 = 2.81$$

Some questions give the pK_a value of the weak acid. In this case, pK_a must be converted to K_a.

$$K_a = 10^{-pK_a}$$

For example, pK_a for methanoic acid = 3.75.

$$K_a = 10^{-3.75} = 1.78 \times 10^{-4} \text{ mol dm}^{-3}$$

The strengths of some weak acids are shown in Table 2.2.

The smaller the value of K_a, the weaker is the acid. Thus, the larger the value of pK_a, the weaker is the acid.

Table 2.2 Acid dissociation constants, K_a, and the pK_a values of some weak acids

	pK_a	K_a/mol dm^{-3}
Inorganic acids		
Hydrogensulfate ion, HSO_4^-	2.0	0.010
Hydrogen fluoride, HF	3.25	5.65×10^{-4}
Carbonic acid, H_2CO_3	6.38	4.17×10^{-7}
Ammonium ion, NH_4^+	9.25	5.62×10^{-10}
Hydrogen cyanide, HCN	9.40	3.98×10^{-10}
Hydrogencarbonate ion, HCO_3^-	10.32	4.79×10^{-11}
Organic acids		
Methanoic, HCOOH	3.75	1.78×10^{-4}
Ethanoic, CH_3COOH	4.76	1.75×10^{-5}
Chloroethanoic, $ClCH_2COOH$	2.86	1.32×10^{-3}
Propanoic, C_2H_5COOH	4.86	1.39×10^{-5}

Weak acids have $K_a < 1$ and $pK_a > 0$.

For organic acids where the hydrogen is bonded to oxygen, the relative strength depends on how $\delta+$ the hydrogen of the $O-H$ group is. The CH_3 group is electron pushing and so the $O-H$ hydrogen in ethanoic acid is less $\delta+$ than in methanoic acid and so it is a weaker acid than methanoic acid.

Test yourself

6 Propanoic acid is a weak acid with $K_a = 1.35 \times 10^{-5}\,mol\,dm^{-3}$. A solution of the acid has a pH = 3.09. Calculate the concentration of the propanoic acid in the solution.

Diprotic acids

Sulfuric acid, H_2SO_4, is only a strong acid in its first ionisation:

$$H_2SO_4 \rightarrow H^+ + HSO_4^-$$

The second ionisation is weak and is suppressed by the H^+ ions from the first ionisation:

$$HSO_4^- \rightleftharpoons H^+ + SO_4^{2-}$$

So, a solution of sulfuric acid of concentration $0.10\,mol\,dm^{-3}$ has $[H^+]$ of just above $0.10\,mol\,dm^{-3}$, *not* $0.20\,mol\,dm^{-3}$ and hence its pH is very slightly less than 1.00. To an accuracy of one decimal place, the second ionisation can be ignored.

Extension for those doing A level maths

For $0.10\,mol\,dm^{-3}$ sulfuric acid, the first ionisation is complete and the second partial, with $K_2 = 0.010\,mol\,dm^{-3}$.

	$H_2SO_4 \rightarrow$	H^+	$+$	HSO_4^-
Concentrations/mol dm^{-3}	0	0.1		0.1

then...

	$HSO_4^- \rightleftharpoons$	H^+	$+$	SO_4^{2-}
Concentrations/mol dm^{-3}	$0.10 - x$	$0.10 + x$		x

$$K_2 = 0.010 = \frac{[H^+][SO_4^{2-}]}{[HSO_4^-]} = \frac{(0.10 + x)x}{(0.10 - x)}$$
$$0.0010 - 0.010x = 0.10x + x^2$$

$$x^2 + 0.11x - 0.0010 = 0$$

Solving for x gives:

$$x = \frac{-0.11 \pm \sqrt{0.11^2 - (4 \times -0.0010)}}{2} = 0.00844$$

$$[H^+] = 0.10 + 0.00844 = 0.1084\,mol\,dm^{-3}$$

$$pH = -\log 0.1084 = 0.96$$

To one decimal place the pH of $0.10\,mol\,dm^{-3}$ H_2SO_4 is 1.0. To two decimal places the pH is 0.96.

$[H^+]$ is the sum of $[H^+]$ from the first and second ionisations

Solutions of equal concentration

The pH of $0.10\,mol\,dm^{-3}$ solutions of a number of acids, bases and salts are shown in Table 2.3.

Table 2.3 The pH of $0.1\,mol\,dm^{-3}$ solutions of some acids, bases and salts

Acid or base	pH	Salt	pH
Strong acid (e.g. HCl)	1.0	Salt of strong acid and strong base (e.g. NaCl)	7.0
Weak acid (e.g. CH_3COOH)	2.9	Salt of a strong acid and weak base (e.g. NH_4Cl)	5.1
Strong base (e.g. NaOH)	13.0	Salt of a weak acid and a strong base (e.g. CH_3COONa)	8.9
Weak base (e.g. NH_3)	11.1	Salt of a weak acid and weak base (e.g. CH_3COONH_4)	7.0

Note how the pH of a solution of a weak acid or a weak base differs by approximately two from that of a strong acid or base (the rule of two — see p. 51.)

Dilution of solutions

The pH values resulting from diluting solutions of strong and weak acids and bases by factors of ten are shown in Table 2.4.

Table 2.4 Effect on pH of dilution

Concentration/ $mol\,dm^{-3}$	pH of a solution of HCl	pH of a solution of NaOH	pH of a solution of CH_3COOH	pH of a solution of NH_3
0.1	1	13	2.9	11.1
0.01	2	12	3.4	10.6
0.001	3	11	3.9	10.1
0.0001	4	10	4.4	9.6

Note that the pH of an acid increases as it is diluted; the pH of a base decreases as it is diluted.

When strong acids or strong bases are diluted, the pH changes by 1 unit for each ten-fold dilution.

When weak acids or weak bases are diluted, the pH changes by half a unit for each ten-fold dilution.

Test yourself

7 Calculate the pH of a $2.0\,mol\,dm^{-3}$ solution of nitric acid, HNO_3, and its pH when it is diluted 100 times.

Calculation of K_a from experimental data

The pH of a solution can be measured using a pH meter (p. 101). If the pH and mass of a weak acid dissolved in a known amount of water are known, the value of its acid dissociation constant, K_a, can be calculated.

Worked example

A solution of propanoic acid, $M_r = 74\,\text{g}\,\text{mol}^{-1}$, was made by dissolving 3.7 g of the acid in water and making the solution up to 250 cm³. This solution had a pH of 2.78. Calculate the value of its acid dissociation constant, K_a.

Answer

amount (moles) of propanoic acid taken = $3.7\,\text{g}/74\,\text{g}\,\text{mol}^{-1} = 0.050\,\text{mol}$

initial concentration of propanoic acid, $[C_2H_5COOH]_{initial}$, = $0.050\,\text{mol}/0.250\,\text{dm}^3$ = $0.200\,\text{mol}\,\text{dm}^{-3}$

Propanoic acid ionises according to the equilibrium:

$$C_2H_5COOH \rightleftharpoons H^+ + C_2H_5COO^-$$

pH = 2.78, so $[H^+] = 10^{-2.78} = 0.00166\,\text{mol}\,\text{dm}^{-3}$

$$K_a = \frac{[H^+][C_2H_5COO^-]}{[C_2H_5COOH]_{initial}}$$

$$= \frac{[H^+]^2}{[C_2H_5COOH]_{initial}}$$

$$= \frac{0.00166^2}{0.200} = 1.38 \times 10^{-5}\,\text{mol}\,\text{dm}^{-5}$$

> **Tip**
>
> Note that in this worked example the simplified equilibrium equation was written, with H^+ being used instead of H_3O^+. Both are acceptable.

$[C_2H_5COOH]_{initial}$ = the concentration as given in the question

In the worked example above, the approximation:

$$[C_2H_5COOH]_{eq} = [C_2H_5COOH]_{initial}$$

need not have been made. The question gives the solution pH of 2.78, so $[H^+] = 10^{-2.78}$ = $0.00166\,\text{mol}\,\text{dm}^{-3}$. Therefore, $0.00166\,\text{mol}\,\text{dm}^{-3}$ of acid must have dissociated, leaving $[C_2H_5COOH]$ = $0.200 - 0.00166 = 0.19834\,\text{mol}\,\text{dm}^{-3}$. This difference is so small that the true value of K_a obtained without using the approximation is $1.39 \times 10^{-5}\,\text{mol}\,\text{dm}^{-3}$, which is hardly any different from that calculated using the approximation. However, with weak acids such as HF and HNO_2, which are stronger than propanoic acid, the approximation should not be made.

Worked example

The pH of a $0.100\,\text{mol}\,\text{dm}^{-3}$ solution of hydrofluoric acid, HF, was found to be 2.14. Calculate the value of the acid dissociation constant, K_a, of hydrofluoric acid.

Answer

$[H^+] = 10^{-pH} = 10^{-2.14} = 0.00724\,\text{mol}\,\text{dm}^{-3}$

$[H^+] = [F^-]$

$0.00724\,\text{mol}\,\text{dm}^{-3}$ of H^+ ions were produced, so 0.00724 mol of HF must have dissociated.

$[HF] = [\text{original}] - [\text{amount dissociated}] = (0.100 - 0.00724) = 0.0928\,\text{mol}\,\text{dm}^{-3}$

$$K_a = \frac{[H^+][F^-]}{[HF]} = \frac{0.00724^2}{0.0928} = 5.65 \times 10^{-4}\,\text{mol}\,\text{dm}^{-3}$$

In the worked example above, if the approximation:

$$[HF] = [\text{original acid}] = 0.100 \, \text{mol dm}^{-3}$$

had been made, the value of K_a would have been $5.24 \times 10^{-4} \, \text{mol dm}^{-3}$.

The pH of weak bases

A **weak base** is partially protonated in water. Ammonia is an example of a weak base:

$$NH_3 + H_2O \rightleftharpoons NH_4^+ + OH^-$$

$$K_b = \frac{[NH_4^+][OH^-]}{[NH_3]}$$

As with weak acids, the term $[H_2O]$ is omitted, as its value is constant.

The same type of assumptions can be made as with weak acids:

$$[NH_4^+] = [OH^-] \text{ and } [NH_3]_{eq} = [NH_3]_{initial}$$

Thus:

$$K_b = \frac{[OH^-]^2}{[NH_3]}$$

$$[OH^-]^2 = K_b \times [NH_3]$$

The value of K_b for ammonia at $25°C = 1.78 \times 10^{-5} \, \text{mol dm}^{-3}$, so the pH of a $0.100 \, \text{mol dm}^3$ ammonia solution can be calculated:

$$[OH^-] = \sqrt{K_b \times [NH_3]} = \sqrt{1.78 \times 10^{-5} \times 0.100} = 0.00133 \, \text{mol dm}^{-3}$$

$$pOH = -\log[OH^-] = -\log 0.00133 = 2.88$$

$$pH = 14 - pOH = 14 - 2.88 = 11.12$$

The strengths of some weak bases are shown in Table 2.5.

Table 2.5 Dissociation constants, K_b, and the pK_b values of some weak bases

Substance	$K_b/\text{mol dm}^{-3}$	pK_b
Ammonia, NH_3	1.78×10^{-5}	4.75
Cyanide ion, CN^-	2.51×10^{-5}	4.60
Ethanoate ion, CH_3COO^-	5.75×10^{-10}	9.24

Salts of weak bases

The cations in the salts of weak bases are their conjugate acids. For example, the ammonium ion, NH_4^+, is the conjugate acid of the weak base ammonia, NH_3.

A solution of ammonium chloride is totally ionised:

$$NH_4Cl \rightarrow NH_4^+ + Cl^-$$

The ammonium ions act as an acid, reacting reversibly with water to produce H_3O^+ ions, which make the solution acidic.

$$NH_4^+ + H_2O \rightleftharpoons H_3O^+ + NH_3$$

$$K_a = \frac{[H_3O^+][NH_3]}{[NH_4^+]}$$

As the K_a for NH_4^+ = 5.62×10^{-10} mol dm^{-3} and using the usual assumptions for a weak acid:

$$[H_3O^+]^2 = K_a \times [\text{weak acid}] = K_a \times [NH_4^+]$$

For a 0.10 mol dm^{-3} solution of ammonium chloride:

$$[H_3O^+] = \sqrt{5.62 \times 10^{-10} \times 0.10} = 7.50 \times 10^{-6} \text{ mol dm}^{-3}$$

$$pH = -\log[H_3O+] = -\log 7.50 \times 10^{-6} = 5.13$$

The pH is less than 7, so the solution is acidic.

> **Tip**
>
> Remember that a solution is acidic if $[H^+]$ or $[H_3O^+]$ > $[OH^-]$. A neutral solution becomes acidic if H^+ ions are produced. NH_4^+ ions produce H^+ ions and so the solution has a pH < 7.

Salts of weak acids

The anions in the salts of weak acids are their conjugate bases. For example, the ethanoate ion in sodium ethanoate is the conjugate base of ethanoic acid, which is a weak acid.

Sodium ethanoate is totally ionised:

$$CH_3COONa \rightarrow CH_3COO^- + Na^+$$

The CH_3COO^- ions react reversibly with water:

$$CH_3COO^- + H_2O \rightleftharpoons CH_3COOH + OH^-$$

The formation of OH^- ions makes the solution alkaline.

$$K_b = \frac{[CH_3COOH][OH^-]}{[CH_3COO^-]}$$

The value of K_b of a conjugate base can be found by using the formula:

$$K_a \times K_b = K_w$$

K_a for ethanoic acid = 1.75×10^{-5} mol dm^{-3}

So:

$$K_b \text{ for the ethanoate ion} = \frac{1.0 \times 10^{-14}}{1.75 \times 10^{-5}} = 5.71 \times 10^{-10} \text{ mol dm}^{-3}$$

The pH of a 0.10 mol dm^{-3} solution of sodium ethanoate can be calculated:

$$[OH^-]^2 = K_b[CH_3COO^-]$$

$$[OH^-] = \sqrt{5.71 \times 10^{-10} \times 0.10} = 7.56 \times 10^{-6} \text{ mol dm}^{-3}$$

$$pOH = -\log[OH^-] = -\log 7.56 \times 10^{-6} = 5.12$$

$$pH = 14 - pOH = 14 - 5.12 = 8.88$$

The pH is greater than 7, so the solution is alkaline.

> **Tip**
>
> Salts of weak bases and strong acids are slightly acidic, so have a pH less than 7. Salts of weak acids and strong bases are slightly alkaline, so have a pH greater than 7.

The weaker the acid, the stronger is its anion as a conjugate base, and the more alkaline is the solution of its salt. For example, carbonic acid, H_2CO_3, is a weaker acid than ethanoic acid, so a solution of its conjugate base sodium carbonate has a higher pH than a solution of sodium ethanoate.

Test yourself

8 Write the equation for the reaction of water with:

   a) NH_4^+ ions

   b) CN^- ions

   c) State whether their solutions would be neutral, acidic or alkaline.

Salts of strong acids and strong bases

The conjugate base of a strong acid, such as HCl, is too weak to react with water. Similarly, the conjugate acid of a strong base does not react, so the salts of strong acids and strong bases dissolve in water without any reaction taking place. Their solutions are neutral, pH 7.

$$Cl^- + H_2O \rightarrow \text{no reaction}$$

$$Na^+ + H_2O \rightarrow \text{no reaction}$$

> The reaction $NaCl + H_2O \rightarrow$ $HCl + NaOH$ does *not* occur. In fact, the reverse reaction goes to completion.

Universal indicator in various salt solutions (left to right: ammonium chloride, sodium chloride, sodium ethanoate and sodium carbonate)

Buffer solutions

> **Tip**
>
> Do not state that a buffer has constant pH. A buffer solution *resists* the change in pH when *small* amounts of H^+ or OH^- ions are added. It does not completely remove all the added H^+ or OH^- ions. Therefore, the pH does change, but only very slightly.

A buffer solution is one that resists a change in pH when a small amount of acid or base is added.

An **acid buffer solution** consists of a mixture of a weak acid and its conjugate base of *similar* concentration — for example, the weak acid ethanoic acid, CH_3COOH, and its salt sodium ethanoate, CH_3COONa.

An **alkaline buffer solution** consists of a weak base and its conjugate acid of *similar* concentration — for example, the weak base ammonia, NH_3, and its salt ammonium chloride, NH_4Cl.

The crucial points are that the members of the acid–base conjugate pair must be at a similar concentration, which should be not less than $0.05\,mol\,dm^{-3}$. The difference in their concentrations should not be more than a factor of ten.

Blood plasma has a pH of 7.4 and acts as a buffer solution. The pH is maintained mainly by the mixture of carbonic acid and hydrogencarbonate ions. Inside the red blood cells, the pH is 7.25. Here, the buffer is also carbonic acid–hydrogencarbonate ions, but haemoglobin molecules are themselves acidic and lower the pH.

It is important that the pH of blood plasma and of the fluid inside the blood cells does not alter significantly. If the pH changes inside a haemoglobin cell, its ability to absorb oxygen is altered. If a person hyperventilates, carbon dioxide is removed from the blood plasma and the pH alters, which causes the person to become unconscious.

Some foods are buffered to prevent deterioration. Decay due to bacteria may release acids, which, in the absence of a buffer, would result in a pH change that would cause the food to deteriorate.

Mode of action of a buffer solution

Consider a buffer solution made of a weak acid, HA, and its sodium salt, NaA. The salt is totally ionised:

$$NaA \rightarrow Na^+ + A^-$$

The weak acid is only slightly ionised:

$$HA \rightleftharpoons H^+ + A^-$$

Its ionisation is *suppressed* by the A^- ions from the totally ionised salt, thus $[A^-] \approx$ [salt] and $[HA] \approx$ [weak acid]:

$$K_a = \frac{[H^+][A^-]}{[HA]} = \frac{[H^+][salt]}{[weak\ acid]}$$

> The acid produces a reservoir of HA molecules and the salt produces a reservoir of A^- ions.

A buffer solution maintains a nearly constant pH because the reservoirs of both the weak acid, HA, and its conjugate base, A^-, are large *relative* to the small amount of H^+ or OH^- added.

When a *small* amount of H^+ ions is added, the ions react with the relatively large reservoir of A^- ions from the salt:

$$H^+ + A^- \rightarrow HA$$

The value of $[A^-]$ decreases slightly and that of [HA] increases slightly, but these changes are insignificant in relation to the original values of $[A^-]$ (from the totally ionised salt) and of [HA] (from the almost unionised weak acid), which remain virtually unchanged. Nothing has changed significantly in the expression for K_a, so the hydrogen ion concentration and hence the pH will not change significantly.

> A weak acid on its own is not a buffer as $[A^-]$ is very small. When H^+ or OH^- is added, the change in $[A^-]$ is significant.

When a *small* amount of OH^- ions is added, the ions react with the relatively large reservoir of HA molecules of the weak acid:

$$OH^- + HA \rightarrow H_2O + A^-$$

The value of $[A^-]$ increases slightly and that of [HA] decreases slightly, but these changes are insignificant in relation to the original values of $[A^-]$ and [HA], which remain virtually unchanged. Nothing has changed significantly in the expression for K_a, so the hydrogen ion concentration and hence the pH will not change greatly.

Tip

The addition of OH^- ions can also be explained by stating that they drive the equilibrium $HA \rightleftharpoons H^+ + A^-$ to the right, by removal of the H^+ ions. This causes an increase in $[A^-]$. However, the increase is not significant because of the relatively large value of $[A^-]$ from the salt. [HA] also decreases slightly, but also by an insignificant amount. Therefore, the pH hardly changes.

The mode of action of a buffer can be summarised as follows:

- The salt is fully ionised, so suppresses the ionisation of the weak acid.
- The amounts of the weak acid *and* its conjugate base are large relative to the small additions of H^+ or OH^-.
- H^+ ions are removed by reaction with the conjugate base: $H^+ + A^- \rightarrow HA$
- OH^- ions are removed by reaction with the weak acid: $OH^- + HA \rightarrow H_2O + A^-$
- Because [weak acid] and [salt] are large relative to the added H^+ or OH^- ions, there is no significant change in pH.

Efficiency of a buffer solution

This can be tested by adding $0.10\,mol\,dm^{-3}$ hydrochloric acid in $5\,cm^3$ portions to $100\,cm^3$ of a buffer solution made by dissolving $0.1\,mol$ of sodium ethanoate in $100\,cm^3$ of $1.0\,mol\,dm^{-3}$ ethanoic acid solution and measuring the pH after each addition. The results are shown in Table 2.6.

Table 2.6

Volume of $0.10\,mol\,dm^{-3}$ HCl added	pH
0	4.76
5	4.76
10	4.77
15	4.77
20	4.78

> **Test yourself**
>
> 9 Which of the following mixtures are buffer solutions and which are not?
>   a) hydrochloric acid and excess ammonia
>   b) equal amounts of hydrochloric acid and sodium chloride
>   c) sodium hydroxide and excess ethanoic acid

Calculation of the pH of a buffer solution

Consider a buffer solution made up of a weak acid, HA, and its sodium salt, NaA. The salt is totally ionised:

$$NaA \rightarrow Na^+ + A^-$$

The weak acid is only slightly ionised:

$$HA \rightleftharpoons H^+ + A^- \qquad K_a = \frac{[H^+][A^-]}{[HA]}$$

Ionisation of the weak acid is *suppressed* by the A^- ions from the totally ionised salt. This means that both [HA] and [A^-] are fairly large and both are much larger than [H^+]. The following assumptions can be made:

- The number of A^- ions from the totally ionised salt is much greater than the few A^- ions from the weak acid, so it can be assumed that [A^-] = [salt] (the concentration of salt originally present).
- The ionisation of the weak acid is so suppressed that [HA] = [weak acid] (the concentration of weak acid originally present).

The equilibrium expression can, therefore, be simplified:

$$K_a = \frac{[H^+][A^-]}{[HA]} = \frac{[H^+][salt]}{[weak\ acid]}$$

So:

$$[H^+] = \frac{K_a[weak\ acid]}{[salt]}$$

The pH of a buffer solution can be calculated given K_a for the weak acid and the concentrations or amounts of the weak acid and its salt.

> **Tip**
>
> In the calculation of the pH of a weak acid, the assumption was made that [H^+] = [A^-]. This is true only when the sole source of A^- ions is the weak acid. In a buffer solution this is not true because A^- ions are formed from the complete ionisation of the salt.

Worked example 1

Calculate the pH of a buffer solution made by adding $50\,cm^3$ of $0.100\,mol\,dm^{-3}$ ethanoic acid to $50\,cm^3$ of $0.200\,mol\,dm^{-3}$ sodium ethanoate. (K_a for ethanoic acid $= 1.80 \times 10^{-5}\,mol\,dm^{-3}$)

Answer

$$CH_3COONa \rightarrow CH_3COO^- + Na^+$$

$$CH_3COOH \rightleftharpoons H^+ + CH_3COO^-$$

$$K_a = \frac{[H^+]\,[CH_3COO^-]}{[CH_3COOH]} = \frac{[H^+]\,[salt]}{[weak\ acid]}$$

$$K_a = 1.80 \times 10^{-5}\,mol\,dm^{-3}$$

$$[H^+] = K_a \times \frac{[weak\ acid]}{[salt]} = 1.80 \times 10^{-5} \times \frac{0.0500}{0.100}$$

$$= 9.00 \times 10^{-6}\,mol\,dm^{-3}$$

$$pH = -\log[H^+] = -\log\,(9.00 \times 10^{-6}) = 5.05$$

Note that mixing the two solutions doubles the total volume. Therefore, the concentration of the weak acid was halved from $0.100\,mol\,dm^{-3}$ to $0.0500\,mol\,dm^{-3}$ and that of the salt was halved from $0.200\,mol\,dm^{-3}$ to $0.100\,mol\,dm^{-3}$.

Extra care must be taken when both the volume and the concentration of the acid and of the salt are different.

Worked example 2

Calculate the pH of a solution made by mixing $30\,cm^3$ of a $0.10\,mol\,dm^{-3}$ solution of benzoic acid with $20\,cm^3$ of a $0.20\,mol\,dm^{-3}$ solution of sodium benzoate. (K_a for benzoic acid $= 6.31 \times 10^{-5}\,mol\,dm^{-3}$)

Answer

$$amount\ (moles)\ of\ acid = 0.10\,mol\,dm^{-3} \times 0.030\,dm^3 = 0.0030\,mol$$

$$[acid] = \frac{0.0030\,mol}{0.050\,dm^3} = 0.060\,mol\,dm^{-3}$$

$$amount\ (moles)\ of\ salt = 0.20\,mol\,dm^{-3} \times 0.020\,dm^3 = 0.0040\,mol$$

$$[salt] = \frac{0.0040\,mol}{0.050\,dm^3} = 0.080\,mol\,dm^{-3}$$

$$K_a = \frac{[H^+][A^-]}{[HA]} = \frac{[H^+][salt]}{[weak\ acid]}$$

$$[H^+] = K_a \times \frac{[weak\ acid]}{[salt]} = 6.31 \times 10^{-5} \times \frac{0.060}{0.080} = 4.73 \times 10^{-5}\,mol\,dm^{-3}$$

$$pH = -\log[H^+] = -\log(4.73 \times 10^{-5}) = 4.32$$

A more complicated calculation involving buffers arises when an *excess* of weak acid is mixed with a strong alkali. All the alkali reacts with some of the acid, forming a salt of the weak acid and, therefore, creating a buffer solution. The amount of salt formed is equal to the amount of alkali. The total volume of the solution is the sum of the volumes of the two solutions that were mixed.

Worked example 3

Calculate the pH of a buffer solution made by mixing $60\,cm^3$ of $0.20\,mol\,dm^{-3}$ ethanoic acid solution with $40\,cm^3$ of sodium hydroxide solution of concentration $0.10\,mol\,dm^{-3}$. (K_a for ethanoic acid $= 1.80 \times 10^{-5}\,mol\,dm^{-3}$)

Answer

amount of alkali taken $= 0.10 \times 0.040 = 0.0040\,mol =$ amount of salt formed

amount of acid taken $= 0.20 \times 0.060 = 0.012\,mol$

amount of acid left $= 0.012 - 0.0040 = 0.0080\,mol$

total volume $= 100\,cm^3$

$$[\text{salt}] = \frac{0.0040}{0.100} = 0.040\,mol\,dm^{-3}$$

$$[\text{weak acid}] = \frac{0.0080}{0.100} = 0.080\,mol\,dm^{-3}$$

$$CH_3COONa \rightarrow CH_3COO^- + Na^+$$

$$CH_3COOH \rightleftharpoons H^+ + CH_3COO^-$$

$$K_a = \frac{[H^+][CH_3COO^-]}{[CH_3COOH]} = \frac{[H^+][\text{salt}]}{[\text{weak acid}]}$$

$$= 1.80 \times 10^{-5}\,mol\,dm^{-3}$$

$$[H^+] = K_a \times \frac{[\text{weak acid}]}{[\text{salt}]} = 1.8 \times 10^{-5} \times \frac{0.0080}{0.040}$$

$$= 3.6 \times 10^{-5}\,mol\,dm^{-3}$$

$$pH = -\log[H^+] = -\log(3.6 \times 10^{-5}) = 4.44$$

It is dangerous to use the Henderson-Hasselbalch formula when calculating the pH of a buffer solution:
$$pH = pK_a + \log\left(\frac{[\text{salt}]}{[\text{weak acid}]}\right)$$
because it is often mis-remembered.

Tip

Always start the calculation of the pH of a buffer solution and also of a weak acid with the expression for the equilibrium constant. Then make the assumptions·

- for a buffer solution: [HA] = [weak acid] and [A$^-$] = [salt]
- for a solution of a weak acid: [HA] = [weak acid] and [H$^+$] = [A$^-$]

Calculation of the composition of a buffer solution

Calculation of the composition of a buffer solution requires the use of the expression for K_a. There are two types of calculation. In the first, the amount of solid salt has to be calculated.

Worked example

Calculate the mass of sodium ethanoate, CH_3COONa, that has to be added to $100\,cm^3$ of a $1.00\,mol\,dm^{-3}$ solution of ethanoic acid to make a buffer solution of pH = 4.38. (K_a for ethanoic acid $= 1.8 \times 10^{-5}\,mol\,dm^{-3}$)

Answer

$[H^+] = 10^{-pH} = 10^{-4.38} = 4.17 \times 10^{-5}\,mol\,dm^{-3}$

$$K_a = \frac{[H^+][CH_3COO^-]}{[CH_3COOH]} = \frac{[H^+][salt]}{[weak\ acid]} = 1.8 \times 10^{-5}\,mol\,dm^{-3}$$

$$[salt] = K_a \times \frac{[weak\ acid]}{[H^+]} = \frac{1.8 \times 10^{-5} \times 1.00}{4.17 \times 10^{-5}} = 0.432\,mol\,dm^{-3}$$

molar mass of $CH_3COONa = 12 + 3 + 12 + (2 \times 16) + 23 = 82\,g\,mol^{-1}$

mass of sodium ethanoate required for $1\,dm^3 = 0.432\,mol \times 82\,g\,mol^{-1} = 35\,g$

mass for $100\,cm^3$ of solution $= 3.5\,g$

In the second type of calculation, the volumes of the solutions of the weak acid and the salt have to be calculated. In this type of calculation there is no unique answer. It is the ratio of the volumes of the two solutions that is found.

Worked example

Calculate the relative volumes of a $1.00\,mol\,dm^{-3}$ solution of ethanoic acid and a $1.00\,mol\,dm^{-3}$ solution of sodium ethanoate that have to be mixed to give a solution of pH = 4.00. (K_a for ethanoic acid $= 1.8 \times 10^{-5}\,mol\,dm^{-3}$)

Answer

$[H^+] = 10^{-pH} = 1.00 \times 10^{-4}\,mol\,dm^{-3}$

$$K_a = \frac{[H^+][CH_3COO^-]}{[CH_3COOH]} = \frac{[H^+][salt]}{[weak\ acid]} = 1.8 \times 10^{-5}\,mol\,dm^{-3}$$

$$\frac{[weak\ acid]}{[salt]} = \frac{[H^+]}{K_a} = \frac{1.00 \times 10^{-4}}{1.8 \times 10^{-5}} = 5.6$$

The ratio of the volumes of solutions of ethanoic acid to sodium ethanoate = 5.6:1, so, mix $56\,cm^3$ of the ethanoic acid solution with $10\,cm^3$ of the sodium ethanoate solution.

Acid–base indicators

In acid–base titrations, the **equivalence point** is the point at which enough alkali has been added from the burette to react with all the acid in the conical flask or when enough acid has been added from the burette to react with all the alkali in the conical flask. For a reaction with a 1:1 stoichiometry, this means an equal number of moles of acid and alkali. If the stoichiometry is 2:1, then the ratio of moles required for the equivalence point is also 2:1.

The pH at the equivalence point is not necessarily 7. This is because at this point the solution consists of the salt of the acid and the alkali. If both the acid and alkali are strong, the solution will be pH 7, but if either is weak, then it will not (see p. 49).

The purpose of an indicator is to show when the equivalence point has been reached. Indicators are weak acids with the colour of the conjugate base being different from that of the weak acid molecule. Shorthand for an indicator molecule is HInd. It dissociates in water according to the equation:

$$HInd \rightleftharpoons H^+ + Ind^-$$

colour 1   colour 2

$$K_{ind} = \frac{[H^+][Ind^-]}{[HInd]}$$

- When acid is added, the equilibrium is driven to the left and the indicator appears as colour 1.
- When alkali is added, the OH^- ions react with the H^+ ions from the indicator and the equilibrium is driven to the right. The indicator turns colour 2.
- The colour at the equivalence point appears when $[HInd] \approx [Ind^-]$. At this point:

$$K_{ind} = [H^+] \text{ or } pH = pK_{ind}$$

With most indicators, the eye can see only either colour 1 or colour 2 if at least 90% of that species is present in the mixture. Thus, the range over which the colour is seen to change is from a ratio of $[HInd]:[Ind^-]$ of just less than 10 to just over 0.1. This is a range of pH of approximately ±1 from the pK_{ind} value.

Table 2.7 lists some common acid–base indicators.

Table 2.7 Some common acid-base indicators

Indicator	pK_{ind}	pH range	Acid colour	Alkaline colour	Neutral colour
Methyl orange	3.7	3.1–4.4	Red	Yellow	Orange
Bromophenol blue	4.0	3.0–4.6	Yellow	Blue	Green
Bromocresol green	4.7	3.8–5.4	Yellow	Blue	Green
Methyl red	5.1	4.2–6.3	Red	Yellow	Orange
Bromothymol blue	7.0	6.0–7.6	Yellow	Blue	Green
Thymol blue*	8.9	8.0–9.6	Yellow	Blue	Green
Phenolphthalein	9.3	8.3–10.0	Colourless	Mauve	Pale pink

*Thymol blue also changes from red to yellow around a pH of 2

The correct choice of indicator depends on the strengths of the acid and base in the titration.

(a) Methyl orange in acid (left) and alkaline (right) solutions; (b) phenolphthalein in acid (left) and alkaline (right) solutions

Titration curves

A titration curve shows how the pH of a solution varies as the reagent in the burette is added. The shape of a titration curve depends upon the strength/weakness of the acid and base.

In order to sketch a titration curve, the following have to be estimated:

- the pH at the start
- the pH at the equivalence point
- the volume of liquid from the burette required to reach the equivalence point
- the pH range of the near vertical part of the graph
- the pH after excess reagent has been added from the burette (final pH)

The pH values at different points during a typical titration are shown in Table 2.8. The figures are only approximate, because they vary depending on the concentrations and on how weak the acids and bases are.

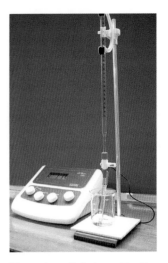

Measuring pH during a titration

Table 2.8 Variation of pH during different types of titration

Reagent in conical flask	Reagent in burette	Initial pH	Equivalence point pH	Vertical range pH	Final pH
Strong acid	Strong base	1	7	3–11	Just < 13
Strong base	Strong acid	13	7	11–3	Just > 1
Weak acid	Strong base	3	9	7–11	Just < 13
Strong base	Weak acid	13	9	11–7	Just > 3
Strong acid	Weak base	1	5	3–7	Just < 11
Weak base	Strong acid	11	5	7–3	Just > 1

Red cabbage extract acts as an acid–base indicator.

Red cabbage extract at (from left) pH 1, 3, 5, 7, 9, 11 and 13

Tip

Note that the rule of *two* (p. 51) applies here:

- A weak acid starts (or finishes if it is being added to the base) at 2 pH units higher than that of a strong acid.
- A weak acid has an equivalence point 2 pH units higher than that of a strong acid.
- A weak base starts or finishes at 2 pH units lower than that of a strong base.
- A weak base has an equivalence point 2 pH units lower than that of a strong base.
- For both weak acids and bases, the vertical range is ± 2 pH units about the equivalence point pH.

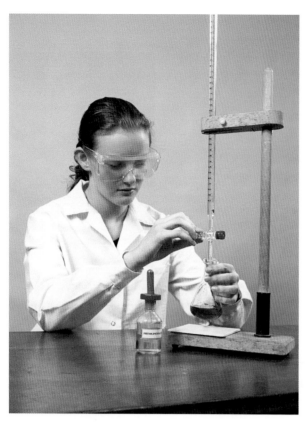
Performing a titration

The volume at the equivalence point has to be worked out by the usual titration method. In most questions the acids and bases react in a 1:1 ratio. For example, if a $0.10\,mol\,dm^{-3}$ solution of a base is added to $20\,cm^3$ of $0.10\,mol\,dm^{-3}$ acid, the equivalence point is at $20\,cm^3$ of added base. Note that if the acid had a concentration of $0.20\,mol\,dm^{-3}$, the equivalence point would be at $40\,cm^3$ of added base.

In the titration curves that follow:

- the starting volume in the flask is $20\,cm^3$
- the equivalence point is at $20\,cm^3$ of added reagent
- the left-hand graph of each pair shows the change in pH as base is added to acid; the right-hand graph shows the pH change as acid is added to base

Strong acid–strong base titration

In an experiment, $20.0\,cm^3$ of hydrochloric acid (a strong acid) of concentration $0.100\,mol\,dm^{-3}$ was titrated with a solution of sodium hydroxide (a strong base) of concentration $0.100\,mol\,dm^{-3}$.

The variation of pH with the volume of sodium hydroxide added can be estimated by calculating the pH at certain points.

pH at the start
The acid concentration is $0.100\,mol\,dm^{-3}$, so $pH = -\log 0.100 = 1.00$.

pH after the addition of $10.0\,cm^3$ sodium hydroxide
$0.0200 \times 0.100 = 0.00200\,mol$ of acid were present originally. Half the acid has reacted, so $\frac{1}{2} \times 0.00200 = 0.00100\,mol$ are present in $30.0\,cm^3$ of solution. Therefore:

$$[H^+] = \frac{0.00100}{0.0300} = 0.0333\,mol\,dm^{-3}$$
$$pH = -\log 0.0333 = 1.48$$

pH at equivalence point (after $20.0\,cm^3$ added)
All the acid has reacted and the solution contains sodium chloride, which is neutral at $pH = 7$.

pH after the addition of $30.0\,cm^3$ sodium hydroxide
Two-thirds of the sodium hydroxide has reacted, so $10.0\,cm^3$ did not react. Therefore, $0.100 \times 0.0100 = 0.00100\,mol$ of NaOH are present in $50.0\,cm^3$ of solution.

$$pOH = \frac{-\log 0.00100}{0.0500} = 1.70$$
$$pH = 14 - 1.70 = 12.30$$

The pH values at different points during this titration are given in Table 2.9.

> **Tip**
>
> You must convert the volume in cm^3 to dm^3 by dividing by 1000.

Table 2.9 pH during the titration of 20 cm³ 0.100 mol dm⁻³ HCl with 0.100 mol dm⁻³ NaOH

Volume of NaOH added/cm³	pH	Volume of NaOH added/cm³	pH
0	1.00	20.0	7.00
10	1.48	20.1	10.40
15	1.85	21.0	11.39
19	2.59	30.0	12.30
19.9	3.60	40.0	12.52

These data can be presented as a graph (Figure 2.6), which is usually called a titration curve.

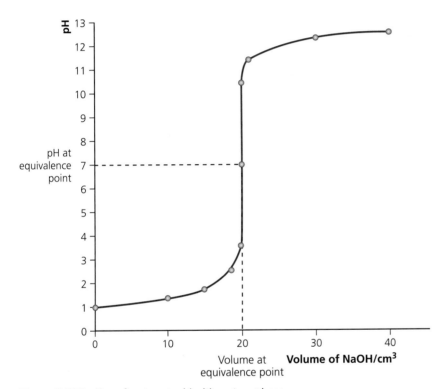

Figure 2.6 Titration of a strong acid with a strong base

Notice that the graph rises slowly to start with, then vertically at the equivalence point, before flattening off just below pH 13.

If the acid were added to 20 cm³ of the alkali, the graph would have a similar shape but would be a mirror image. It would start at pH 13, fall slowly, and then just before the equivalence volume of 20.0 cm³ of acid, it would plunge vertically from about pH 10 to pH 3. Finally, it would flatten off just above pH 1.

Titrations involving weak acids or weak bases

The pH at the end point of these titrations can be found using the rule of two.

The rule of two

Remember that a weak acid has a bigger pH than a strong acid and a weak base a smaller pH than a strong base.

- The pH of a 0.1 mol dm⁻³ solution of a strong acid is 1 and that of a 0.1 mol dm⁻³ solution of a strong base is 13.
- The pH of a solution of a salt of a strong acid and a strong base is 7.

Tip

The rule for going from strong to weak is to add 2 pH units for a weak acid; subtract 2 pH units for a weak base.

The 'rule of two' gives an approximate pH of $0.1 \, mol \, dm^{-3}$ weak acids, weak bases and their salts:

- pH of weak acid = pH of strong acid + 2 = 1 + 2 = 3
- pH of weak base = pH of strong base − 2 = 13 − 2 = 11
- pH of salt of weak acid and strong base = 7 + 2 = 9
- pH of salt of weak base and strong acid = 7 − 2 = 5
- pH of salt of weak acid and weak base ≈ pH of salt of strong acid +2 and strong base −2 = 7 + 2 − 2 = 7

Weak acid–strong base titration

The graphs in Figure 2.7 show the variation of pH during the reaction between solutions of a weak acid, such as ethanoic acid, and a strong base, such as sodium hydroxide. The concentration of both reagents is $0.10 \, mol \, dm^{-3}$.

Figure 2.7 Weak acid/strong base

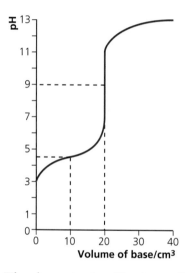
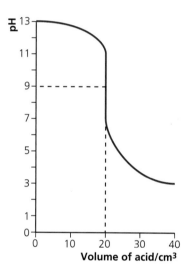

The sharp rise in pH when a little base is added is because the solution is not yet buffered. From about $5 \, cm^3$ of base added to $5 \, cm^3$ short of the equivalence point, the solution is buffered and so the pH changes gradually.

Strong acid–weak base titrations

The graphs in Figure 2.8 on p. 53 show the variation of pH during the reaction between solutions of a strong acid, such as hydrochloric acid, and a weak base such as ammonia. The concentration of both reagents is $0.10 \, mol \, dm^{-3}$.

Choice of indicator

For an indicator to work, the entire range during which it changes colour must lie *completely* within the vertical section of the titration curve.

For a strong acid–strong base titration, the pH range of the indicator must lie *completely* within the range of pH 3–11. Therefore, all the indicators listed in Table 2.7 (p. 48) will give an accurate result. The indicators most usually chosen are methyl orange and phenolphthalein.

For a weak acid–strong base titration, the range must be *completely* within pH 7–11. Of the indicators in Table 2.7, only thymol blue and phenolphthalein will give the correct result.

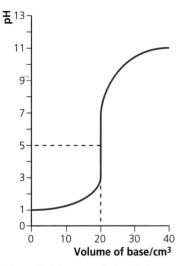

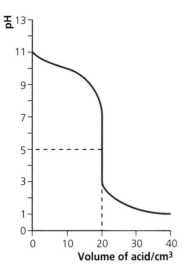

Figure 2.8 Strong acid/weak base

For a weak base–strong acid titration, the colour change of the indicator must be *completely* within the range of pH 3–7. Methyl orange, bromophenol blue, bromocresol green and methyl red are all suitable indicators.

Evaluation of K_a and K_b from titration curves

When a strong base is added to a solution of a weak acid, the point halfway to the equivalence point is when half the acid has been neutralised. For a weak acid, HA:

$$K_a = \frac{[H^+][A^-]}{[HA]}$$

At the half-neutralisation point, $[HA] = [A^-]$. Therefore, at this point, $K_a = [H^+]$ and so $pK_a = pH$. The pH at the half-neutralisation point can be read off the graph.

At the half-neutralisation point, the mixture is a buffer solution because both the weak acid and its conjugate base are present in equal and, therefore, significant, quantities.

The evaluation is similar for a weak base. If a strong acid is added to a weak base, the pH at the half-neutralisation point is equal to pK_b of the weak base, B.

$$B + H_2O \rightleftharpoons BH^+ + OH^-$$

$$K_b = \frac{[BH^+][OH^-]}{[B]}$$

At the half-neutralisation point, $[B] = [BH^+]$. Therefore, at this point $K_b = [OH^-]$, so $pK_b = pOH$. The pH at the half-neutralisation point can be read off the graph.

Buffer region in titration curves

When a strong base is added to a weak acid, a buffer solution is produced when there are significant amounts of both the salt formed and unreacted weak acid present. This occurs in the fairly flat part of the curve between the addition of 5 cm³ of strong base to within 5 cm³ of the equivalence point.

The buffered region would look much flatter if the scale of the *x*-axis were extended. This would then show clearly that the pH alters only slightly for small additions (less than 1 cm³) of acid or alkali.

Similarly, when a strong acid is added to a weak base, the fairly flat part of the curve occurs when there are significant amounts of both the salt formed and unreacted weak base present. This occurs in the region between the addition of $5\,cm^3$ of strong acid to within $5\,cm^3$ of the equivalence point.

Buffers are most resistant to pH changes when the amounts of the components of the acid–base conjugate pair are equal.

Enthalpy of neutralisation of acids

The standard enthalpy of neutralisation, ΔH_{neut}, is defined as the enthalpy change when an acid and a base react to form 1 mol of water under standard conditions of $1.0\,mol\,dm^{-3}$ solutions, 100 kPa pressure and a stated temperature, usually 298 K (25°C).

For example, it is the molar enthalpy change for:

$HCl(aq) + NaOH(aq) \rightarrow NaCl(aq) + H_2O(l)$

$\frac{1}{2}H_2SO_4(aq) + KOH(aq) \rightarrow \frac{1}{2}K_2SO_4(aq) + H_2O(l)$

$CH_3COOH(aq) + NaOH(aq) \rightarrow CH_3COONa(aq) + H_2O(l)$

Strong acids neutralised by strong bases

Strong acids and strong bases are both totally ionised, so the equation for the reaction between them can be written ionically. For example, for the neutralisation of hydrochloric acid by sodium hydroxide the full ionic equation is:

$H^+(aq) + Cl^-(aq) + Na^+(aq) + OH^-(aq) \rightarrow Na^+(aq) + Cl^-(aq) + H_2O(l)$

The spectator ions can be crossed out, leaving the net ionic equation:

$H^+(aq) + OH^-(aq) \rightarrow H_2O(l)$

This equation represents the neutralisation of all strong acids by strong bases. Therefore, ΔH for all these reactions is approximately the same.

For a strong acid neutralised by a strong base, $\Delta H_{neut} \approx -57.2\,kJ\,mol^{-1}$.

Weak acids neutralised by strong bases

The ionic equation given above does not apply to the neutralisation of a weak acid by a strong base because the acid is not totally ionised. The neutralisation can be regarded as the sum of two reactions:

$HA(aq) \rightleftharpoons H^+(aq) + A^-(aq)$ $\qquad\qquad\qquad \Delta H_1$

$H^+(aq) + OH^-(aq) \rightarrow H_2O(l)$ $\qquad\qquad\qquad \Delta H_2$

Adding gives:

$HA(aq) + OH^-(aq) \rightarrow A^-(aq) + H_2O(l)$ $\qquad \Delta H_{neut}$

$\Delta H_{neut} = \Delta H_1 + \Delta H_2$

where $\Delta H_2 \approx -57.2\,kJ\,mol^{-1}$.

- If ΔH_1 is endothermic, the value of ΔH_{neut} is less exothermic than ΔH_{neut} of a strong acid.

Even though the acid is only about 1% ionised, the removal of H^+ ions by the base drives the equilibrium to the right until all the acid has been neutralised.

- If ΔH_1 is exothermic, the value of ΔH_{neut} is more exothermic than ΔH_{neut} of a strong acid.

Hydrofluoric acid, HF, is a weak acid. It ionises exothermically because of the small size of the F^- ion (the smallest anion that can exist in solution), which forms strong hydrogen bonds with water molecules.

Other weak acids ionise endothermically. The weaker the acid, the more endothermic is its ionisation. Some examples are given in Table 2.10.

Table 2.10 Enthalpy of neutralisation of some weak acids

Acid	K_a/mol dm^{-3}	Base	ΔH_{neut}/kJ mol^{-1}
HF	5.6×10^{-4}	NaOH	−68.6
CH_3COOH	1.8×10^{-5}	NaOH	−55.2
H_2S	8.9×10^{-7}	NaOH	−32.2
HCN	4.9×10^{-10}	NaOH	−11.7

The enthalpy of ionisation of ethanoic acid is only $+2\,kJ\,mol^{-1}$. This is why its enthalpy of neutralisation is so close to that of a strong acid.

Tip

In oxo-acids containing an element that can have more than one oxidation state, the lower the oxidation state the weaker the acid is. For example, sulfuric acid (oxidation state of sulfur = +6) is a stronger acid than sulfuric(IV) acid (oxidation state of sulfur = +4).

The structure of acids

Acids can be classified according to three types. In the first type of acid, a hydrogen atom is joined to an oxygen atom in a molecule. The oxo-acids (e.g. sulfuric, nitric, carbonic) and all the organic acids fall into this category.

In addition to the oxygen attached to the hydrogen, an oxo-acid also contains one or more X=O groups. For example, the structure of sulfuric acid is shown in Figure 2.9, that of nitric acid is shown in Figure 2.10, and that of carbonic acid is shown in Figure 2.11.

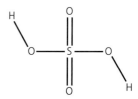

Figure 2.9

In the second type of acid, a hydrogen atom is joined to an electronegative atom other than oxygen. Well-known examples of this type of acid are HF, HCl, HBr and HI. The strength of these acids depends mainly on the strength of the H–X bond: the stronger the bond, the weaker the acid. This is why HF is the weakest acid of the hydrogen halide acids and HI is the strongest. The bond enthalpies are:

H–F: $+562\,kJ\,mol^{-1}$ H–I: $+299\,kJ\,mol^{-1}$

Figure 2.10

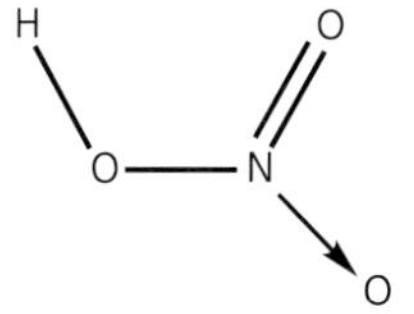

The third type of acid is a hydrated metal ion. The polarising power of the cation, especially small 3+ ions such as Al^{3+} or Fe^{3+}, draws electrons away from the H–O bond in the surrounding water molecules. This means that a water molecule can be deprotonated easily by solvent water molecules:

$$[Al(H_2O)_6]^{3+} + H_2O \rightleftharpoons [Al(H_2O)_5OH]^{2+} + H_3O^+$$

H_3O^+ ions are produced and so the solution becomes acidic (see Chapter 10).

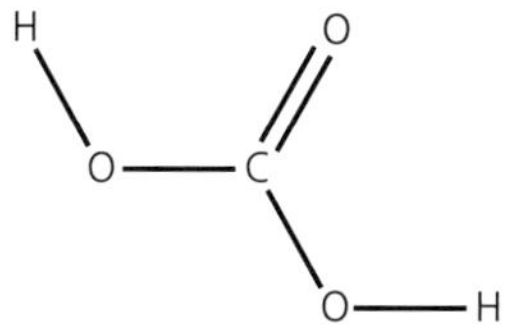

Figure 2.11

Test yourself

10 Draw the displayed formula of sulfuric(IV) acid, H_2SO_3.

Summary tasks

Make sure that you can:

- identify acid/base conjugate pairs
- define acid, base, strong acid, weak acid and buffer solution
- understand the pH scale and the concept of neutrality
- write expressions for K_a of a weak acid and use it to calculate the pH of weak acids and of buffer solutions
- write expressions for K_b of a weak base and use it to calculate the pH of weak bases
- calculate the pH of solutions of salts of weak bases and strong acids and salts of weak acids and strong bases
- explain the mode of action of a buffer solution
- draw titration curves and use them to calculate the K_a value of weak acids
- understand the choice of indicators
- explain why $\Delta H_{neutralisation}$ of strong acids with strong bases are approximately the same but those of weak acids differ.

Questions

1 Hydrogen chloride gas reacts with water. Write the equation for the reaction and use it to explain why HCl can be classified as a Brønsted–Lowry acid and why the solution is acidic.

2 State the conjugate bases of the following acids:

   a) HCN   c) OH^-

   b) $HClO_3$ d) $[Fe(H_2O)_6]^{3+}$

3 Write the formulae for the conjugate acids of the following bases:

   a) CH_3NH_2 b) OH^- c) HNO_3

4 Explain why the pH of pure water is not always 7.

5 At 25°C, pK_w = 14. Calculate the $[OH^-]$ of the following solutions and state whether the solutions are acidic or alkaline:

   a) $[H^+] = 1.0 \times 10^{-2}\,mol\,dm^{-3}$

   b) $[H^+] = 2.2 \times 10^{-7}\,mol\,dm^{-3}$

6 At 25°C, $K_w = 1.0 \times 10^{-14}\,mol^2\,dm^{-6}$. Calculate the pH of the following solutions in which:

   a) $[H^+] = 4.4 \times 10^{-5}\,mol\,dm^{-3}$

   b) $[H^+] = 5.5 \times 10^{-9}\,mol\,dm^{-3}$

   c) $[OH^-] = 7.7 \times 10^{-11}\,mol\,dm^{-3}$

7 Calculate the concentration of hydrogen ions in solutions with the following pH values:

   a) pH = 1.33   b) pH = 7.00

8 Calculate the ratio of $[H^+]$ to $[OH^-]$ ions in solutions of pH:

   a) 7   b) 10   c) 3

9 Calculate the pH of the following solutions:

   a) $0.200\,mol\,dm^{-3}$ hydrobromic acid, HBr, which is a strong acid

   b) $0.0500\,mol\,dm^{-3}$ strontium hydroxide, $Sr(OH)_2$, which is a strong base

10 Calculate the pH of a $2.0\,mol\,dm^{-3}$ solution of a strong acid such as nitric acid, HNO_3. Then calculate its pH when it is diluted 10 times and 1 000 000 times.

11 Chloric(I) acid, HOCl, is a weak acid with $K_a = 3.02 \times 10^{-11}\,mol\,dm^{-3}$.

   a) Write the equation for its ionisation in water and hence the expression for the acid dissociation constant, K_a.

   b) Calculate the pH of a $0.213\,mol\,dm^{-3}$ solution of chloric(I) acid.

12 Nitrous acid, HNO_2, is also called nitric(III) acid. It is a weak acid. A $0.200 \, mol \, dm^{-3}$ solution of HNO_2 has a pH of 2.02. Calculate the value of its acid dissociation constant, K_a.

13 Hydroxyethanoic acid, $CH_2(OH)COOH$, has a $pK_a = 3.83$. Calculate the pH of a $1.05 \, mol \, dm^{-3}$ solution of this weak acid.

14 Methylamine is a weak base, with $K_b = 4.36 \times 10^{-4} \, mol \, dm^{-3}$:

$$CH_3NH_2 + H_2O \rightleftharpoons CH_3NH_3^+ + OH^-$$

a) Give the expression for K_b.

b) Calculate the pH of $0.200 \, mol \, dm^{-3}$ methylamine solution.

15 Thymol blue can be regarded as a weak acid of formula HThy. Use the data in Table 2.7 (p. 48) to explain the colour changes that take place when dilute hydrochloric acid, followed by an excess of sodium hydroxide solution, is added to a solution of thymol blue.

16 Calculate the pH of a buffer solution made by adding $50 \, cm^3$ of $2.00 \, mol \, dm^{-3}$ sodium hydroxide solution to $150 \, cm^3$ of $1.00 \, mol \, dm^{-3}$ ethanoic acid solution. (K_a for ethanoic acid $= 1.8 \times 10^{-5} \, mol \, dm^{-3}$)

17 What volume of $1.00 \, mol \, dm^{-3}$ propanoic acid, $pK_a = 4.87$, is needed to make a buffer solution of pH 4.50 with $50 \, cm^3$ of $1.00 \, mol \, dm^{-3}$ sodium propanoate solution?

18 What mass of calcium ethanoate, $Ca(CH_3COO)_2$, must be added to $100 \, cm^3$ of $1.25 \, mol \, dm^{-3}$ ethanoic acid solution to make a buffer solution of pH $= 5.00$? (K_a for ethanoic acid $= 1.80 \times 10^{-5} \, mol \, dm^{-3}$)

19 What volume of $1.00 \, mol \, dm^{-3}$ sodium hydroxide must be added to $100 \, cm^3$ of $1.00 \, mol \, dm^{-3}$ ethanoic acid solution to make a buffer solution of pH $= 4.44$? (K_a for ethanoic acid $= 1.80 \times 10^{-5} \, mol \, dm^{-3}$)

20 Write the equation for the reaction, if any, of the following ions with water and state whether their solutions would be neutral, acidic or alkaline:

a) $CH_3NH_3^+$ b) CO_3^{2-} c) I^-

21 a) Sketch the titration curve obtained when $40 \, cm^3$ of $0.20 \, mol \, dm^{-3}$ hydrochloric acid is added to $40 \, cm^3$ of $0.10 \, mol \, dm^{-3}$ ammonia solution. Use Table 2.7 (p. 48) to select a suitable indicator. Justify your choice.

b) Mark on your curve a place where the solution is acting as a buffer.

22 $20 \, cm^3$ of a $0.100 \, mol \, dm^{-3}$ solution of a weak acid, HA, was placed in a conical flask. Sodium hydroxide solution of concentration $0.100 \, mol \, dm^{-3}$ was added in portions and the pH of the stirred solution read after each addition. The readings obtained are given in the table below.

Volume of NaOH/cm³	pH	Volume of NaOH/cm³	pH
0	2.9	19.9	7.0
2.5	3.9	20.1	10.4
5.0	4.3	20.5	11.1
15.0	5.2	21.0	11.4
17.5	5.6	25.0	12.0
19.0	6.0	30.0	12.3
19.5	6.3	35.0	12.4

a) Plot a graph of pH (y-axis) against the volume of sodium hydroxide (x-axis).

b) Use the graph to find a value for the acid dissociation constant, K_a, of the weak acid, HA.

c) Estimate the pH of a $0.050 \, mol \, dm^{-3}$ solution of the salt, NaA.

d) Use the data in Table 2.7 (p. 48) to select a suitable indicator for this titration. Justify your choice.

23 a) Explain why the standard enthalpies of neutralisation of hydrobromic acid and hydrochloric acid by aqueous sodium hydroxide are both $-57 \, kJ \, mol^{-1}$.

b) Ethanoic acid is only about 1% ionised in solution, yet its enthalpy of neutralisation is $-55 \, kJ \, mol^{-1}$. Explain why its value is so similar to that of hydrobromic and hydrochloric acids.

c) Explain why the very weak acid, hydrocyanic acid, HCN, has a much lower exothermic enthalpy of neutralisation than that for a strong acid.

24 Draw the structural formula, showing all the bonds, of each of the following:

a) chloric(v) acid, $HClO_3$

b) hydrocyanic acid (hydrogen cyanide), HCN

Exam practice questions

1 a) Calculate the pH of a solution of hydrochloric acid of concentration $2.0 \, mol \, dm^{-3}$. (1)

b) Explain why the pH of a solution of sulfuric acid, H_2SO_4, of concentration $2.0 \, mol \, dm^{-3}$ is less negative than -0.60. (2)

c) Sulfuric acid reacts with nitric acid in the equilibrium reaction:

$$H_2SO_4 + HNO_3 \rightleftharpoons H_2NO_3^+ + HSO_4^-$$

Which of the following statements is correct? (1)

A H_2SO_4 and HNO_3 are an acid–conjugate base pair

B HNO_3 and $H_2NO_3^+$ are a base–conjugate acid pair

C the nitric acid is reduced as it gains hydrogen

D the nitric acid is oxidised as it loses an electron and forms a positive ion

(Total 4 marks)

2 Glycolic acid, $CH_2OHCOOH$, is a weak acid that is used in some skin-care products.

$$CH_2OHCOOH \rightleftharpoons H^+ + CH_2OHCOO^-$$

$$K_a = \frac{[H^+][CH_2OHCOO^-]}{[CH_2OHCOOH]}$$

$$= 1.48 \times 10^{-4} \, mol \, dm^{-3}$$

a) Calculate the pH of a solution of glycolic acid of concentration $0.15 \, mol \, dm^{-3}$ (3)

b) Another solution of glycolic acid has a pH of 2.48. Calculate its concentration. (2)

c) Explain why an aqueous solution of sodium glycolate, $CH_2OHCOONa$, has a pH greater than 7. (2)

d) When $20.0 \, cm^3$ of a $0.15 \, mol \, dm^{-3}$ solution of glycolic acid was mixed with $10 \, cm^3$ of a $0.15 \, mol \, dm^{-3}$ solution of sodium hydroxide, a buffer solution was formed. Calculate the pH of this buffer solution. (3)

e) Explain the mode of action of this buffer solution when a small amount of H^+ ions is added. (3)

(Total 13 marks)

3 a) Define 'buffer solution'. (2)

b) Which of the following is **not** a buffer solution? (1)

A $10 \, cm^3$ of $1.0 \, mol \, dm^{-3}$ CH_3COONa + $10 \, cm^3$ of $1.0 \, mol \, dm^{-3}$ CH_3COOH

B $10 \, cm^3$ of $1.0 \, mol \, dm^{-3}$ $NaOH$ + $10 \, cm^3$ of $1.0 \, mol \, dm^{-3}$ CH_3COOH

C $10 \, cm^3$ of $1.0 \, mol \, dm^{-3}$ $NaHSO_4$ + $10 \, cm^3$ of $1.0 \, mol \, dm^{-3}$ Na_2SO_4

D $10 \, cm^3$ of $1.0 \, mol \, dm^{-3}$ NH_3 + $10 \, cm^3$ of $1.0 \, mol \, dm^{-3}$ NH_4Cl

c) Calculate the pH of a buffer solution made by mixing $100 \, cm^3$ of $1.00 \, mol \, dm^{-3}$ ethanoic acid solution with $5.65 \, g$ of sodium ethanoate, CH_3COONa. (K_a for ethanoic acid $= 1.8 \times 10^{-5} \, mol \, dm^{-3}$) (4)

(Total 7 marks)

4 a) i) Define the term **acid**. (1)

ii) Explain what is meant by the term **weak acid**. (1)

b) i) Sketch the titration curve obtained when $40 \, cm^3$ of $0.10 \, mol \, dm^{-3}$ sodium hydroxide is slowly added to $20 \, cm^3$ of $0.10 \, mol \, dm^{-3}$ solution of a weak acid of pH 2.8. (3)

ii) Select from the list below a suitable indicator for this titration and state the colour at the end point. Justify your answers. (3)

Indicator	pK_{ind}	pH range	Acid colour	Alkaline colour
Bromophenol blue	4.0	3.0 to 4.6	Yellow	Blue
Methyl red	5.1	4.2 to 6.3	Red	Yellow
Thymol blue	8.9	8.0 to 9.6	Yellow	Blue

c) i) Explain what is meant by a neutral aqueous solution. (1)

ii) The pH of a neutral solution at blood temperature is 6.8. Explain why neutral at this temperature is not 7.0. (2)

(Total 11 marks)

Energetics II (Topic 13)

Energetics of ionic bonding

Ion-pair formation

It is often taught at GCSE that a sodium atom 'gives' one electron to a chlorine atom 'so that they both gain the stability of a noble gas'. This is a gross oversimplification. The enthalpy change for the formation of separate sodium and chloride ions from their atoms is the sum of the energies for the endothermic removal of an electron from the sodium atom and for the exothermic addition of an electron to the chlorine atom, thus:

$ΔH_2$ is the electron affinity of chlorine.

$$Na(g) \rightarrow Na^+(g) + e^- \qquad ΔH_1 = +494\,kJ\,mol^{-1}$$

$$Cl(g) + e^- \rightarrow Cl^-(g) \qquad ΔH_2 = -364\,kJ\,mol^{-1}$$

$$Na(g) + Cl(g) \rightarrow Na^+(g) + Cl^-(g) \qquad ΔH = ΔH_1 + ΔH_2 = +130\,kJ\,mol^{-1}$$

This is very endothermic and, therefore, cannot be the driving force for the reaction. In addition, sodium metal has to be vaporised and chlorine molecules have to be split into atoms, making the whole process even more endothermic.

$ΔH_3$ and $ΔH_4$ are the enthalpies of atomisation of sodium and chlorine.

$$Na(s) \rightarrow Na(g) \qquad ΔH_3 = +109\,kJ\,mol^{-1}$$

$$\frac{1}{2}Cl(g) \rightarrow Cl(g) \qquad ΔH_4 = +121\,kJ\,mol^{-1}$$

Overall:

$$Na(s) + \frac{1}{2}Cl_2(g) \rightarrow Na^+(g) + Cl^-(g) \quad ΔH = +360\,kJ\,mol^{-1}$$

When sodium and chlorine react, solid sodium chloride is formed and not separate gaseous sodium and chloride ions. The energy released when the ions come together and form the solid more than compensates for the endothermic formation of the separate ions. This energy is called the **lattice energy**.

> **The lattice energy, $ΔH_{latt}$ or LE, of an ionic compound is the energy change when *1 mol* of the *solid* is formed from its constituent *gaseous ions* that start infinitely far apart. It is always exothermic, so its value is always negative.**

Born–Haber cycles

The enthalpy of formation of NaCl(s) is the enthalpy change for the reaction of solid sodium with gaseous chlorine molecules. The enthalpy change for this direct one-step reaction will, by Hess's law, be equal to the sum of the enthalpy changes involved if the reaction were to take place in several steps. Born and Haber were the first to think of the formation of an ionic compound in this way. In this case, the steps are:

- turning solid sodium atoms into gaseous atoms
- splitting gaseous chlorine molecules into gaseous atoms

- removing an electron from each gaseous sodium atom
- adding an electron to each gaseous chlorine atom
- bringing the ions together into an ionic lattice

These processes are shown in Figure 3.1:

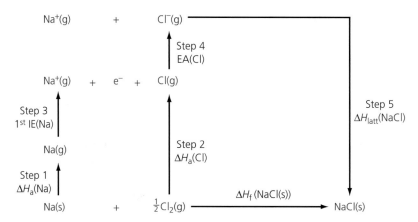

Figure 3.1

Step 1: the enthalpy of atomisation of sodium, $\Delta H_a(\text{Na})$ $(+109\,\text{kJ}\,\text{mol}^{-1})$

Step 2: the enthalpy of atomisation of chlorine, $\Delta H_a(\text{Cl})$ $(+121\,\text{kJ}\,\text{mol}^{-1})$

Step 3: the first ionisation energy of sodium, 1st IE(Na) $(+494\,\text{kJ}\,\text{mol}^{-1})$

Step 4: the first electron affinity of chlorine, EA(Cl) $(-364\,\text{kJ}\,\text{mol}^{-1})$

Step 5: the lattice energy of sodium chloride, $\Delta H_{\text{latt}}(\text{NaCl})$ $(-771\,\text{kJ}\,\text{mol}^{-1})$

$\Delta H_f(\text{NaCl(s)})$ = sum of the ΔH values for steps 1–5

$$= \Delta H_a(\text{Na}) + \Delta H_a(\text{Cl}) + \text{1st IE(Na)} + \text{EA(Cl)} + \Delta H_{\text{latt}}(\text{NaCl})$$

$$= +109 + 121 + 494 + (-364) + (-771) = -411\,\text{kJ}\,\text{mol}^{-1}$$

The enthalpy of atomisation, ΔH_a, of an element is the enthalpy change when *1 mol* of *gaseous* atoms is made from an element in its standard state. It is always endothermic.

The *first* electron affinity of an element is the energy change when 1 mol of gaseous 1− ions is formed from 1 mol of gaseous atoms. It is always exothermic.

The *second* electron affinity is the energy change when an electron is added to a gaseous 1− ion, forming a 2− ion. It is always endothermic.

Tip

The first electron affinity is always negative (exothermic). The second is always positive (endothermic) as a negative electron is brought towards a negative ion.

For example, the enthalpy of atomisation of:

- chlorine is for the change $\frac{1}{2}\text{Cl}_2(\text{g}) \rightarrow \text{Cl}(\text{g})$

- bromine is for the change $\frac{1}{2}\text{Br}_2(\text{l}) \rightarrow \text{Br}(\text{g})$

- sulfur is for the change $\frac{1}{8}\text{S}_8(\text{s}) \rightarrow \text{S}(\text{g})$

For example, the first electron affinity for oxygen is for the change $\text{O}(\text{g}) + \text{e}^- \rightarrow \text{O}^-(\text{g})$ and the second electron affinity is for the change $\text{O}^-(\text{g}) + \text{e}^- \rightarrow \text{O}^{2-}(\text{g})$.

If the ionic radii and the arrangement of the ions in the lattice are known, theoretical lattice energies can be calculated. The only way that they can be found experimentally is by using a Born–Haber cycle.

$$\Delta H_f(NaCl(s)) = \Delta H_a(Na) + \Delta H_a(Cl) + 1^{st}\ IE(Na) + EA(Cl) + \Delta H_{latt}(NaCl)$$

$$\Delta H_{latt}(NaCl) = \Delta H_f(NaCl(s)) - \{\Delta H_a(Na) + \Delta H_a(Cl) + 1^{st}\ IE(Na) + EA(Cl)\}$$

$$= -411 - \{+109 + (+121) + (+494) + (-364)\} = -771\ kJ\,mol^{-1}$$

Calculation of lattice energy from Born–Haber cycle data

Born–Haber cycles can also be drawn as energy-level diagrams. For example, for calcium chloride, $CaCl_2$, the energy-level diagram is shown in Figure 3.2.

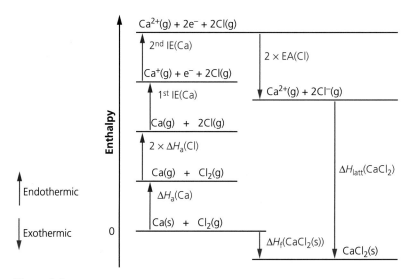

Figure 3.2

$$\Delta H_f(CaCl_2(s)) = \Delta H_a(Ca) + 2 \times \Delta H_a(Cl) + 1st\ IE(Ca) + 2nd\ IE(Ca)$$
$$+ 2 \times EA(Cl) + \Delta H_{latt}(CaCl_2)$$

$$\Delta H_{latt}(CaCl_2) = \Delta H_f(CaCl_2(s)) - \{\Delta H_a(Ca) + 2 \times \Delta H_a(Cl) + 1st\ IE(Ca)$$
$$+ 2nd\ IE(Ca) + 2 \times EA(Cl)\}$$

$$= -795 - \{+193 + 2(+121) + (+590) + (+1150) + 2(-364)\}$$

$$= -2242\ kJ\,mol^{-1}$$

Note that as 2 Cl atoms are formed from Cl_2, the enthalpy change is $2 \times \Delta H_a$. Also, because 2 Cl⁻ ions are formed, the enthalpy change is $2 \times EA$.

Tip

The second ionisation energy is the energy change when an electron is removed from a gaseous 1+ ion. It is the energy required to remove the second electron, not the energy for the removal of both electrons.

Extent of covalency: polarisation of the anion

The positive cation exerts an attraction on the electrons in the negative anion. If the electrons are significantly pulled towards the cation, the anion is **polarised**.

- Cations with a high charge and a small radius have a high polarising power.
- The smaller magnesium ion is more polarising than the larger calcium ion, both of which have the same charge of 2+.
- A magnesium ion is more polarising than a sodium ion, because it is 2+ and it is smaller than the larger, 1+ sodium ion.
- The polarising power is measured by the charge density of the cation.
- Anions with a high charge are easily polarised.
- Anions with a large number of electrons have a large radius and so are easily polarised.
- An iodide ion, I^-, is more easily polarised than the smaller chloride ion, Cl^-.
- A sulfide ion, S^{2-}, is more easily polarised than a chloride ion because it has a greater charge and a larger radius (Table 3.1).

The charge density of a cation is the charge divided by the volume of the ion. Assuming the ion to be spherical, the charge density is the charge divided by $\frac{4}{3}\pi r^3$, where r is the ionic radius.

Cations with a large charge and a small radius are highly polarising. Anions with a large charge and a large radius are highly polarisable. If either type of ion is present, the anion will be significantly polarised, resulting in the bond being partially covalent.

This causes the experimental (or Born–Haber) lattice energy to be greater than the theoretical value, which is calculated assuming that the solid is 100% ionic.

> The charge density of a cation can be thought of as its charge divided by the cube of its ionic radius.

> Partially covalent means that the electron cloud around the anion is distorted. This is because a pair of electrons on the **anion** is slightly drawn towards the cation and so becoming partially shared.

Table 3.1 Ionic radii

Cation	Radius/nm	Anion	Radius/nm
Na^+	0.095	Cl^-	0.181
K^+	0.133	I^-	0.216
Mg^{2+}	0.065	S^{2-}	0.184

As the polarising power of a cation depends on its charge density, the magnesium ion is the most polarising cation in Table 3.2. The iodide ion is the biggest anion, so magnesium iodide should be the most covalent compound and have the biggest difference between the experimental and the theoretical lattice energies (Table 3.2).

> **Tip**
>
> If you use the term 'charge density' in an examination, you must explain what it means.

Table 3.2 Lattice energies

Substance	Experimental lattice energy/kJ mol^{-1}	Theoretical lattice energy/kJ mol^{-1}	Difference/kJ mol^{-1}	Extent of covalency
NaCl	−780	−770	10	Almost none
K_2S	−2052	−1933	119	Significant
MgI_2	−2327	−1944	383	Considerable

The effect that covalency has on the experimental value of lattice energy is very much less than the effects of the charges and the radii of the ions.

The greater the difference between the theoretically calculated and the experimental Born–Haber values, the more covalent is the bond.

Worked example

Explain why calcium chloride is more covalent than potassium chloride.

Answer

The calcium ion is 2+ and has a smaller radius than the 1+ potassium ion. Therefore, its charge density is greater. This means that it polarises the Cl^- ion to a greater extent, causing the bond in calcium chloride to be more covalent than the bond in potassium chloride.

Tip

Magnitude means the value regardless of the sign. Thus the value −100 has a greater magnitude than the value −10.

Table 3.3 shows that the **magnitude** of the lattice energy:

- steadily decreases down a group of the periodic table as the size of the cation increases
- steadily decreases down the group as the size of the anion increases
- increases as the charge on either or both the cation and the anion increases

---

Test yourself

2 Which will have a greater degree of covalency, CaS or KCl?

Table 3.3 Lattice energies of some ionic compounds

	Lattice energy/kJ mol⁻¹				
Halides	LiF −1022	NaF −902	KF −801	RbF −767	CsF −716
	LiCl −846	NaCl −771	KCl −701	RbCl −675	CsCl −645
	LiBr −800	NaBr −733	KBr −670	RbBr −647	CsBr −619
	LiI −744	NaI −684	KI −629	RbI −609	CsI −585
	$BeCl_2$ −3006	$MgCl_2$ −2500	$CaCl_2$ −2237	$SrCl_2$ −2112	$BaCl_2$ −2018
Oxides	Li_2O −2814	Na_2O −2478	K_2O −2232	Rb_2O −2161	Cs_2O −2063
	BeO −4444	MgO −3890	CaO −3513	SrO −3310	BaO −3152
Sulfides	Li_2S −2500	Na_2S −2200	K_2S −2052	Rb_2S −1944	Cs_2S −1850
	BeS −3832	MgS −3300	CaS −3013	SrS −2850	BaS −2725
Hydroxides		$Mg(OH)_2$ −2842	$Ca(OH)_2$ −2553	$Sr(OH)_2$ −2354	$Ba(OH)_2$ −2228

Formulae of ionic compounds

The reason why sodium and chlorine form NaCl rather than $NaCl_2$ is not because of the mythical stability of a noble gas electronic configuration. The answer lies in comparing the enthalpy change of the two reactions:

$$Na(s) + \frac{1}{2}Cl(g) \rightarrow NaCl(s)$$

$$Na(s) + Cl_2(g) \rightarrow NaCl_2(s)$$

ΔH_f for the formation of NaCl(s) can be measured. The value is $-411\,kJ\,mol^{-1}$.

ΔH_f for the formation of $NaCl_2(s)$ can be calculated from a Born–Haber cycle (Figure 3.3), assuming that the lattice energy of $NaCl_2$ would be similar to that of $MgCl_2$ ($-2500\,kJ\,mol^{-1}$).

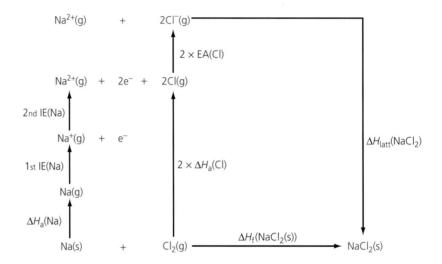

Figure 3.3

$$\Delta H_f(NaCl_2(s)) = \Delta H_a(Na) + 2 \times \Delta H_a(Cl) + \text{1st IE(Na)} + \text{2nd IE(Na)} +$$
$$2 \times EA(Cl) + \Delta H_{latt}(NaCl_2)$$

$$= 109 + 2(121) + 494 + 4560 + 2(-364) + (-2500)$$

$$= +2177\,kJ\,mol^{-1}$$

This process is very endothermic, so $NaCl_2$ is not formed.

The reason why it is so endothermic is that the extra 4560 kJ of energy, required to remove a second electron from sodium, is too great to be compensated for by the increased attraction between a 2+ cation and a 1− anion in the theoretical $NaCl_2$ solid. This huge jump in energy from the first to the second ionisation energy of sodium occurs because the second electron has to be removed from an inner (2*p*) shell. In this shell, the electron is screened from the 11+ nucleus by only the two 1*s*-electrons. Therefore, it is held very firmly.

This concept of whether the extra energy required to remove another electron is compensated for by the more negative lattice energy (or the hydration energy if the reaction is carried out in aqueous solution) is important in the chemistry of the transition metals.

In year 11 (GCSE) chemistry, it is often suggested that the driving force behind the formation of ions is gaining the stability of a noble gas electron configuration. However, this ignores the huge number of ionic compounds of the *d*-block metals that do not gain this so-called stability. A more accurate explanation is that the substances react to give the product with the lowest energy.

Magnesium chloride is $MgCl_2$, not $MgCl$, because the energy required to remove the second outer or $3s$-electron is more than compensated for by the extra energy released by the attraction between the 2+ ion and the Cl^- ion. Figure 3.4 shows the dot-and-cross diagram for $MgCl_2$.

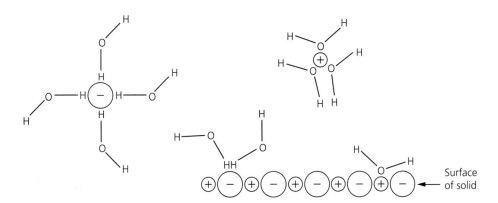

Figure 3.4

Whether or not a change takes place depends on the value of the change in entropy. This concept is covered later in this chapter.

> **Tip**
>
> Never state that atoms gain or lose electrons in order to reach the stability of the electron configuration of a noble gas.

Solubility of ionic compounds

When an ionic solid dissolves in water, the lattice breaks down and the ions are separated. This is very endothermic, so you might expect that ionic solids would not dissolve in water. To explain this apparent paradox, you must think about what happens to the ions as the solid dissolves.

Cations become surrounded by water molecules. Strong ion–dipole forces act between the positive cations and the $\delta-$ oxygen atoms in the water. Similarly, the anions become surrounded by water molecules with the $\delta+$ hydrogen atoms of the water molecules being strongly attracted to the negative anions (Figure 3.5). This process is called **hydration**. It is the highly exothermic nature of hydration that compensates for the endothermic break-up of the lattice.

> **Tip**
>
> The change from atom to cation is endothermic. Ionic bonding only occurs if the ions form a solid or, in solution, are hydrated by water molecules (see p. 59).

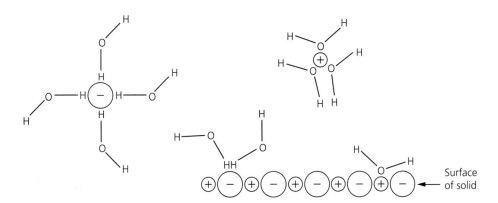

Figure 3.5 An ionic solid dissolving

> **The enthalpy of solution of a solid, ΔH_{soln}, is the enthalpy change when 1 mol of the solid is dissolved in sufficient solvent to give an infinitely dilute solution.**
>
> **The hydration enthalpy of an ion, ΔH_{hyd}, is the enthalpy change when 1 mol of gaseous ions is dissolved in sufficient solvent to give an infinitely dilute solution.**

> **Tip**
>
> An infinitely dilute solution can be thought of as one in which further dilution does not cause a heat change.

Step 1:

$$NaCl(s) \rightarrow Na^+(g) + Cl^-(g) \qquad \Delta H = -\Delta H_{latt}$$

Step 2:

$$Na^+(g) \xrightarrow{H_2O} Na^+(aq) \qquad \Delta H = \Delta H_{hyd}(Na^+)$$

$$Cl^-(g) \xrightarrow{H_2O} Cl^-(aq) \qquad \Delta H = \Delta H_{hyd}(Cl^-)$$

On addition, the gaseous ions cancel, giving:

$$NaCl(s) \xrightarrow{H_2O} Na^+(aq) + Cl^-(aq) \quad \Delta H_{soln} = -\Delta H_{latt} + \Delta H_{hyd}(Na^+) + \Delta H_{hyd}(Cl^-)$$

This can be shown as a Hess's law cycle (Figure 3.6).

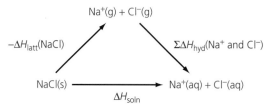

Figure 3.6

$$\Delta H_{soln} = -\Delta H_{latt} + \Delta H_{hyd}(Na^+) + \Delta H_{hyd}(Cl^-)$$

From this equation, it can be seen that:

- the more exothermic the lattice energy, the more endothermic the enthalpy of solution
- the more exothermic either of the hydration enthalpies, the more exothermic the enthalpy of solution

The sign of the enthalpy of solution is determined by the difference in magnitude between the lattice energy and the sum of the hydration energies (Figure 3.7).

Tip

Remember that the lattice energy is defined in the exothermic direction. It is the energy change when 1 mol of an ionic solid is formed from its constituent gaseous ions infinitely far apart.

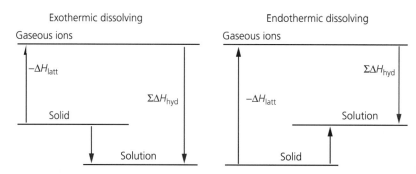

Figure 3.7

If the magnitude of the lattice enthalpy (blue arrow) is *less* than the sum of the hydration enthalpies of the two ions (red arrow), dissolving will be exothermic.

If the magnitude of the lattice enthalpy is *greater* than the sum of the hydration enthalpies of the two ions, dissolving will be endothermic.

A general relationship can be deduced from Figure 3.7:

$$\Delta H_{soln} = -\text{lattice energy} + \text{the sum of the hydration energies of all the ions}$$

Factors that affect lattice energy

The magnitude of the lattice energy depends on the strength of the forces acting on the ions. In a lattice, each ion is surrounded by a number of ions of opposite charge, resulting in strong forces of attraction and some forces of repulsion. This is illustrated in Figure 3.8. The red lines represent forces of attraction; the blue lines represent forces of repulsion.

The strength of these forces depends on:

- the magnitude of the charges on the ions
- the sum of the radii of the cation and the anion
- the arrangement of the ions in the lattice
- the relative sizes of the ions
- the extent of covalency

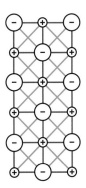

Figure 3.8 The forces acting between the ions in a planar slice through a crystal of sodium chloride

Charge and size of ions

The force between two ions of opposite charge depends upon the value of the ionic charges and how close the centres of the ions are. The stronger the force of attraction between the ions in the solid, the more exothermic is the lattice energy.

The lattice energy is proportional to the product of the charges on the two ions divided by the sum of their radii:

$$\Delta H_{latt} \propto \frac{q(+) \times q(-)}{\{r(+) + r(-)\}}$$

where $q(+)$ = the charge on the cation

$q(-)$ = the charge on the anion

$r(+)$ = the ionic radius of the cation

$r(-)$ = the ionic radius of the anion

> **Tip**
>
> There are small forces of repulsion between neighbouring ions of the same charge. This is only significant when the anion is much larger than the cation, which causes the anions to be crowded together.

The lattice energy is a measure of the strength of the ionic bond. The more negative the lattice energy, the stronger the bond.

Worked example 1

Explain why the lattice energy of sodium fluoride is more exothermic than the lattice energy of potassium chloride.

Answer

It is because Na^+ has a smaller ionic radius than K^+, and F^- is smaller than Cl^-. Therefore, the forces between sodium ions and fluoride ions are stronger than those between potassium ions and chloride ions.

Worked example 2

Explain why the lattice energy of calcium oxide is approximately four times more negative than that of potassium fluoride.

Answer

This is because in calcium oxide the product of the ionic charges is 4, whereas in potassium fluoride it is 1. The sums of the ionic radii of the two compounds are not very different. However, the value is smaller in CaO than in KF, so the lattice energy ratio is further increased.

The answer to worked example 2 can be explained more fully by looking at the values involved (Table 3.4).

Table 3.4 Lattice energy and ionic charge

Substance	ΔH_{latt}/kJ mol^{-1}	Product of ionic charges	Sum of ionic radii/nm
CaO	−3513	4	0.239
KF	−801	1	0.269

The lattice energy depends on the product of the charges on the ions divided by the sum of the ionic radii.

$$\frac{\text{product of ionic charges divided by sum of ionic radii for CaO}}{\text{product of ionic charges divided by sum of ionic radii for KF}}$$

$$= \frac{4/0.239}{1/0.269} = 4.5$$

$$\frac{\Delta H_{latt}(\text{CaO})}{\Delta H_{latt}(\text{KF})}$$

$$= \frac{-3513}{-801} = 4.4$$

The fact that these two values are so similar supports the theory.

Arrangement and relative size

Ions take up an arrangement in the lattice that maximises the lattice energy released. This is the position of minimum potential energy of the ions. If a small cation is surrounded by too many larger anions, a considerable amount of repulsion occurs between the larger anions. This is shown by the structures of ionic compounds of formula AB that are given in Table 3.5.

In sodium chloride, fitting eight chloride ions around the smaller sodium ion would result in considerable repulsion between the closely packed chloride ions. Each Na$^+$ ion is surrounded by six Cl$^-$ ions; each Cl$^-$ ion is surrounded by six Na$^+$ ions. This is called 6:6 coordination. This arrangement minimises repulsion.

Table 3.5 Ionic radii and coordination numbers

Substance	Cationic radius/nm	Anionic radius/nm	Ratio of anionic radius to cationic radius	Coordination number
CsCl	0.169	0.181	1.1:1	8
NaCl	0.095	0.181	1.9:1	6
ZnS	0.074	0.184	2.5:1	4

The type of lattice depends upon the ratio of the ionic radii. Compounds with a ratio of approximately 1:1 have a lattice structure similar to that of caesium chloride. Those with a ratio nearer to 2:1 have a structure similar to that of sodium chloride (Figure 3.9).

> **Tip**
>
> The coordination number of an ion in an ionic lattice is the number of ions of opposite charge that are most closely arranged around it.

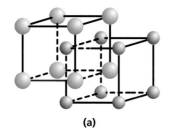

(a)

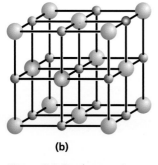

(b)

Figure 3.9 Structures of (a) caesium chloride and (b) sodium chloride

Factors that affect hydration enthalpy

The magnitude of the hydration enthalpy of an ion depends on the strength of the force between the ion and the water molecules surrounding it. Positive ions are attracted to the $\delta-$ oxygen atoms of the water and negative ions to the $\delta+$ hydrogen atoms.

The strength of the forces depends on:

- the magnitude of the charge on the ion — the greater the charge, the greater is the force
- the radius of the ion — the smaller the radius, the greater is the force

Test yourself

3 The ionic radius of M^{2+} is 0.076 nm and that of Q^{3+} is 0.064 nm. Explain which ion would have a more exothermic hydration enthalpy.

Hydration enthalpies of some gaseous ions are shown in Table 3.6.

Table 3.6 Hydration enthalpies of ions

Cation	$\Delta H_{hyd}/kJ\,mol^{-1}$	Anion	$\Delta H_{hyd}/kJ\,mol^{-1}$
Li^+	−519	F^-	−506
Na^+	−406	Cl^-	−364
K^+	−322	Br^-	−335
Mg^{2+}	−1920	I^-	−293
Ca^{2+}	−1650	OH^-	−460
Sr^{2+}	−1480		
Ba^{2+}	−1360		

Table 3.6 shows that

- the hydration energies become less exothermic as the radius of the ions in a group increases
- the magnitude of the hydration energy increases as the charge on the cation increases

Calculation of enthalpy of solution

Worked example

Use data from Tables 3.3 and 3.6 to predict the enthalpy of solution of sodium chloride.

Answer

$\Delta H_{soln} = -\Delta H_{latt} + \Delta H_{hyd}(Na^+) + \Delta H_{hyd}(Cl^-)$

$= -(-771) + (-406) + (-364) = +1\,kJ\,mol^{-1}$

Using lattice energies and hydration energies to predict the enthalpy of solution may be inaccurate, because slight errors in any of the quantities could result in an answer with the wrong sign. For example, if the data in the above worked example had been taken from a different source, the calculation could have been:

$$\Delta H_{\text{soln}} = -\Delta H_{\text{latt}} + \Delta H_{\text{hyd}}(\text{Na}^+) + \Delta H_{\text{hyd}}(\text{Cl}^-)$$

$$= -(-780) + (-444) + (-340) = -4\,\text{kJ}\,\text{mol}^{-1}$$

The true value of ΔH_{soln} of NaCl(s) is $+3.9\,\text{kJ}\,\text{mol}^{-1}$.

Extra care must be taken with ionic compounds of formula MX_2. This can be illustrated using a Hess's law cycle (Figure 3.10).

Figure 3.10

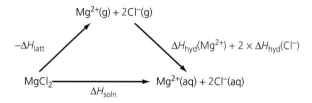

The hydration enthalpy of the chloride ion must be multiplied by two, because there are two Cl$^-$ ions in the equation.

$$\Delta H_{\text{soln}} = -\Delta H_{\text{latt}}(\text{MgCl}_2) + \Delta H_{\text{hyd}}(\text{Mg}^{2+}) + 2 \times \Delta H_{\text{hyd}}(\text{Cl}^-)$$

$$= -(-2500) + (-1920) + 2(-364) = -148\,\text{kJ}\,\text{mol}^{-1}$$

As can be seen from Table 3.7, many ionic solids have endothermic enthalpies of solution and are still soluble. Others have exothermic enthalpies of solution and are insoluble. The concept that exothermic changes will take place spontaneously and endothermic changes will not is an oversimplification. The criteria for spontaneity include the **entropy** change of the system (p. 72).

Table 3.7 Enthalpies ($\text{kJ}\,\text{mol}^{-1}$) of solutions of anhydrous compound at 25°C

Cation	Anion							
	F$^-$	Cl$^-$	Br$^-$	I$^-$	OH$^-$	CO$_3$$^{2-}$	NO$_3$$^-$	SO$_4$$^{2-}$
Li$^+$	+4.9**	−37	−49	−63	−24	−18	−3	−30
Na$^+$	+1.9	+3.9	−0.6	−7.5	−45	−27	+21	−2.4
K$^+$	−18	+17	+20	+20	−57	−31	+35	+24
NH$_4$$^+$	−1.2	+15	+16	+14	–	–	+26	+6.6
Ag$^+$	−23	+66*	+84*	+112*	–	+42*	+23	+18
Mg^{2+}	−18*	−160	−186	−213	+2.3*	−25.3*	−91	−91
Ca^{2+}	+12*	−81	−103	−120	−16.7**	−13*	−19	−18**
Al^{3+}	−27**	−330	−370	−390	*	–	–	−350

* insoluble ** slightly soluble

Entropy

It is often assumed that exothermic reactions will take place and endothermic reactions will not. This is an oversimplification, as can be seen by studying the solubilities and the enthalpies of solution of many salts. For example:

- ΔH_{soln} of ammonium nitrate is endothermic, yet it is very soluble in water.
- ΔH_{soln} of calcium carbonate is exothermic, yet it is insoluble in water.

During an exothermic process, the enthalpy of the chemicals decreases (ΔH is negative). However, the energy of the surroundings increases by exactly the same amount. In an endothermic reaction, the chemicals gain energy (ΔH is positive) and the surroundings lose an equal quantity of energy. So what is the driving force of spontaneous change?

The answer lies in the simple concept that **energy and matter tend to spread out or disperse**.

When a highly ordered crystalline solid, such as sodium chloride, dissolves in water, the solid becomes dispersed throughout the liquid. When the denser gas carbon dioxide is added to air, it does not form a lower layer, but spreads throughout the air. The same happens with energy. If a hot piece of iron is placed in a beaker of water, the heat from the iron disperses into the water until both the iron and the water are at the same temperature. You cannot boil a kettle of water by putting it on a block of ice and expect the ice to become colder as the water heats up. Such a change would not break the first law of thermodynamics (the conservation of energy), but experience tells us that it never happens. Heat spontaneously flows from a hotter body to a colder body.

The spreading out of a solute into water, the spontaneous mixing of carbon dioxide and air, the heat transfer from the hot iron to the colder water are all examples of an increase in disorder. The scientific term for disorder is **entropy**, symbol S.

Top: ordered, therefore low entropy; bottom: disordered, therefore high entropy

The second law of thermodynamics states that spontaneous changes result in an increase in disorder or entropy.

The second law of thermodynamics determines the direction of any physical, chemical or biological changes, for example:

- whether a change of state or chemical reaction is likely to happen at a particular temperature
- whether redox reactions will take place
- the position of equilibrium

It can be said that the second law of thermodynamics explains all of chemistry.

Care must be taken to include not only the entropy change of the chemicals (ΔS_{system}) but also the entropy change of the surroundings (ΔS_{surr}). For example, when hydrochloric acid solution is added to sodium hydroxide, the mixture of the two chemicals is called the system. The test tube, the solvent (water) and the air in the room are regarded as the surroundings. For a change to happen spontaneously, ΔS_{total} must be positive:

$$\Delta S_{total} = \Delta S_{system} + \Delta S_{surr}$$

This is another way of expressing the second law of thermodynamics.

The entropy of the *system* will increase if:

- a solid melts or a liquid boils, for example:

$$H_2O(s) \rightarrow H_2O(l) \text{ or } H_2O(l) \rightarrow H_2O(g)$$

> **Tip**
>
> In any spontaneous change, ΔS_{total} will be positive.

- a gas is produced or if a smaller number of moles of gas produce a larger number of moles of gas, for example:

$$Mg(s) + H_2SO_4(aq) \rightarrow MgSO_4(aq) + H_2(g) \quad \text{or} \quad PCl_5(g) \rightarrow PCl_3(g) + Cl_2(g)$$

- the number of moles of products is greater than the number of moles of reactants, for example:

$$[Cr(H_2O)_6]^{3+}(aq) + 3NH_2CH_2CH_2NH_2(aq) \rightarrow [Cr(NH_2CH_2CH_2NH_2)_3]^{3+}(aq) + 6H_2O(l)$$
$$\text{4 moles} \hspace{10cm} \text{7 moles}$$

Conversely the entropy of the system will decrease when a gas reactant forms a solid or more moles of gas produce fewer moles of gas. For example:

$$2Mg(s) + O_2(g) \rightarrow 2MgO(s) \quad \text{or} \quad 2H_2(g) + O_2(g) \rightarrow 2H_2O(g)$$

Entropy change of the system

A solid is much more ordered (or less disordered) than a liquid, which in turn is more ordered than a gas. So gaseous water is more disordered and has a larger entropy than liquid water, which has a greater entropy than ice. In general, this can be expressed as:

$$S_{solid} < S_{liquid} < S_{gas}$$

Table 3.8 shows the entropy changes for melting and boiling some substances.

Table 3.8 Some entropy changes

	$\Delta S_{melting}$ /J K^{-1}mol^{-1}	Melting temperature/K	$\Delta S_{boiling}$ /J K^{-1}mol^{-1}	Boiling temperature/K
O_2	8.2	54	76	90
H_2O	22	273	109	373
NH_3	29	195	97	246

In the combustion of phosphorus, the reaction goes from a solid plus a gas to a solid:

$$P_4(s) + 5O_2(g) \rightarrow P_4O_{10}(s)$$

The disorder of a gas is replaced by the order of a solid. Therefore, the extent of disorder decreases and ΔS_{system} is negative:

$$\Delta S^{\ominus}_{system} = S \text{ of } P_4O_{10}(s) - [S \text{ of } P_4(s) + 5 \times S \text{ of } O_2(g)]$$

When dilute hydrochloric acid is added to solid calcium carbonate, carbon dioxide gas is produced:

$$CaCO_3(s) + 2HCl(aq) \rightarrow CaCl_2(aq) + H_2O(l) + CO_2(g)$$
$$\text{solid} \quad + \text{ solution} \rightarrow \text{ solution} \quad + \hspace{3cm} \text{gas}$$

As a gas is produced, the disorder increases, and so ΔS_{system} is positive.

Table 3.9 shows the standard entropy values of some substances. Table 3.9 also shows that entropy increases as the complexity of a substance increases. For example, the entropy of ethane is greater than that of methane; the entropy of calcium carbonate is greater than that of calcium oxide. Note the difference between this table and one of enthalpies of formation.

Table 3.9 Standard entropies of some elements and compounds at 25°C

Gas	Entropy, $S^\ominus/\text{J K}^{-1}\text{mol}^{-1}$	Liquid	Entropy, $S^\ominus/\text{J K}^{-1}\text{mol}$	Solid	Entropy, $S^\ominus/\text{J K}^{-1}\text{mol}^{-1}$
H_2	131	C_2H_5OH	161	P_4	164
O_2	205	CCl_4	216	P_4O_{10}	229
N_2	192	C_6H_6	174	C	5.7
$H_2O(g)$	189	$H_2O(l)$	70	$H_2O(s)$	43
CO_2	214			CaO	40
NH_3	192			$CaCO_3$	93
CH_4	186				
C_2H_6	230				

> **Tip**
>
> When looking up the entropy of H_2O make sure that you use the value for the state (gas, liquid or solid) given in the question.

The standard enthalpy of formation of an element in its standard state is defined as zero. The same is not true about the standard entropy values of an element: $\Delta H^\ominus_f$ of $O_2(g) = 0\,\text{kJ mol}^{-1}$; $S^\ominus$ of $O_2(g) = -205\,\text{J K}^{-1}\text{mol}^{-1}$.

A third general point is that ΔS_{system} increases if the number of moles in a given state (all gases or all liquids) increases or ΔS_{system} decreases if the number of moles of product gases is less than the number of moles of gaseous reactants. For example the entropy of the system decreases in the reaction:

$$N_2(g) + 3H_2(g) \rightleftharpoons 2NH_3(g)$$
$$\text{4 mol of gas} \qquad \text{2 mol of gas}$$

Test yourself

4 State whether the reactions below result in an increase or decrease in the entropy of the systems:

   a) $SO_2(g) + \frac{1}{2}O_2(g) \rightarrow SO_3(g)$ b) $NH_4Cl(s) + OH^-(aq) \rightarrow NH_3(g) + Cl^-(aq) + H_2O(l)$

Effect of temperature on entropy

The third law of thermodynamics states that the entropy of a perfect crystalline substance at absolute zero (0 K or −273°C) is zero. As the crystalline substance is heated, it gains in entropy until its melting temperature is reached. On melting there is a large jump in entropy, followed by a steady increase as the liquid is heated to its boiling temperature. There is another large jump in entropy as its physical state changes, followed by a gradual increase as the gas is heated. This is shown in Figure 3.11.

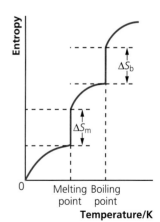

Figure 3.11

Test yourself

5 State and explain whether $H_2O(l)$ at 25°C has a higher or lower entropy than $H_2O(l)$ at 35°C.

The values in Table 3.9 are *standard* entropy values, which means that they are the values at a stated temperature, usually 298 K (25°C), and 100 kPa (1 atm) pressure. The entropy of liquid water at 100°C is $80 \, \text{J K}^{-1} \, \text{mol}^{-1}$, which is $10 \, \text{J K}^{-1} \, \text{mol}^{-1}$ more than its value at 25°C.

Calculation of $\Delta S^{\ominus}_{\text{system}}$

The entropy change of the system can be calculated from the formula:

$$\Delta S^{\ominus}_{\text{system}} = \Sigma n S^{\ominus}(\text{products}) - \Sigma n S^{\ominus}(\text{reactants})$$

where n represents the stoichiometric numbers in the chemical equation.

Worked example 1

Use the data in Table 3.9 to calculate the entropy change of the system for the reaction:

$$2H_2O(g) \rightarrow 2H_2(g) + O_2(g)$$

Answer

$\Delta S_{\text{system}} = 2 \times S(\text{hydrogen}) + S(\text{oxygen}) - 2 \times S(\text{gaseous water}) = 2 \times 131 + 205 - (2 \times 189) = +89 \, \text{J K}^{-1} \, \text{mol}^{-1}$

Worked example 2

Use data from Table 3.9 to calculate the standard entropy change of the system for the reaction between phosphorus and oxygen:

$$P_4(s) + 5O_2(g) \rightarrow P_4O_{10}(s)$$

Answer

$\Delta S^{\ominus}_{\text{system}} = \Sigma n S^{\ominus}(\text{products}) - \Sigma n S^{\ominus}(\text{reactants})$

$= 229 - (+164 + 5 \times 205) = -960 \, \text{J K}^{-1} \, \text{mol}^{-1}$

At first sight you might think that the reaction in worked example 2 should not take place because the entropy decreases. However, this is only the entropy change of the system. Both this reaction (negative ΔS value) and the reaction of acid with calcium carbonate (positive ΔS value) take place spontaneously. What has not been taken into account is the entropy change of the surroundings (the reactions are exothermic).

Entropy change of the surroundings

When an exothermic reaction takes place, heat energy is transferred to the surrounding air or to the solvent, causing an increase in disorder of the air or solvent molecules. This can be seen from the Maxwell–Boltzmann distribution of energies at two temperatures (Figure 3.12).

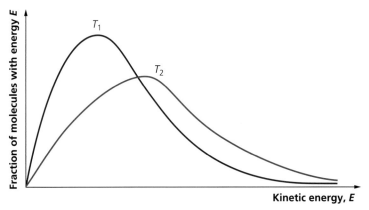

Figure 3.12 Maxwell–Boltzmann distribution of molecular energies at two temperatures ($T_2 > T_1$)

At the higher temperature (T_2), the molecules have a much greater range of energy and so are more random or disordered. This leads to the following important conclusions:

- $\Delta S_{surr}^{\ominus}$ is positive for all exothermic reactions.
- $\Delta S_{surr}^{\ominus}$ is negative for all endothermic reactions.

This is shown pictorially in Figure 3.13.

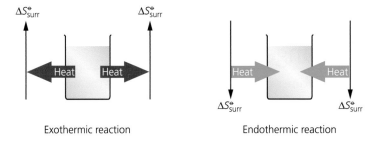

Figure 3.13 $\Delta S_{surr}^{\ominus}$ and exothermic and endothermic reactions

If the surroundings are hot, the entropy increase is small because the molecules have high entropy and are already in chaotic motion. Conversely, if the surroundings are cold, the entropy change is much greater. The entropy change in the surroundings, caused by transfer of heat, depends on the value of the heat change and is also inversely proportional to the temperature of the surroundings. The heat change of the surroundings is the negative of the enthalpy change of the system:

$$\Delta S_{surr}^{\ominus} = \frac{-\Delta H^{\ominus}}{T}$$

Tip

If the system is exothermic, it loses enthalpy, which is transferred as heat to the surroundings (which gain entropy).

Test yourself

6 State whether an endothermic reaction will have a positive or negative value of ΔS_{surr}.

Tip

The temperature must be in kelvin (K = °C + 273).

Worked example 1

Calculate the value of ΔS_{surr} at 25°C and at 100°C for a reaction with $\Delta H = -123\,kJ\,mol^{-1}$.

Answer

$$\Delta S_{surr}\,(\text{at }25°C) = \frac{-\Delta H}{T} = \frac{-(-123\,000\,J\,mol^{-1})}{298\,K} = +413\,J\,K^{-1}\,mol^{-1}$$

$$\Delta S_{surr}\,(\text{at }100°C) = \frac{-\Delta H}{T} = \frac{-(-123\,000\,J\,mol^{-1})}{373\,K} = +330\,J\,K^{-1}\,mol^{-1}$$

> Note that the value of ΔH was converted from kJ to J and the temperature from °C to K.

Worked example 2

Calculate the entropy change of the surroundings when 1 mol of phosphorus, P_4, burns in air.

$$P_4(s) + 5O_2(g) \rightarrow P_4O_{10}(s)\ \Delta H_c = -2984\,kJ\,mol^{-1}\ \text{at }25°C\ (298\,K)$$

Answer

$$\Delta S_{surr}^{\ominus} = \frac{-\Delta H^{\ominus}}{T}$$

$$= \frac{-(-2984)}{298} = +10.0\,kJ\,K^{-1}\,mol^{-1} = +10\,000\,J\,K^{-1}\,mol^{-1}$$

> **Tip**
>
> As with ΔH calculations, you should always include a sign and units in the answer for ΔS.

Total entropy change

The total entropy change (sometimes called the entropy change of the universe) is the sum of the entropy changes of the system and the surroundings:

$$\Delta S_{total}^{\ominus} = \Delta S_{system}^{\ominus} + \Delta S_{surr}^{\ominus} = \Delta S_{system}^{\ominus} - \frac{\Delta H^{\ominus}}{T}$$

Worked example

Calculate the total entropy change for the combustion of magnesium and comment on its feasibility at 298 K.

$$2Mg(s) + O_2(g) \rightarrow 2MgO(s)\qquad \Delta H_{reaction} = -1203\,kJ\,mol^{-1}$$

The entropy change of the *system* is $-217\,J\,K^{-1}\,mol^{-1}$.

Answer

$$\Delta S_{surr} = \frac{-\Delta H}{T} = \frac{-(-1\,203\,000)}{298} = +4037\,J\,K^{-1}\,mol^{-1}$$

$$\Delta S_{total} = -217 + 4037 = +3820\,J\,K^{-1}\,mol^{-1}$$

This is a positive number so the reaction is thermodynamically feasible at a temperature of 298 K. However, the oxidation of magnesium at 298 K is so slow that it is not observed. This is because the activation energy for the reaction is very high.

> Remember that entropy data are in joules (per kelvin per mole) and enthalpy data are in kilojoules (per mole). You must either divide the entropy value by 1000 or multiply the enthalpy value by 1000.

Changes are thermodynamically feasible if the *total* entropy change is positive.

This means that an unfavourable (negative) entropy change of the system can be compensated for by a favourable (positive) entropy change of the surroundings.

Table 3.10 Entropy changes and feasibility

$\Delta S^{\ominus}_{system}$	$\Delta S^{\ominus}_{surr}$	Feasible
Positive	Positive (exothermic reaction)	Always
Negative	Negative (endothermic reaction)	Never
Negative	Positive (exothermic reaction)	If the numerical value of $\Delta H/T > \Delta S^{\ominus}_{system}$ (more likely at low temperatures)
Positive	Negative (endothermic reaction)	If the numerical value $\Delta S^{\ominus}_{system} > \Delta H/T$ (more likely at high temperatures)

Numerical value means the value ignoring any sign, so -40 is numerically larger than -30.

Test yourself

7 Use the data in Table 3.9 on p. 73 to calculate the thermodynamic feasibility of the following reactions at 298 K.

a) $N_2(g) + 3H_2(g) \rightarrow 2NH_3(g)$ $\Delta H = -92\,kJ\,mol^{-1}$

b) $CaCO_3(s) \rightarrow CaO(s) + CO_2(g)$ $\Delta H = +178\,kJ\,mol^{-1}$

Spontaneous endothermic reactions

When pure ethanoic acid is added to solid ammonium carbonate, bubbles of gas are rapidly produced. This appears to be a violent reaction, but if a thermometer is placed in the acid before the ammonium carbonate is added, it will be observed that the temperature falls considerably as the reaction takes place.

$$2CH_3COOH(l) + (NH_4)_2CO_3(s) \rightarrow 2CH_3COONH_4(s) + H_2O(l) + CO_2(g)$$

Even though the reaction is endothermic, there is a considerable increase in entropy of the system because a gas is produced. This makes ΔS_{total} positive and the reaction thermodynamically spontaneous.

Hydrated barium hydroxide reacts with solid ammonium chloride in a rapid endothermic reaction at room temperature:

$$Ba(OH)_2 \cdot 8H_2O(s) + 2NH_4Cl(s) \rightarrow BaCl_2(s) + 10H_2O(l) + 2NH_3(g)$$

As with the previous example, the driving force of the reaction is ΔS_{system}, which overcomes the endothermic nature of the reaction. The reactants are solids and the products are a solid, a liquid and a gas, and three substances make 13 substances, so there is a considerable gain in disorder.

Another easily observed endothermic change is the dissolving of ammonium nitrate in water.

$$NH_4NO_3(s) + aq \rightarrow NH_4^+(aq) + NO_3^-(aq)$$

As the reaction is spontaneous, the negative value of ΔS_{surr} must be outweighed by the positive value of ΔS_{system}.

All three of the above examples are thermodynamically spontaneous. The activation energies are low and so all three reactions take place rapidly at room temperature. They are examples of reactants that are thermodynamically and kinetically unstable relative to their products.

- A positive ΔS_{total} means that the reactants are thermodynamically unstable relative to the products.
- A negative ΔS_{total} means that the reactants are thermodynamically stable relative to the products.
- A small activation energy means that the reactants are kinetically unstable relative to the products.
- A large activation energy means that the reactants are kinetically stable relative to the products.

Free energy, G

The free energy measured at constant pressure is called the Gibbs free energy (or Gibbs function), symbol G, and is named after the American scientist J. Willard Gibbs. It is a measure of the chemical potential, μ, that a mole of a substance has when on its own. It is defined as:

$$G = H - TS$$

where H is the enthalpy of the substance and S its entropy. T is the temperature in kelvin.

When 1 mol of substance A reacts to form 1 mol of substance B, the change in free energy is given by:

$$\Delta G^{\ominus} = G_B^{\ominus} - G_A^{\ominus} = (H_B^{\ominus} - TS_B^{\ominus}) - (H_A^{\ominus} - TS_A^{\ominus})$$

which becomes:

$$\Delta G^{\ominus} = \Delta H^{\ominus} - T\Delta S^{\ominus}$$

where $\Delta S^{\ominus}$ is the entropy change of the system.

For spontaneous processes, the value of $\Delta G^{\ominus}$ is negative, as the change is from a position of higher chemical potential to one at a lower chemical potential. This is similar to a rock rolling down a hill. The rock loses potential energy, so Δ(potential energy) is negative.

In equilibrium reactions, the position of equilibrium is where the system has minimum free energy. This is shown in Figure 3.14.

The composition of the equilibrium mixture is given by the minimum in this curve. If there is more A in the system than that at the minimum, the reaction will proceed from A to B until equilibrium is reached. Likewise if there is more B in the mixture, the reaction will proceed from B to A until equilibrium is reached.

> Chemical potential is similar to gravitational potential energy, but applied to chemical changes.

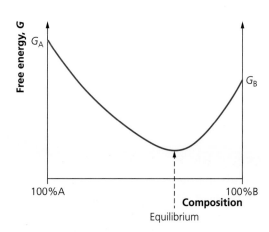

Figure 3.14 The change of free energy as A changes to B

$\Delta G^{\ominus}$ and total entropy change

The relationship between total entropy change and the entropy changes of the system and surroundings was given on p. 76.

$$\Delta S^{\ominus}_{\text{total}} = \Delta S^{\ominus}_{\text{system}} + \Delta S^{\ominus}_{\text{surroundings}} = \Delta S^{\ominus}_{\text{system}} - \frac{\Delta H}{T}$$

Multiplying both sides by $-T$:

$$-T\Delta S^{\ominus}_{\text{total}} = \Delta H - T\Delta S^{\ominus}_{\text{system}}$$

But the definition of ΔG is:

$$\Delta G^{\ominus} = \Delta H - T\Delta S^{\ominus}_{\text{system}}$$

This gives the relationship between ΔG and ΔS_{total}:

$$\Delta G^{\ominus} = -T\Delta S^{\ominus}_{\text{total}}$$

For a spontaneous change $\Delta G^{\ominus} \leq 0$:

$$\Delta H^{\ominus} - T\Delta S^{\ominus} \leq 0$$

$$\Delta H^{\ominus} \leq T\Delta S^{\ominus}$$

This important inequality expresses the criterion for spontaneous change solely in terms of the system and so the subscript system can be dropped.

Exothermic reactions will be spontaneous if:

- $\Delta S^{\ominus}$ is positive

or if

- $\Delta S^{\ominus}$ is negative but $T\Delta S^{\ominus}$ is less negative than $\Delta H^{\ominus}$

An endothermic reaction will only be spontaneous if $\Delta S^{\ominus}$ is positive *and* $T\Delta S^{\ominus}$ is more positive than $\Delta H^{\ominus}$.

Tip

$\Delta G^{\ominus}$ is negative for any spontaneous change.

Direction of change

This can be predicted in one of two ways.

In terms of ΔS_{total}

If ΔS_{total} is positive the change is said to be thermodynamically spontaneous (thermodynamically feasible). Thus the change will occur, providing that the kinetics of the change are favourable. If ΔS_{total} is negative, the reverse reaction is thermodynamically spontaneous. The value of ΔS_{total} can be altered by altering the temperature. For an exothermic reaction an increase in temperature will cause ΔS_{surr} to become less positive, which in turn will make ΔS_{total} less positive.

A positive value of ΔS_{total} is favoured by a negative value of ΔH and a positive value of ΔS_{system}.

The relationship between total entropy change and the entropy changes of the system and surroundings was given above:

$$\Delta S^{\ominus}_{\text{total}} = \Delta S^{\ominus}_{\text{system}} - \frac{\Delta H^{\ominus}}{T}$$

For a spontaneous change $\Delta S^{\ominus}_{\text{total}} \geq 0$:

$$\Delta S^{\ominus}_{\text{total}} = \Delta S^{\ominus}_{\text{system}} - \frac{\Delta H^{\ominus}}{T} \geq 0 \text{ (a positive number)}$$

The value of ΔS_{total} also determines the extent of the reaction. The more positive its value, the more the position of equilibrium will lie to the right as $\Delta S_{\text{total}} = R \ln K$ (see p. 82).

In terms of free energy

If ΔG is negative the change is said to be thermodynamically spontaneous. Thus the change will occur, providing that the kinetics of the change are favourable. If ΔG is positive, the reverse reaction is thermodynamically spontaneous.

A negative value of ΔG is favoured by a negative value of ΔH and a positive value of ΔS.

The relationship between ΔG and ΔH and the entropy changes of the system and surroundings was given above:

$$\Delta G^{\ominus} = \Delta H - T\Delta S^{\ominus}$$

For a spontaneous change $\Delta G^{\ominus} < 0$.

> The value of ΔG also determines the extent of the reaction. The more negative its value, the more the position of equilibrium will lie to the right as $\Delta G = -RT\ln K$ (see p. 82).

Test yourself

8 State whether a reaction with a value of $\Delta G^{\ominus} = +23\,kJ\,mol^{-1}$ is thermodynamically feasible.

Worked example 1

Comment on the feasibility of the following reaction occurring at a temperature of 298 K:

$$C_2H_5OH(l) + PCl_5(s) \rightarrow C_2H_5Cl(g) + HCl(g) + POCl_3(l)$$

$$\Delta H = -107\,kJ\,mol^{-1} \quad \Delta S_{system} = +368\,J\,K^{-1}\,mol^{-1}$$

> ΔS_{system} is positive because the reaction involves liquid + solid → two gases + liquid (getting more random).

Answer

As ΔH is negative, ΔS_{surr} will be positive. Both ΔS_{surr} and ΔS_{system} are favourable (positive), so the reaction is thermodynamically feasible (spontaneous) at all temperatures.

> **Tip**
>
> As both factors are favourable, there is no need to work out the value of ΔS_{total}. However, the reaction may be too slow (reactants kinetically stable) at low temperatures.

Worked example 2

Comment on the feasibility of the following reaction occurring at a temperature of 298 K.

$$2C(s) + 2H_2(g) \rightarrow H_2C{=}CH_2(g)$$

$$\Delta H = +52.2\,kJ\,mol^{-1} \quad \Delta S_{system} = -184\,J\,K^{-1}\,mol^{-1}$$

Answer

Both ΔH and ΔS_{system} are unfavourable, so the reaction will not take place. Carbon and hydrogen are thermodynamically stable relative to ethene at all temperatures.

> **Tip**
>
> As both factors are unfavourable, there is no need to work out the value of ΔS_{total}.

Worked example 3

Comment on the feasibility of the following reaction occurring at a temperature of 298 K:

$$H_2(g) + \frac{1}{2}O_2(g) \rightarrow H_2O(l)$$

$$\Delta H = -286\,kJ\,mol^{-1} \quad \Delta S_{system} = -45\,J\,K^{-1}\,mol^{-1}$$

This reaction mixture is kinetically stable at room temperature. Either a catalyst or a spark is needed for reaction to occur. Water decomposes into its elements only at very high temperatures.

Standard free energy of formation, $\Delta G_f^{\ominus}$

The standard free energy of formation is the change in free energy that occurs when a compound is formed from its elements in their most thermodynamically stable states under standard conditions of 100 kPa (1 atm) pressure and a temperature of 298 K. It is the difference between the free energy of a substance and the free energies of its elements in their most thermodynamically stable states at standard conditions.

The standard free *energy* of formation of an element in its standard state is zero, as is the *enthalpy* of formation of an element in its standard state.

The standard free energy of reaction can be calculated from the standard free energies of formation. It is the sum of the free energies of formation of the products minus the sum of the free energies of formation of the reactants:

$$\Delta G^{\ominus} = \Sigma(\Delta G_f^{\ominus}\text{of products}) - \Sigma(\Delta G_f^{\ominus}\text{of reactants})$$

where Σ means the sum of all the substances, using their stoichiometry in the equation.

Table 3.11 Some free energy of formation data

Substance	Formula	$\Delta G_f^{\ominus}$/kJ mol^{-1}	Substance	Formula	$\Delta G_f^{\ominus}$/kJ mol^{-1}
Methane	$CH_4(g)$	−12	Water	$H_2O(g)$	−229
Ethane	$C_2H_6(g)$	−7.7	Water	$H_2O(l)$	−237
Ethanol	$C_2H_5OH(l)$	−175	Carbon dioxide	$CO_2(g)$	−394
Glucose	$C_6H_{12}O_6(s)$	−911	Carbon monoxide	$CO(g)$	−33

Worked example 1

Calculate the free energy change when 1 mol of glucose is burnt in excess oxygen.

$$C_6H_{12}O_6(s) + 6O_2(g) \rightarrow 6CO_2(g) + 6H_2O(l)$$

Answer

$$\Delta G^{\ominus} = \Sigma(\Delta G_f^{\ominus}\text{ of products}) - \Sigma(\Delta G_f^{\ominus}\text{of reactants})$$

$$= (6 \times -394) + (6 \times -237) - (-911 + 6 \times 0) = -2875\,\text{kJ mol}^{-1}$$

Tip

Remember that the free energy of formation of an element in its standard state is zero.

Free energy change for a reaction can also be calculated from enthalpy and entropy data using the expression:

$$\Delta G^{\ominus} = \Delta H^{\ominus} - T\Delta S^{\ominus}$$

Worked example 2

Calculate the standard free energy change for the reaction at 298 K.

$$C_2H_5OH(l) + PCl_5(s) \rightarrow C_2H_5Cl(g) + HCl(g) + POCl_3(l)$$

Given $\Delta H^{\ominus} = -107$ kJ mol^{-1} and $\Delta S^{\ominus}_{system} = +368$ J K^{-1} mol^{-1}.

Answer

$$\Delta G^{\ominus} = \Delta H^{\ominus} - T\Delta S^{\ominus} = -107\,\text{kJ}\,\text{mol}^{-1} - 298\,\text{K} \times 0.368\,\text{kJ}\,\text{K}^{-1}\,\text{mol}^{-1}$$

$$= -216.7\,\text{kJ}\,\text{mol}^{-1}$$

As the value is negative, this reaction is thermodynamically spontaneous.

If ΔG is negative the change is said to be thermodynamically feasible (spontaneous). Thus the change will occur, providing that the kinetics of the change are favourable. However if the activation energy for the reaction is too high, the reaction is described as being kinetically inhibited.

If ΔG is positive, the reverse reaction is thermodynamically feasible.

Calculation of equilibrium constant from thermodynamic data

From entropy data

The value of the equilibrium constant depends on $\Delta S^{\ominus}_{total}$:

$$\Delta S^{\ominus}_{total} = R\ln K$$

where R is the gas constant, which equals $8.31\,\text{J}\,\text{K}^{-1}\,\text{mol}^{-1}$.

So:

$$\ln K = \frac{\Delta S^{\ominus}_{total}}{R} \qquad \text{or} \qquad K = e^{\Delta S/R}$$

The value of $\Delta S^{\ominus}_{total}$ depends on the entropy change of the system and the entropy change of the surroundings:

$$\Delta S^{\ominus}_{total} = \Delta S^{\ominus}_{system} + \Delta S^{\ominus}_{surroundings} = \Delta S^{\ominus}_{system} - \Delta H/T$$

$\Delta S^{\ominus}_{total}$ and hence K depend on:

- the nature of the reaction, which determines $\Delta H^{\ominus}$ and $\Delta S^{\ominus}_{system}$
- the temperature at equilibrium

The value of K_c does *not* depend on the pressure or the presence of a catalyst.

From free energy data

The standard free energy change for a reaction, $\Delta G^{\ominus}_r$, can be calculated from the standard free energy of formation, $\Delta G^{\ominus}_f$ or from $\Delta S^{\ominus}_r$ and $\Delta H^{\ominus}_r$ values.

The value of K can then be calculated using the expression $\Delta G^{\ominus}_r = -RT\ln K$.

Tip

Remember that ΔS and R are quoted in joules but ΔH in kilojoules.

Tip

The standard free energy of *formation* of an element in its stable state is zero.

Worked example 1

(from standard free energy of formation data)

Use the standard free energy of formation data in Table 3.11 (p. 81) to calculate the value of the standard free energy change and hence the value of the equilibrium constant K for the reaction below at 600 K.

$$CO(g) + H_2O(g) \rightleftharpoons H_2(g) + CO_2(g)$$

$$[R = 8.31\,\text{J}\,\text{mol}^{-1}\,\text{K}^{-1}]$$

Answer

$\Delta G = \Sigma \Delta G_f \text{ (of products)} - \Sigma \Delta G_f \text{ (of reactants)}$

$\quad = -394 + 0 - (-33) - (229) = -132\,\text{kJ}\,\text{mol}^{-1}$

$\quad = -RT \ln K$

$\ln K = -\Delta G / RT = -(-132\,000\,\text{J}\,\text{mol}^{-1})/(8.31\,\text{J}\,\text{mol}^{-1}\,\text{K}^{-1} \times 600\,\text{K}) = 26.47$

$K = e^{-\Delta G/RT} = e^{26.47} = 3.14 \times 10^{11}$

> **Tip**
>
> Remember to have both R and $\Delta G^\ominus$ in terms of joules.

Worked example 2

(from entropy and enthalpy data)

Hydrogen is manufactured by the reaction at 800°C.

$$CH_4(g) + H_2O(g) \rightleftharpoons CO(g) + 3H_2(g)$$

Use the data below to calculate $\Delta G^\ominus$ and hence K at this temperature.

$$[R = 8.31\,\text{J}\,\text{mol}^{-1}\,\text{K}^{-1}]$$

Substance	$\Delta H_f/\text{kJ}\,\text{mol}^{-1}$	$S/\text{J}\,\text{mol}^{-1}\,\text{K}^{-1}$
$CH_4(g)$	−74.8	186.2
$H_2O(g)$	−248.1	188.7
$CO(g)$	−110.5	197.6
$H_2(g)$	0	130.6

Answer

$\Delta G = \Delta H - T\Delta S$

$\Delta H = -110.5 + 0 - (-74.8) - (-242.8) = +206.1\,\text{kJ}\,\text{mol}^{-1}$

$\Delta S = 197.6 + (3 \times 130.6) - (186.2 + 188.7) = 214.5\,\text{J}\,\text{mol}^{-1}\,\text{K}^{-1} = +0.2145\,\text{J}\,\text{mol}^{-1}\,\text{K}^{-1}$

$\Delta G = +206.1 - (1073 \times 0.2145) = -24.1\,\text{kmol}^{-1}\,\text{K}^{-1} = -RT\ln K$

$\ln K = -(-24\,100\,\text{J}\,\text{mol}^{-1})/(8.31 \times 1073) = 2.698$

$K = e^{2.698} = 14.9$

> Thermodynamically derived values of K have no units.

Summary

The equilibrium constant, K, is linked to $\Delta G^{\ominus}$ and to $\Delta S^{\ominus}_{\text{total}}$ by the expressions:

$$\Delta G^{\ominus} = -RT\ln K$$

$$\Delta S^{\ominus}_{\text{total}} = R\ln K$$

Effect of a change in temperature on *K* and hence on position of equilibrium

In terms of ΔS_{total}

$$\Delta S^{\ominus}_{\text{total}} = \Delta S^{\ominus}_{\text{system}} - \frac{\Delta H^{\ominus}}{T}$$

If the reaction is exothermic, $\Delta H^{\ominus}$ is negative, so $-\Delta H^{\ominus}/T$ is positive.

If T increases, the value of $-\Delta H^{\ominus}/T$ becomes less positive (smaller), so $\Delta S^{\ominus}_{\text{total}}$ becomes less positive.

Because $\Delta S^{\ominus}_{\text{total}}$ becomes less positive, $\ln K$ and hence K become smaller and the position of equilibrium lies more to the left.

For an endothermic reaction, $\Delta H^{\ominus}$ is positive, so $-\Delta H^{\ominus}/T$ is negative and gets less negative at a higher temperature. This makes $\Delta S^{\ominus}_{\text{total}}$ more positive (or less negative) and so the value of K rises and the position of equilibrium moves to the right.

The logic of the explanation is:

1 What is the effect of the change in temperature on the value of $\Delta S^{\ominus}_{\text{total}}$?

2 Hence what is the effect of the change in temperature on the value of K?

3 If K decreases (exothermic reaction) the quotient Q is now larger than K.

4 The position of equilibrium moves to the left, making the quotient smaller until the new value of Q equals the new value of K.

In terms of ΔG

$$\Delta G^{\ominus} = \Delta H^{\ominus} - T\Delta S^{\ominus} = -RT\ln K$$

$$\ln K = \frac{\Delta S^{\ominus}}{R} - \frac{\Delta H^{\ominus}}{RT}$$

- If the reaction is exothermic, $\Delta H^{\ominus}$ is negative, so $-\Delta H^{\ominus}/T$ is positive.
- If T increases, the value of $-\Delta H^{\ominus}/T$ becomes less positive (smaller).
- The right-hand side of the expression for $\ln K$ becomes less positive, so $\ln K$ and hence K become smaller and the position of equilibrium moves to the left.
- For an endothermic reaction, $\Delta H^{\ominus}$ is positive, so $-\Delta H^{\ominus}/T$ is negative.
- If T increases, the value of $-\Delta H^{\ominus}/T$ becomes less negative.
- The right-hand side of the expression for $\ln K$ becomes larger, so $\ln K$ and hence K become larger and the position of equilibrium moves to the right.

The logic of the explanation is:

1 What is the effect of the change in temperature on the value of $-\Delta H^{\ominus}/T$?

2 Hence what is the effect of the change in temperature on the value of K?

> **Tip**
>
> Both the explanations in terms of $\Delta G^{\ominus}$ and that in terms of $\Delta S^{\ominus}_{\text{total}}$ assume that neither $\Delta H^{\ominus}$ nor $\Delta S^{\ominus}_{\text{system}}$ change with a change in temperature. This is a reasonable assumption.

3 As K decreases (reaction is exothermic) the quotient Q is now larger than K.

4 The position of equilibrium moves to the left, making the quotient smaller until the new value of Q equals the new value of K.

Change of feasibility

When ΔS_{total} is positive or $\Delta G^{\ominus}$ is negative the reaction is said to be thermodynamically feasible, but it may not take place if the activation energy is too high.

A reaction is unfeasible if ΔS_{total} is negative or $\Delta G^{\ominus}$ is positive.

The change when an unfeasible reaction becomes feasible is when a negative ΔS_{total} becomes zero or a positive ΔG becomes zero. The temperature when this happens can be calculated:

$$\Delta S_{total} = \Delta S_{system} - \frac{\Delta H}{T} = 0 \qquad \text{or} \qquad \Delta G = \Delta H - T\Delta S = 0$$

$$\Delta S_{system} = \frac{\Delta H}{T} \qquad\qquad\qquad T\Delta S = \Delta H$$

$$T = \frac{\Delta H}{\Delta S_{system}} \qquad\qquad\qquad T = \frac{\Delta H}{\Delta S}$$

Do not try to explain the effect of a change in temperature in terms of the change in ΔG as this results in a very complex explanation, especially if ΔS is positive.

> **Tip**
>
> The term 'spontaneous' is sometimes used in place of 'feasible'.

Worked example 1

Calculate the temperature at which the decomposition of calcium nitrate becomes feasible.

$$Ca(NO_3)_2(s) \rightleftharpoons CaO(s) + 2NO_2(g) + \frac{1}{2}O_2(g) \qquad \Delta H_r = +369.7\,kJ\,mol^{-1}$$
$$\Delta S_{system} = +428.5\,J\,K^{-1}\,mol^{-1}$$

Answer

The temperature is when $\Delta S_{total} = 0$.

$$\Delta S_{total} = \Delta S_{system} - \frac{\Delta H}{T} = 0$$

$$T = \frac{\Delta H}{\Delta S_{system}} = \frac{(+369.7 \times 1000\,J\,mol^{-1})}{(+428.5\,J\,K^{-1}\,mol^{-1})} = 863\,K = 590°C$$

> **Tip**
>
> The value for magnesium nitrate is 213°C. This shows that the decomposition temperature of the group 2 nitrates increases down the group.

Worked example 2

a) Calculate the Gibbs free energy change at a temperature of 435 K for the reaction below and comment on its feasibility.

$$PCl_5(g) \rightleftharpoons PCl_3(g) + Cl_2(g)$$

$$\Delta H_r = +92\,kJ\,mol^{-1} \qquad \Delta S = +182\,J\,mol^{-1}\,K^{-1}$$

b) Calculate the temperature at which the reaction changes to becoming feasible.

Answer

a) $\Delta G = \Delta H - T\Delta S = +92 - 435 \times 0.182 = +12.8\,kJ\,mol^{-1}$, so the reaction is thermodynamically unfeasible as ΔG is positive.

b) The temperature will be when $\Delta G = 0$.

$$\Delta H - T\Delta S = 0$$

$$T = \frac{\Delta H}{\Delta S} = \frac{92}{0.182} = 505\,K$$

> **Tip**
>
> Remember to have both ΔH and ΔS in kilojoules.

Worked example 3

Calculate the temperature at which the following reaction becomes thermodynamically feasible:

$$CaCO_3(s) \rightarrow CaO(s) + CO_2(g)$$

$$\Delta H = +178\,kJ\,mol^{-1} \qquad \Delta S_{system} = +164\,J\,K^{-1}\,mol^{-1}$$

Answer in terms of ΔS_{total}

ΔH is unfavourable (positive), but ΔS_{system} is favourable (positive). Therefore, the reaction will only be thermodynamically feasible when ΔS_{system} is greater than $\Delta H/T$.

$$\Delta S_{total} = \Delta S_{system} + \Delta S_{surr} = \Delta S_{system} - \frac{\Delta H}{T}$$

At a temperature of 298 K:

$$\Delta S_{total} = +164\,J\,K\,mol^{-1} - (+178\,000\,J\,K^{-1}\,mol^{-1})/298\,K = -433\,J\,K^{-1}\,mol^{-1}$$

This is a negative value and so the reaction is not feasible at 298 K.

As the reaction is endothermic, it will become spontaneous at a higher temperature. The conditions at which it changes from being not feasible to being feasible is when $\Delta S_{total} = 0$.

$$\Delta S_{total} = \Delta S_{system} - \frac{\Delta H}{T} = 0$$

$$\Delta S_{system} = \frac{\Delta H}{T}$$

$$T = \frac{\Delta H}{\Delta S_{system}} = \frac{+178\,000\,J\,mol^{-1}}{+164\,J\,K^{-1}\,mol^{-1}} = 1085\,K\ (or\ 812°C)$$

Answer in terms of ΔG

ΔH is positive (unfavourable) and ΔS is positive (favourable). Therefore, the reaction will only be thermodynamically feasible when $T\Delta S$ is more positive than ΔH. The change in feasibility is when the two are equal.

$$T\Delta S = \Delta H$$

$$T = \frac{\Delta H}{\Delta S} = \frac{+178\,000\,J\,mol^{-1}}{+164\,J\,K^{-1}\,mol^{-1}} = 1085\,K\ (or\ 812°C)$$

Tip

Remember that endothermic reactions have a positive ΔH.

At A level, it is assumed that an increase in temperature results in a negligible change in the value of ΔS_{system} because the entropies of the reactants and products change by similar amounts. It is also assumed that the value of ΔH does not alter either. These are good approximations unless there is a change of state of one of the species between the two temperatures.

Thermodynamics gives no information about reaction rate. A thermodynamically feasible reaction might have such high activation energy that it does not proceed at room temperature.

Tip

At a higher temperature, the *magnitude* of ΔS_{surr} always gets smaller. Thus a negative ΔS_{surr} becomes less negative and a positive ΔS_{surr} becomes less positive.

Solubility

Solubility of gases

Dissolving a gas always results in a negative ΔS_{system} because the system becomes more ordered. Therefore, for a gas to be soluble it must always dissolve exothermically (the surroundings become more disordered). This means that the equilibrium:

$$X(g) \rightleftharpoons X(aq)$$

is driven to the left by an increase in temperature. Gases, such as carbon dioxide, are less soluble in hot water than in cold water.

$$CO_2(g) \rightleftharpoons CO_2(aq) \qquad \Delta H \text{ negative}$$

Solubility of solids

Contrary to the expected approach to entropy, dissolving solids does not always result in a positive $\Delta S^{\ominus}_{system}$ (the system becoming more disordered). The solute becomes more disordered as it goes from highly ordered solid to a more random solution, but the solvent can become more ordered due to the forces of attraction between solute and solvent. This is particularly the case when compounds containing ions of high charge density dissolve in water (p. 62). $\Delta H^{\ominus}_{soln}$ can be either negative (hence the surroundings also become more disordered) or slightly positive (hence the surroundings become slightly less disordered). The equilibrium:

$$X(s) \rightleftharpoons X(aq)$$

is driven to the left (less soluble) if $\Delta H^{\ominus}_{soln}$ is exothermic and to the right (more soluble) if $\Delta H^{\ominus}_{soln}$ is endothermic.

Extent of solubility

Solubility of a solid is determined by the total entropy change for 1 mol of that solid.

$$\Delta S^{\ominus}_{total} = \Delta S^{\ominus}_{system} + \Delta S^{\ominus}_{surr} = \Delta S^{\ominus}_{system} + \frac{\Delta H^{\ominus}_{soln}}{T}$$

For an ionic solid to dissolve significantly, $\Delta S^{\ominus}_{total}$ must be positive. Its value depends on both the entropy change of the system and the enthalpy change.

Entropy changes on dissolving an ionic solid

When ammonium chloride dissolves in water, the enthalpy change is $+15\,kJ\,mol^{-1}$.

This is endothermic and the system moves spontaneously to a state of higher enthalpy. The entropy of the surroundings *decreases* by $15\,000/298 = 50\,J\,K^{-1}\,mol^{-1}$ ($\Delta S^{\ominus}_{surr} = -50\,J\,K^{-1}\,mol^{-1}$). However, this is balanced by an increase in the entropy of the system, as the ordered ammonium chloride lattice is broken down and the ions are dispersed into the solvent. The value of $\Delta S^{\ominus}_{system}$ is $+167\,J\,K^{-1}\,mol^{-1}$. The total entropy change is:

$$\Delta S^{\ominus}_{total} = \Delta S^{\ominus}_{system} + \Delta S^{\ominus}_{surr} = +167 + (-50) = +117\,J\,K^{-1}\,mol^{-1}$$

This is a positive number and so the dissolving of ammonium chloride is thermodynamically spontaneous.

Entropy of the surroundings

Because $\Delta S^{\ominus}_{surr} = -\Delta H^{\ominus}_{soln}/T$, the sign of the entropy change depends on the sign of the enthalpy change:

- For endothermic enthalpies of solution, $\Delta S^{\ominus}_{surr}$ is negative.
- For exothermic enthalpies of solution, $\Delta S^{\ominus}_{surr}$ is positive.

Entropy of the system

This is made up of the entropy change of the solute and the entropy change of the solvent:

$$\Delta S^{\ominus}_{system} = \Delta S^{\ominus}_{solute} + \Delta S^{\ominus}_{solvent}$$

When any solid solute is dissolved, its entropy increases as the particles go from being arranged in a regular pattern in the solid to being distributed randomly in the solution. This applies to both covalent substances, such as glucose, and to ionic substances such as sodium chloride.

$$\Delta S^{\ominus}_{solute} > 0 \qquad (\Delta S^{\ominus}_{solute} \text{ positive})$$

In the case of many solutions, there is also an increase in the entropy of the solvent as it becomes mixed with solute particles. However, when anhydrous ionic substances are dissolved in water, there is also a considerable amount of ordering of water molecules. The positive ions become surrounded by water molecules, as the $\delta-$ oxygen atoms in the water bond with the positive cations. This makes the $\delta+$ hydrogen atoms more positive, causing them to bind a second sphere of water molecules. The extent to which this happens depends on the charge density of the cation.

The charge density of the ammonium ion is small because the single positive charge is delocalised over the whole ion and so the entropy of the water is not significantly altered. The lithium ion, Li^+, decreases the entropy of the solvent water to a greater extent than the other group 1 ions, as its ionic radius is much smaller. The group 2 cations have a much larger charge density than group 1 ions. They are doubly charged and, for each, the ionic radius is much less than that of the group 1 ion in the same period. The extent to which the $\Delta S^{\ominus}_{water}$ is negative (more ordered) decreases as the group is descended. Thus barium ions, Ba^{2+}, order the water less than magnesium ions, Mg^{2+}.

Negative ions also cause a slight ordering of water molecules, as the negative ions are surrounded by $\delta+$ hydrogen atoms in water molecules.

For the process:

ionic solid + water $\rightarrow$ aqueous ions

the following assumptions can be made:

- Dissolving group 1 compounds, ammonium compounds and silver compounds causes only a small change in the entropy of the water, so $\Delta S^{\ominus}_{system}$ is always positive as these all contain singly charged cations.
- Dissolving compounds containing doubly charged cations, such as those of the group 2 metals, causes a large decrease in the entropy of the water, so $\Delta S^{\ominus}_{system}$ is negative.

This can be demonstrated by filling a burette with water and then adding some *anhydrous* aluminium chloride or iron(III) chloride. The volume of the water shrinks noticeably as water molecules bond to the ions and become less randomly arranged. The high charge density of Al^{3+} ions means that when aluminium chloride is dissolved, ΔS_{system} is negative.

It is possible to calculate the value of $\Delta S^{\ominus}_{system}$. It has been estimated that $\Delta S^{\ominus}_{system}$ for dissolving ammonium chloride in water is $+167\,J\,K^{-1}\,mol^{-1}$; the theoretical value for barium sulfate is $-104\,J\,K^{-1}\,mol^{-1}$.

Some enthalpy and entropy changes for ionic solids dissolving in water, i.e. for the change at 298 K

$$MX(s) + aq \rightarrow M^{n+}(aq) + X^{n-}(aq)$$

are shown in Table 3.12.

It can be seen from the table that all the compounds containing singly charged cations have a positive $\Delta S^{\ominus}_{system}$. This is the main reason why group 1 compounds are water soluble, the exception being lithium fluoride. This is caused by the fluoride ion forming strong hydrogen bonds with water molecules and by the high charge density of the small Li^+ ion. Both these factors cause a more ordered arrangement of the water molecules. Silver chloride is insoluble in spite of the favourable $\Delta S^{\ominus}_{system}$, because its $\Delta S^{\ominus}_{soln}$ is highly endothermic.

Table 3.12 Enthalpy and entropy changes for ionic solids dissolving in water

Substance	$\Delta H^{\ominus}_{soln}/$ $kJ\,mol^{-1}$	$\Delta S^{\ominus}_{surr}/$ $J\,K^{-1}\,mol^{-1}$	$\Delta S^{\ominus}_{system}/$ $J\,K^{-1}\,mol^{-1}$	$\Delta S^{\ominus}_{total}/$ $J\,K^{-1}\,mol^{-1}$	Solubility
LiCl(s)	−37	+124	+11	+135	Soluble
NaCl(s)	+4	−13	+43	+30	Soluble
KCl(s)	+17	−57	+77	+20	Soluble
LiF(s)	+5	−17	−37	−54	Insoluble
NH₄Cl(s)	+15	−51	+167	+116	Soluble
AgCl(s)	+66	−221	+33	−188	Insoluble
MgSO₄(s)	−91	+305	−213	+92	Soluble
CaSO₄(s)	−18	+60	−145	−85	Insoluble
BaSO₄(s)	+19	−65	−104	−169	Insoluble
CuSO₄(s)	−73	+245	−192	+53	Soluble

The substances with an exothermic $\Delta H^{\ominus}_{soln}$ are shown in red; those with an endothermic $\Delta H^{\ominus}_{soln}$ are in blue.

The reverse is true for compounds containing doubly positive cations. All have a negative $\Delta S^{\ominus}_{system}$. This is why many of their compounds (carbonates, phosphates and hydroxides) are insoluble. They are only soluble if the enthalpy of solution is sufficiently exothermic. This is the case with magnesium sulfate and copper sulfate, but not with calcium sulfate. For barium sulfate, $\Delta H^{\ominus}_{soln}$ is endothermic *and* $\Delta S^{\ominus}_{system}$ is negative, so it is extremely insoluble.

The relationship between enthalpy of solution, solubility and the entropy of the system is summarised in Table 3.13.

Tip

Exothermic indicates a positive $\Delta S^{\ominus}_{surr}$; endothermic indicates a negative $\Delta S^{\ominus}_{surr}$.

Table 3.13 Enthalpy, solubility and entropy

$\Delta H^{\ominus}_{soln}$	Solubility	$\Delta S^{\ominus}_{system}$
Endothermic (+)	Soluble	Must be more positive than $\Delta H_{soln}/T$
Endothermic (+)	Insoluble	Negative or less positive than $\Delta H_{soln}/T$
Exothermic (−)	Soluble	Positive or less negative than $\Delta H_{soln}/T$
Exothermic (−)	Insoluble	Must be more negative than $\Delta H_{soln}/T$

Solubility trends in a group

The enthalpy of solution of an ionic solid can be calculated by means of a Hess's law cycle (p. 66). The reason for the trend in the value of $\Delta H^{\ominus}_{soln}$ is found in the way that the lattice energies and hydration energies change down a group.

The enthalpy of solution is a balance between lattice energy and the sum of the hydration energies of the ions:

$$\Delta H_{soln} = -\text{lattice energy} + \text{sum of the hydration energies of the ions}$$

In any group of the periodic table:

- The lattice energies become less exothermic as the group is descended.
- The hydration energies of the cations become less exothermic down the group.

Therefore, the change in ΔH_{soln} down the group is determined by which quantity shows the *greater decrease*.

If the lattice energy decreases more than the hydration energy, the process of dissolving is more exothermic (or less endothermic).

The lattice energy and hydration enthalpy values for group 2 hydroxides and sulfates are shown in Table 3.14.

Table 3.14 Lattice energy and hydration enthalpy values for group 2 hydroxides and sulfates.

Substance	Lattice energy/kJ mol^{-1}	Hydration enthalpy of cation/kJ mol^{-1}
$Mg(OH)_2(s)$	−2842	−1920
$Ca(OH)_2(s)$	−2553	−1650
$Sr(OH)_2(s)$	−2354	−1480
$Ba(OH)_2(s)$	−2228	−1360
Change down the group	**614**	**560**
$MgSO_4(s)$	−2874	−1920
$CaSO_4(s)$	−2677	−1650
$SrSO_4(s)$	−2516	−1480
$BaSO_4(s)$	−2424	−1360
Change down the group	**450**	**560**

Table 3.14 shows that, for the hydroxides of group 2, on descending the group there is a greater change in lattice energy than there is in hydration enthalpy. This results in the enthalpy of solution becoming steadily more exothermic.

The lattice energy changes more than the hydration enthalpy because of the way in which the two factors depend on the ionic radius:

- The hydration energy of a cation depends upon its charge density — the charge divided by the radius.
- The lattice energy depends upon the charges of the two ions multiplied together divided by the sum of the two ionic radii — $\{r(+) + (r(-)\}$.
- The OH^- ion is a small anion, similar in size to the group 2 cations. Therefore, the value of $\{r(+) + r(-)\}$ increases considerably as the value of the radius of the cation, $r(+)$, increases.

The opposite is true for the group 2 sulfates. The sulfate ion is much larger than any of the group 2 cations. Therefore, as $r(-) >> r(+)$, the value of $\{r(+) + r(-)\}$ changes by only a small amount. This means that the decrease in the magnitude of the lattice energy is more than the decrease in the magnitude of the hydration enthalpy of the ions. This makes the enthalpy of solution increasingly less exothermic as the group is descended.

The values of $\Delta H^\ominus_{soln}$ are shown in Table 3.15.

The value of $\Delta H^\ominus_{soln}$ is not the only factor determining solubility. The other factor is the change in entropy of the system. For many ionic solids, this is difficult to determine accurately. A guide is the relative entropy values of the ions, which are also shown in Table 3.15. Note how the entropy of the ion increases as the ionic radius increases.

Solubility of group 2 hydroxides

Table 3.15 Enthalpy and entropy changes involved in dissolving ionic solids – group 2 hydroxides

Substance	$\Delta H^\ominus_{soln}$ /kJ mol^{-1}	$\Delta S^\ominus_{surr} = \Delta H^\ominus_{soln}/T$ /J K^{-1} mol^{-1}	Hydrated ion	Relative* entropy value of hydrated ion/J K^{-1} mol^{-1}
$Mg(OH)_2$	+3	−10	$Mg^{2+}(aq)$	−138
$Ca(OH)_2$	−16	+54	$Ca^{2+}(aq)$	−53
$Sr(OH)_2$	−46	+154	$Sr^{2+}(aq)$	−33
$Ba(OH)_2$	−52	+174	$Ba^{2+}(aq)$	+10
Change down the group from Mg to Ba	More exothermic	−184, so more likely to dissolve	Change down the group from $Mg^{2+}(aq)$ to Ba^{2+}	−148, so more likely to dissolve

*The values of the entropy of hydrated ions are relative to the value for $H^+(aq)$

The enthalpy of solution becomes more negative down the group. This means that $\Delta S^\ominus_{surr}$ becomes more positive and so favours solubility. The change in the entropy of the cation gets less negative and this also favours solubility. As both factors favour an increase in solubility, barium hydroxide is more soluble than magnesium hydroxide.

Solubility of group 2 sulfates

Table 3.16 Enthalpy and entropy changes involved in dissolving ionic solids – group 2 sulfates

Substance	$\Delta H^{\ominus}_{soln}/$ $kJ\,mol^{-1}$	$\Delta S^{\ominus}_{surr} =$ $-\Delta H^{\ominus}_{soln}/T$ $/J\,K^{-1}mol^{-1}$	Hydrated ion	Relative* entropy value of hydrated ion/$J\,K^{-1}mol^{-1}$
$MgSO_4$	−91	+305	$Mg^{2+}(aq)$	−138
$CaSO_4$	−18	+60	$Ca^{2+}(aq)$	−53
$SrSO_4$	−9	+30	$Sr^{2+}(aq)$	−33
$BaSO_4$	+19	−63	$Ba^{2+}(aq)$	+10
Change down the group from Mg to Ba	Less exothermic	−368, so less likely to dissolve	Change down the group from $Mg^{2+}(aq)$ to $Ba^{2+}(aq)$	+148, so more likely to dissolve

*The values of the entropy of hydrated ions are relative to the value for $H^+(aq)$

The enthalpy of solution becomes *less* negative down the group. This means that $\Delta S^{\ominus}_{surr}$ becomes less positive and, therefore, favours insolubility. The change in the entropy of the cation gets less negative, which favours solubility, but the change in entropy of the hydrated cation ($148\,J\,K^{-1}mol^{-1}$) is much less than the change in entropy of the surroundings ($368\,J\,K^{-1}mol^{-1}$). This results in the solubility of the sulfates decreasing down the group.

Melting and boiling points

At equilibrium, the value of $\Delta S^{\ominus}_{total}$ is zero. At 0°C, there is equilibrium between ice and water. The ice does not melt, nor does the water freeze, unless heat is added to or taken from the system. Neither direction is thermodynamically feasible, so the two forms of water remain in equilibrium:

$$\Delta S_{total} = \Delta S_{system} + \Delta S_{surr}$$

$$= \Delta S_{system} - \frac{\Delta H}{T} = 0$$

$$\Delta S_{system} = \frac{\Delta H}{T} \quad \text{or} \quad T = \frac{\Delta H}{\Delta S_{system}}$$

ΔH for ice melting = $+6012\,J\,mol^{-1}$

$\Delta S_{system} = S(\text{water}) - S(\text{ice}) = +22\,J\,K^{-1}mol^{-1}$

$$\text{melting temperature of ice} = \frac{\Delta H}{\Delta S_{system}} = \frac{6012}{22} = 273\,K = 0°C$$

ΔH for water boiling = $+40\,700\,J\,mol^{-1}$

$\Delta S_{system} = S(\text{steam}) - S(\text{water}) = +109\,J\,K^{-1}mol^{-1}$

$$\text{boiling temperature of water} = \frac{\Delta H}{\Delta S_{system}} = \frac{40\,700}{109} = 373\,K = 100°C$$

It can be seen from the expression $T = \Delta H/\Delta S$ that the melting or boiling temperature depends upon the amount of energy required for the change of state. This explains

3 Energetics II (Topic 13)

why boiling and melting temperatures depend on the strength of the forces between the particles:

strong force = large amount of energy needed to separate the particles
= high melting or boiling temperature

Summary

- The reactants are thermodynamically unstable relative to the products if ΔS_{total} for the change is positive or ΔG is negative. This means that the reaction is thermodynamically feasible.
- Endothermic reactions can happen only if the entropy change of the system is positive.
- Endothermic reactions are more likely to take place at higher temperatures.
- Exothermic reactions are always thermodynamically favourable if the entropy change of the system is positive.
- Exothermic reactions are thermodynamically favourable even when the entropy of the system is negative, if the entropy change of the surroundings outweighs the entropy change of the system.

Summary tasks

Make sure that you can:

- define lattice energy and electron affinity
- define enthalpy of atomisation, hydration and solution
- draw and interpret Born–Haber cycles
- explain the factors that affect the value of lattice energy
- explain the extent of covalency in ionic compounds

Make sure that you:

- can calculate ΔS_{system} using the data booklet and ΔS_{surr} from enthalpy data
- know the relationship between ΔS_{total}, ΔS_{system} and $\Delta S_{surrounding}$
- realise that reactions producing a gas have a positive ΔS_{system}
- understand that the *magnitude* of ΔS_{surr} decreases as the temperature rises
- know that for a reaction to be thermodynamically feasible, ΔS_{total} must be positive or that ΔG must be negative
- realise that a feasible reaction may not take place if the activation energy is too high
- can calculate the temperature at which a reaction becomes feasible
- can calculate $\Delta H_{solution}$ of ionic compounds from lattice and hydration energies
- know and can explain the trends in solubility of group 1 and 2 compounds
- can explain the extent of solubility and the effect of a change in temperature on solubility

Questions

1 Use the data in Table 3.9 on p. 73 to calculate the thermodynamic feasibility of the following reaction at 298 K:

$$N_2(g) + 3H_2(g) \rightarrow 2NH_3(g) \quad \Delta H = -92\,kJ\,mol^{-1}$$

2 Hydrated barium hydroxide reacts with solid ammonium chloride according to the equation:

$$Ba(OH)_2 \cdot 8H_2O(s) + 2NH_4Cl(s) \rightarrow$$
$$BaCl_2(s) + 10H_2O(l) + 2NH_3(g)$$

The total standard entropy change at 298 K, $\Delta S^{\ominus}_{total} = +150\,J\,K^{-1}\,mol^{-1}$.

Some enthalpy and entropy data are given in the table.

Substance	Standard enthalpy of formation/kJ mol⁻¹	Standard entropy/J K⁻¹ mol⁻¹
Ba(OH)₂·8H₂O(s)	−3245	
NH₄Cl(s)	−315	92
BaCl₂(s)	−860	130
H₂O(l)	−286	70
NH₃(g)	−46	193

Use the data to:

a) Calculate $\Delta H^{\ominus}$ for this reaction.

b) Calculate ΔS_{system} and hence calculate the standard entropy of hydrated barium hydroxide.

3 The reaction between hydrogen and oxygen does not take place at a temperature of 298 K.

$$H_2(g) + \frac{1}{2}O_2(g) \rightarrow H_2O(l)$$
$$\Delta H = -286\,kJ\,mol^{-1}$$

Use the data above and those in Table 3.9 on page 73 to explain the concepts of thermodynamic stability and kinetic inertness.

4 Draw a Hess's law diagram, and use it together with the data here, to calculate ΔH_{soln} of lithium fluoride, LiF. Comment on the likely solubility of lithium fluoride in water.

	Enthalpy change/kJ mol⁻¹
$\Delta H_{hyd}(Li^+(g))$	−519
$\Delta H_{hyd}(F^-(g))$	−506
$\Delta H_{latt}(LiF(s))$	−1022

5 Draw a Hess's law diagram for dissolving calcium chloride. Use it and the data here to calculate ΔH_{hyd} of a chloride ion, Cl^-.

	Enthalpy change/kJ mol⁻¹
$\Delta H_{hyd}(Ca^{2+}(g))$	−1650
$\Delta H_{latt}(CaCl_2(s))$	−2237
$\Delta H_{soln}(CaCl_2(s))$	−83

6 Study the data in the table.

Substance	$\Delta H^{\ominus}_{soln}$/kJ mol⁻¹	Ion	$S^{\ominus}$/J K⁻¹ mol⁻¹
MgF₂(s)	−18	Mg²⁺(aq)	−138
CaF₂(s)	+13	Ca²⁺(aq)	−55
AgBr(s)	+85	Br⁻(aq)	+57
AgI(s)	+112	I⁻(aq)	+111

a) Use the data to suggest and explain the relative solubility of the group 2 fluorides, magnesium fluoride, MgF_2, and calcium fluoride, CaF_2.

b) Use the data to suggest and explain the relative solubility of the silver halides, silver bromide, AgBr, and silver iodide, AgI.

7 State and explain whether $H_2O(l)$ at 100°C has a higher or lower entropy than $H_2O(g)$ at 100°C.

8 Use the following equations to state and explain whether the reactions result in an increase or decrease in the entropy of the systems:

a) $SO_2(g) + \frac{1}{2}O_2(g) \rightarrow SO_3(g)$

b) $CaCO_3(s) \rightarrow CaO(s) + CO_2(g)$

c) $NH_4NO_3(s) + aq \rightarrow NH_4^+(aq) + NO_3^-(aq)$

9 a) Calculate ΔS_{system} for the following reaction at 85°C:

$$N_2O_4(g) \rightarrow 2NO_2(g) \quad \Delta H = +57.4\,kJ\,mol^{-1}$$

Compound	Entropy, S, at 85°C/J K⁻¹ mol⁻¹
N₂O₄(g)	325
NO₂(g)	256

b) Calculate ΔS_{total} for the reaction at 85°C.

c) Comment on the feasibility of this reaction.

d) Explain the term **thermodynamic stability** with reference to this reaction.

Exam practice questions

1 a) Predict which of the following changes, W to Z, will take place at a temperature of 298 K.

Change	$\Delta H/\text{kJ mol}^{-1}$	$\Delta S_{\text{system}}/\text{J K}^{-1}\text{mol}^{-1}$
W	−170	+600
X	−170	−600
Y	+170	−600
Z	+170	+600

A W only   **C** Y and Z only
B X only   **D** W and Z only   (1)

b) Dinitrogen tetroxide decomposes spontaneously at 50°C:

$$N_2O_4(g) \rightarrow 2NO_2(g) \qquad \Delta H = +58\,\text{kJ mol}^{-1}$$

State and explain the sign of ΔS_{system} for this reaction. (3)

(Total 4 marks)

2 a) i) Which will have the greatest effect on the value of the lattice energy of an ionic solid? (1)
   A both ions having a high charge and a large radius
   B both ions having a high charge and a small radius
   C both ions having a low charge and a small radius
   D both ions having a low charge and a large radius

ii) Which factors maximise the solubility of an ionic solid MX? (1)
   A a large negative lattice energy and a large negative sum of $\Delta H_{\text{hydration}}$ of the ions
   B a small negative lattice energy and a large negative sum of $\Delta H_{\text{hydration}}$ of the ions
   C a large positive lattice energy and a small negative sum of $\Delta H_{\text{hydration}}$ of the ions
   D a large positive lattice energy and a large negative sum of $\Delta H_{\text{hydration}}$ of the ions

b) Use the data below to draw a Born–Haber cycle and hence calculate the lattice energy of magnesium fluoride, MgF_2. (4)
ΔH_a for magnesium = $+150\,\text{kJ mol}^{-1}$
ΔH_a for fluorine = $+79\,\text{kJ mol}^{-1}$
1st ionisation energy for magnesium = $+736\,\text{kJ mol}^{-1}$

2nd ionisation energy = $+1450\,\text{kJ mol}^{-1}$
electron affinity for fluorine = $-328\,\text{kJ mol}^{-1}$
ΔH_f for MgF_2(s) = $-1102\,\text{kJ mol}^{-1}$

c) i) Use your answer to (b) and the data below to calculate the enthalpy of solution of MgF_2. (3)
$\Delta H_{\text{hydration}}$ of Mg^{2+}(g) = $-1920\,\text{kJ mol}^{-1}$
$\Delta H_{\text{hydration}}$ of F^-(g) = $-506\,\text{kJ mol}^{-1}$

ii) What does your answer to (c) (i) tell you about the solubility of magnesium fluoride? (1)

d) Which substance will have the greatest difference between the experimental (Born–Haber) and the theoretical lattice energies? (1)
   A sodium fluoride, NaF
   B sodium chloride, NaCl
   C calcium oxide, CaO
   D calcium sulfide, CaS

(Total 11 marks)

3 Methanol can be manufactured by the reaction of carbon monoxide and hydrogen

$$CO(g) + 2H_2(g) \rightleftharpoons CH_3OH(g)$$
$$\Delta H = -92\,\text{kJ mol}^{-1}$$

a) i) Use the data below to calculate $\Delta S^{\ominus}_{\text{system}}$ of this reaction. Give a sign and units with your answer. (3)

	Standard entropy/$\text{J K}^{-1}\text{mol}^{-1}$
CO(g)	198
H_2(g)	131
CH_3OH(g)	353

ii) Comment on the sign of your answer. (1)

iii) Calculate $\Delta G^{\ominus}$ for this reaction at 298 K. Give a sign and units with your answer. (3)

iv) Comment on the feasibility of this reaction. (1)

v) Explain why this reaction is not observed at a temperature of 298 K. (1)

b) Use your answer to (a) (iii) to calculate the equilibrium constant, K, at a temperature of 298 K. (3)

c) Calculate the temperature at which the feasibility of the reaction will change. (2)

(Total 14 marks)

Redox II (Topic 14)

Year 1 topics

This topic assumes knowledge of the redox chemistry covered in the first year (AS) of the A level course. There are some important concepts that must be revisited before embarking on the new second year work.

The definitions of oxidation and reduction are as follows:

> **Oxidation is loss of electrons by an atom, ion or molecule or the increase in oxidation number of an element.**
>
> **Reduction is gain of electrons by an atom, ion or molecule or the decrease in oxidation number of an element.**

Tip

OIL RIG — oxidation is loss; reduction is gain.

Oxidation numbers

Oxidation numbers can be worked out using a series of rules:

- The oxidation number of an uncombined element is zero.
- The oxidation number of the element in a monatomic ion is the charge on the ion.
- The sum of the oxidation numbers of the atoms in a neutral compound is zero.
- The sum of the oxidation numbers in a polyatomic ion equals the charge on the ion.
- All group 1 metals have an oxidation number of +1 in their compounds, and all group 2 metals have an oxidation number of +2 in their compounds.
- Fluorine always has the oxidation number −1 in its compounds.
- Hydrogen has the oxidation number +1 in its compounds, apart from when it is combined with a metal, when the oxidation number is −1.
- Oxygen has the oxidation number −2 in its compounds, apart from in peroxides and superoxides or when it is combined with fluorine.

Test yourself

1 Give the oxidation number of sulfur in:

   a) H_2S b) SO_4^{2-} c) S_2Cl_2 d) H_2SO_3

Ionic half-equations

Ionic half-equations always have electrons on either the left-hand side or the right-hand side.

When zinc is added to dilute hydrochloric acid, the hydrogen ions are reduced to hydrogen, because their oxidation number decreases from +1 to zero. The half-equation is:

$$2H^+(aq) + 2e^- \rightleftharpoons H_2(g)$$

Tip

Half-equations must balance for charge as well as for numbers of atoms.

As this is a reduction reaction, the electrons are on the left-hand side of the half-equation. The zinc atoms are oxidised to zinc ions, because their oxidation number increases from zero to +2:

$$Zn(s) \rightleftharpoons Zn^{2+}(aq) + 2e^-$$

As this is oxidation, the electrons are on the right-hand side of the equation.

Test yourself

2 Write the half-equations for:

a) the reduction of $Cr_2O_7{}^{2-}$ ions in acid solution to Cr^{3+} ions and water

b) the oxidation of iodide ions to iodine

Overall ionic equations

When half-equations are combined to give the overall equation, the stoichiometry must be such that the numbers of electrons cancel. To do this, one or both half-equations must be multiplied by integers so that the number of electrons is the same in both. The two half-equations are then added together to get the overall equation.

The total change in oxidation number of the species being oxidised is equal to the total change in oxidation number of the species being reduced.

Worked example

a) Write the half-equation for the oxidation of Sn^{2+} ions to Sn^{4+} ions in aqueous solution.

b) Write the half-equation for the reduction of $MnO_4{}^-$ ions to Mn^{2+} ions in aqueous acidic solution.

c) Hence, write the overall equation for the oxidation of tin(II) ions by manganate(VII) ions in aqueous acidic solution.

Answer

a) This is oxidation, so the electrons are on the right-hand side of the half-equation. The oxidation number of tin changes by 2, so there are two electrons in the half-equation:

$$Sn^{2+}(aq) \rightarrow Sn^{4+}(aq) + 2e^-$$

b) This is reduction, so the electrons are on the left-hand side. Five electrons are needed because the oxidation number of manganese changes by 5 (from +7 to +2):

$$MnO_4{}^-(aq) + 8H^+(aq) + 5e^- \rightarrow Mn^{2+}(aq) + 4H_2O(l)$$

c) Multiply the first equation by 5 and the second equation by 2 to obtain the same number of electrons in each equation. Then add the two equations and cancel the electrons. The overall equation is:

$$5Sn^{2+}(aq) + 2MnO_4{}^-(aq) + 16H^+(aq) \rightarrow 5Sn^{4+}(aq) + 2Mn^{2+}(aq) + 8H_2O(l)$$

Test yourself

3 Use your answers to test yourself question 2 (p. 97) to write overall equations for the reaction between acidified dichromate(VI) ions and iodide ions.

Year 2 topics

Electrochemical cells

When a piece of zinc is placed in a solution of copper(II) sulfate, a reaction takes place in which the zinc is oxidised to zinc ions and the copper ions are reduced to copper metal. This reaction can also occur without the copper ions and the zinc atoms coming into contact (Figure 4.1).

Figure 4.1 An electrochemical cell of Zn/Zn^{2+} and Cu/Cu^{2+}

A simple salt bridge is a strip of filter paper soaked in saturated potassium nitrate.

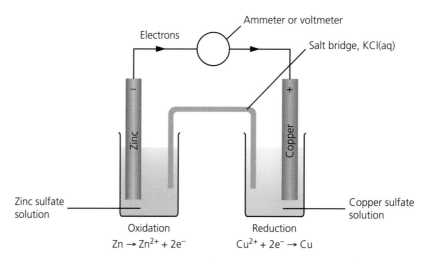

Oxidation
$Zn \rightarrow Zn^{2+} + 2e^-$

Reduction
$Cu^{2+} + 2e^- \rightarrow Cu$

On the surface of the zinc rod

The zinc rod is in equilibrium with the solution of zinc ions:

$$Zn(s) \rightleftharpoons Zn^{2+}(aq) + 2e^-$$

Some of the zinc atoms in the rod lose two electrons. The zinc ions formed go into solution and the released electrons stay on the rod, making it negatively charged. The process is oxidation, as zinc atoms have lost electrons.

In electrochemical cells, where a chemical reaction causes electricity to be produced, and in electrolysis, where electricity causes a chemical reaction, oxidation occurs at the anode and reduction at the cathode. This means that the zinc rod is the anode.

Tip

Oxidation and anode begin with a vowel.

On the surface of the copper rod

The copper ions are in equilibrium with the copper rod:

$$Cu^{2+}(aq) + 2e^- \rightleftharpoons Cu(s)$$

The copper ions in the solution take electrons from the copper rod, which makes the rod positively charged.

Tip

Reduction and cathode begin with a consonant.

As reduction (of copper ions) takes place at the copper rod, it is called the cathode.

This sets up a potential difference (emf) between the two metal rods. A current will flow when the rods are connected by a wire and the solutions are connected by a **salt bridge**, which contains a concentrated solution of an inert electrolyte, such as saturated potassium nitrate or potassium chloride.

The current is carried in the solution and in the salt bridge by the movement of the ions. The anions (e.g. SO_4^{2-} and Cl^- or NO_3^-) move towards the anode and the cations (e.g. Zn^{2+} and K^+) move towards the cathode. In the external circuit (the wire), the current is carried by the flow of electrons from the negative zinc rod to the positive copper rod, which is from left to right in Figure 4.1.

At first sight, it appears that negative SO_4^{2-} ions are being attracted to the negative zinc anode. In fact, the solution around the anode has an excess of positive zinc ions and it is these that attract the negative SO_4^{2-} ions in the solution. (Remember that anions always go to the anode.)

The convention for diagrams such as that in Figure 4.1 is to put the electrode at which oxidation is taking place (the anode) on the left.

Remember that, in electrochemical cells, oxidation occurs at the anode, which becomes negative, and reduction occurs at the cathode which becomes positive.

Electrode potentials

Standard electrode potential, $E^\ominus$

Standard electrode potential is also called the standard reduction potential, because the equation is normally written as a reduction half-equation with the electrons on the left.

A zinc rod dipped into a solution of zinc ions generates a potential relative to the solution. However, an electric potential cannot be measured. To avoid this problem, the electrode potential difference is measured against another electrode. By convention, the standard electrode potential of hydrogen is defined as zero.

The term *standard* means that:

- all ions in the solution are at a concentration of $1.0\,mol\,dm^{-3}$
- all gases are at a pressure of $100\,kPa$ ($1.0\,atm$)
- the system is at a stated temperature, usually $298\,K$ ($25°C$)

For metals, the standard reduction potential is for a piece of the metal dipping into a $1.0\,mol\,dm^{-3}$ solution of its ions. For zinc it is written either as:

$$Zn^{2+}(aq) + 2e^- \rightleftharpoons Zn(s) \qquad E^\ominus = -0.76\,V$$

or as:

$$Zn^{2+}(aq) \mid Zn(s) \qquad E^\ominus = -0.76\,V$$

If the substance is a gas, such as hydrogen or chlorine, the electrode consists of a platinum plate dipping into a $1.0\,mol\,dm^{-3}$ solution of ions of the element with the gaseous element, at $100\,kPa$ pressure, bubbling over the surface of the platinum. For example, a platinum electrode dipping into a $1.0\,mol\,dm^{-3}$ solution of H^+ ions with hydrogen gas at a pressure of $100\,kPa$ bubbling over the platinum.

If the reduction involves two cations — for example, M^{3+} being reduced to M^{2+} — the electrode consists of a platinum rod dipping into a solution containing M^{3+} ions and M^{2+} ions, both at a concentration of $1.0\,mol\,dm^{-3}$. An example is the reduction of Fe^{3+} to Fe^{2+} with *both* ions at a concentration of $1.0\,mol\,dm^{-3}$.

$$Fe^{3+}(aq) + e^- \rightleftharpoons Fe^{2+}(aq) \qquad or \qquad Fe^{3+}(aq), Fe^{2+}(aq) \mid Pt \quad E^\ominus = +0.77\,V$$

The oxidised form of the couple is written on the left, followed by an equilibrium sign or a vertical line and then the reduced form is written on the right.

For manganate(VII) ions|manganese(II) ions in acid solution, a platinum electrode dipping into a solution containing MnO_4^-, Mn^{2+} and H^+ ions, all at a concentration of $1.0\,mol\,dm^{-3}$ is used.

$$MnO_4^-(aq) + 8H^+(aq) + 5e^- \rightleftharpoons Mn^{2+}(aq) + 4H_2O(l)$$

or $\quad [MnO_4^-(aq) + H^+(aq)], Mn^{2+}(aq) \mid Pt \qquad E^\ominus_{cell} = +1.51\,V$

Types of electrode

Standard hydrogen electrode (SHE)

A **standard hydrogen electrode** consists of hydrogen gas at $100\,kPa$ pressure bubbling over a platinum plate, which is dipping into a solution that is $1.0\,mol\,dm^{-3}$ in H^+ ions (such as $1.0\,mol\,dm^{-3}$ HCl), at a temperature of $298\,K$.

$$H^+(aq) + e^- \rightleftharpoons \frac{1}{2}H_2(g) \quad E^\ominus = 0V$$

or

$$H^+(aq) \mid \frac{1}{2}H_2(g), Pt \qquad E^\ominus = 0V$$

A standard hydrogen electrode (Figure 4.2) should always be drawn on the left in a diagram of the apparatus for measuring a cell potential or written on the left in a cell diagram.

Calomel electrode

A standard hydrogen electrode is not easy to use, so a secondary standard is normally used as the reference electrode. This is a **calomel electrode**, which consists of mercury in contact with a saturated solution of mercury(I) chloride (Figure 4.3). This has a reduction potential of $+0.27\,V$.

For a $Zn \mid Zn^{2+}$ electrode joined to a calomel electrode:

$$E^\ominus_{cell} = E(calomel) - E^\ominus(Zn^{2+} \mid Zn)$$

where $E^\ominus(Zn^{2+} \mid Zn)$ is the standard *reduction* potential of zinc ions to zinc and $E^\ominus_{cell} = +1.03V$.

$$E^\ominus(Zn^{2+} \mid Zn) = E(calomel) - E^\ominus_{cell} = +0.27 - 1.03 = -0.76V$$

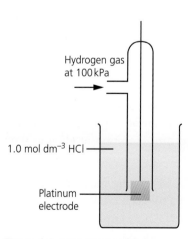

Figure 4.2 A standard hydrogen electrode

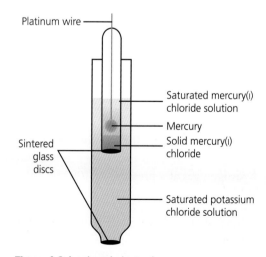

Figure 4.3 A calomel electrode

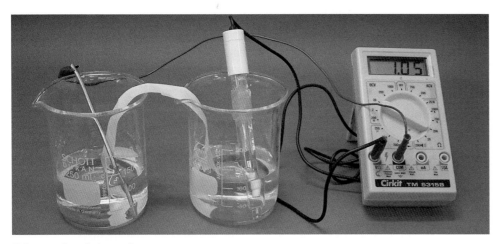

Using a calomel electrode

Glass electrode

A pH meter utilises a half-cell that is based on the reduction of hydrogen ions:

$$H^+(aq) + e^- \rightleftharpoons \frac{1}{2}H_2(g)$$

which is linked to a reference electrode, such as a calomel electrode.

The potential of the $H^+ \mid \frac{1}{2}H_2$ half-cell depends on the concentration of H^+ ions. This means that the voltage produced is a measure of $[H^+]$ and therefore of the pH of the solution. The hydrogen half-cell, which acts as an $H^+ \mid \frac{1}{2}H_2$ system, is called a **glass electrode**.

Measurement of electrode potentials

Standard electrode potential of a metal

The standard electrode potential of a metal is measured using the system illustrated in Figure 4.4. The hydrogen electrode should be drawn on the left and then the sign of the standard electrode potential is the sign of the right-hand electrode.

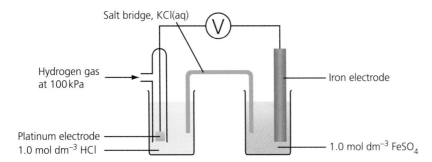

Figure 4.4 Measurement of the standard electrode potential of iron

The metal is dipping into a $1.0 \, \text{mol} \, \text{dm}^{-3}$ solution of its ions with a salt bridge of saturated potassium nitrate to a standard hydrogen electrode, SHE, or a calomel electrode. The two are connected externally by a high-resistance voltmeter or a potentiometer. The high resistance means that little reaction takes place and so the concentrations of the ions involved remain approximately constant.

Using the apparatus shown in Figure 4.4, the iron electrode would be negative and the voltmeter would read $0.44 \, \text{V}$.

The convention for all electrode systems is that:

$$E^{\ominus}_{cell} = E^{\ominus}(\text{right-hand electrode}) - E^{\ominus}(\text{left-hand electrode})$$

The iron electrode is negative relative to the hydrogen electrode and so the electrons flow from the iron electrode to the hydrogen electrode.

The standard electrode potential of iron is:

$$E^{\ominus}_{cell} = -0.44\,\text{V} = E^{\ominus}(\text{Fe}^{2+}\mid\text{Fe}) - E^{\ominus}(\text{standard hydrogen electrode})$$
$$= E^{\ominus}(\text{Fe}^{2+}\mid\text{Fe}) - 0$$

So the standard electrode potential of the $\text{Fe}^{2+}\mid\text{Fe}$ system $= -0.44\,\text{V}$.

This information can be written as a half-equation:

$$\text{Fe}^{2+}(\text{aq}) + 2\text{e}^- \rightleftharpoons \text{Fe}(\text{s}) \qquad E^{\ominus} = -0.44\,\text{V}$$

or as:

$$E^{\ominus}(\text{Fe}^{2+}(\text{aq})\mid\text{Fe}(\text{s})) = -0.44\,\text{V}$$

Copper and other metals below hydrogen in the electrochemical series have positive standard electrode potentials.

If a calomel electrode ($E^{\ominus} = +0.27\,\text{V}$) is used in place of a standard hydrogen electrode, the measured cell potential, $E^{\ominus}_{cell}$, is $0.71\,\text{V}$ and the iron electrode is negative.

The standard electrode potential is then calculated as:

$$E^{\ominus}_{cell} = -0.71\,\text{V} = E^{\ominus}(\text{right-hand electrode}) - E^{\ominus}(\text{left-hand electrode})$$

$$-0.71\,\text{V} = E^{\ominus}(\text{Fe}^{2+}\mid\text{Fe}) - E(\text{calomel electrode})$$

$$E^{\ominus}(\text{Fe}^{2+}\mid\text{Fe}) = E^{\ominus}_{cell} + E(\text{calomel electrode}) = -0.71 + 0.27 = -0.44\,\text{V}$$

Standard electrode potential of a gas

If the standard electrode potential of a gas such as chlorine is required, the iron electrode compartment in Figure 4.4 is replaced by a compartment with a platinum plate dipping into a $1.0\,\text{mol}\,\text{dm}^{-3}$ solution of sodium chloride, with chlorine gas, at 100 kPa pressure, bubbling over the platinum.

$$\tfrac{1}{2}\text{Cl}_2(\text{g}) + \text{e}^- \rightleftharpoons \text{Cl}^-(\text{aq})\ E^{\ominus} = +1.36\text{V}$$

Standard electrode potential of an ion pair

Manganate(VII) is a powerful oxidising agent in acid solution. The half-equation is:

$$\text{MnO}_4^-(\text{aq}) + 8\text{H}^+(\text{aq}) + 5\text{e}^- \rightleftharpoons \text{Mn}^{2+}(\text{aq}) + 4\text{H}_2\text{O}(\text{l})$$

One electrode compartment is made of a piece of platinum dipping into a solution that is $1.00\,\text{mol}\,\text{dm}^{-3}$ in MnO_4^-, H^+ *and* Mn^{2+} ions. This is connected to a standard hydrogen or calomel electrode, as in Figure 4.5.

$$[\text{MnO}_4^-(\text{aq}) + 8\text{H}^+(\text{aq})], [\text{Mn}^{2+}(\text{aq}) + 4\text{H}_2\text{O}(\text{l})]\mid\text{Pt}\quad E^{\ominus} = +1.52\,\text{V}$$

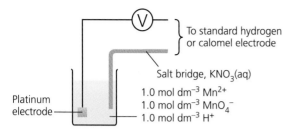

To standard hydrogen or calomel electrode

Salt bridge, $KNO_3(aq)$

$1.0 \text{ mol dm}^{-3} \text{ Mn}^{2+}$
$1.0 \text{ mol dm}^{-3} \text{ MnO}_4^-$
$1.0 \text{ mol dm}^{-3} \text{ H}^+$

Platinum electrode

Figure 4.5 Measurement of the standard electrode potential of $MnO_4^-|Mn^{2+}$

Comparative values of $E^{\ominus}$

Standard electrode potentials can be listed either in alphabetical order or in numerical order. Alphabetical order has the advantage of easy use in a long list of data. Numerical order lists the electrode potentials with the most negative first, then in order of increasing value, finishing with the most positive.

The numerical-order method means that the weakest oxidising agent is the left-hand species at the top of the list ($Li^+(aq)$ in Table 4.1 on p. 104) and the strongest reducing agent is the right-hand species at the top of the list ($Li(s)$ in Table 4.1). Similarly, the strongest oxidising agent is the left-hand species at the bottom of the list ($F_2(g)$ in Table 4.1) and the weakest reducing agent is the right-hand species at the bottom of the list ($F^-(aq)$ in Table 4.1).

> These are written as reduction half-equations.

Test yourself

4 Refer to Table 4.1 and select:

a) the strongest oxidising agent
b) the weakest oxidising agent
c) the strongest reducing agent
d) the weakest reducing agent

Tip

In the A level exam a data book is supplied and this lists the standard electrode potentials in a numerical list.

Non-standard conditions

If the conditions are not standard, the value of the electrode potential will alter. The direction of change can be predicted using Le Châtelier's principle.

Change in concentration

Consider the redox half-equation:

$$Cr_2O_7^{2-}(aq) + 14H^+(aq) + 6e^- \rightleftharpoons 2Cr^{3+}(aq) + 7H_2O(l) \quad E^{\ominus} = +1.33 \text{ V}$$

If the concentrations of dichromate(VI) ions or of hydrogen ions are increased above 1.0 mol dm^{-3}, the position of equilibrium is driven to the right. This causes the value of the electrode potential, E, to be more positive than the standard value: $E > +1.33 \text{ V}$.

Consider the redox equilibrium:

$$\frac{1}{2}Cl_2(g) + e^- \rightleftharpoons Cl^-(aq) \quad E^{\ominus} = +1.36 \text{V}$$

If the concentration of chloride ions is increased, the equilibrium position will shift to the left. This causes the value of the electrode potential, E, to be lower than the standard value: $E < +1.36 \text{ V}$.

This can have a serious effect on the spontaneity of a reaction.

Table 4.1 Standard electrode potential values at 298 K

Alphabetical list		Numerical list	
Electrode reaction	$E^\ominus$/V	**Electrode reaction**	$E^\ominus$/V
$Ag^+(aq) + e^- \rightleftharpoons Ag(s)$	+0.80	$Li^+(aq) + e^- \rightleftharpoons Li(s)$	−3.04
$Al^{3+}(aq) + 3e^- \rightleftharpoons Al(s)$	−1.66	$Ba^{2+}(aq) + 2e^- \rightleftharpoons Ba(s)$	−2.90
$Ba^{2+}(aq) + 2e^- \rightleftharpoons Ba(s)$	−2.90	$Ca^{2+}(aq) + 2e^- \rightleftharpoons Ca(s)$	−2.87
$\frac{1}{2}Br_2(l) + e^- \rightleftharpoons Br^-(aq)$	+1.07	$Al^{3+}(aq) + 3e^- \rightleftharpoons Al(s)$	−1.66
$Ca^{2+}(aq) + 2e^- \rightleftharpoons Ca(s)$	−2.87	$Zn^{2+}(aq) + 2e^- \rightleftharpoons Zn(s)$	−0.76
$\frac{1}{2}Cl_2(g) + e^- \rightleftharpoons Cl^-(aq)$	+1.36	$Fe^{2+}(aq) + 2e^- \rightleftharpoons Fe(s)$	−0.44
$HOCl(aq) + H^+(aq) + e^- \rightleftharpoons \frac{1}{2}Cl_2(g) + H_2O(l)$	+1.64	$Cr^{3+}(aq) + e^- \rightleftharpoons Cr^{2+}(aq)$	−0.41
$Cr^{3+}(aq) + e^- \rightleftharpoons Cr^{2+}(aq)$	−0.41	$Sn^{2+}(aq) + 2e^- \rightleftharpoons Sn(s)$	−0.14
$Cr_2O_7^{2-}(aq) + 14H^+(aq) + 6e^- \rightleftharpoons 2Cr^{3+}(aq) + 7H_2O(l)$	+1.33	$H^+(aq) + e^- \rightleftharpoons \frac{1}{2}H_2(g)$	0.00
$Cu^+(aq) + e^- \rightleftharpoons Cu(s)$	+0.52	$S(s) + 2H^+(aq) + 2e^- \rightleftharpoons H_2S(g)$	+0.14
$Cu^{2+}(aq) + 2e^- \rightleftharpoons Cu(s)$	+0.34	$Cu^{2+}(aq) + e^- \rightleftharpoons Cu^+(aq)$	+0.15
$Cu^{2+}(aq) + e^- \rightleftharpoons Cu^+(aq)$	+0.15	$Sn^{4+}(aq) + 2e^- \rightleftharpoons Sn^{2+}(aq)$	+0.15
$\frac{1}{2}F_2(g) + e^- \rightleftharpoons F^-(aq)$	+2.87	$Cu^{2+}(aq) + 2e^- \rightleftharpoons Cu(s)$	+0.34
$Fe^{2+}(aq) + 2e^- \rightleftharpoons Fe(s)$	−0.44	$\frac{1}{2}O_2(g) + H_2O(l) + 2e^- \rightleftharpoons 2OH^-(l)$	+0.40
$Fe^{3+}(aq) + e^- \rightleftharpoons Fe^{2+}(aq)$	+0.77	$Cu^+(aq) + e^- \rightleftharpoons Cu(s)$	+0.52
$H^+(aq) + e^- \rightleftharpoons \frac{1}{2}H_2(g)$	0.00	$\frac{1}{2}I_2(s) + e^- \rightleftharpoons I^-(aq)$	+0.54
$\frac{1}{2}I_2(s) + e^- \rightleftharpoons I^-(aq)$	+0.54	$MnO_4^-(aq) + e^- \rightleftharpoons MnO_4^{2-}(aq)$	+0.56
$Li^+(aq) + e^- \rightleftharpoons Li(s)$	−3.04	$MnO_4^{2-}(aq) + 2H_2O(l) + 2e^- \rightleftharpoons MnO_2(s) + 4OH^-(aq)$	+0.59
$MnO_4^-(aq) + 8H^+(aq) + 5e^- \rightleftharpoons Mn^{2+}(aq) + 4H_2O(l)$	+1.52	$O_2(g) + 2H^+(aq) + 2e^- \rightleftharpoons H_2O_2(aq)$	+0.68
$MnO_4^-(aq) + e^- \rightleftharpoons MnO_4^{2-}(aq)$	+0.56	$Fe^{3+}(aq) + e^- \rightleftharpoons Fe^{2+}(aq)$	+0.77
$MnO_4^{2-}(aq) + 2H_2O(l) + 2e^- \rightleftharpoons MnO_2(s) + 4OH^-(aq)$	+0.59	$Ag^+(aq) + e^- \rightleftharpoons Ag(s)$	+0.80
$\frac{1}{2}H_2O_2(aq) + H^+(aq) + e^- \rightleftharpoons H_2O(l)$	+1.77	$\frac{1}{2}Br_2(l) + e^- \rightleftharpoons Br^-(aq)$	+1.07
$\frac{1}{2}O_2(g) + 2H^+(aq) + 2e^- \rightleftharpoons H_2O(l)$	+1.23	$\frac{1}{2}O_2(g) + 2H^+(aq) + 2e^- \rightleftharpoons H_2O(l)$	+1.23
$\frac{1}{2}O_2(g) + H_2O(l) + 2e^- \rightleftharpoons 2OH^-(l)$	+0.40	$Cr_2O_7^{2-}(aq) + 14H^+(aq) + 6e^- \rightleftharpoons 2Cr^{3+}(aq) + 7H_2O(l)$	+1.33
$O_2(g) + 2H^+(aq) + 2e^- \rightleftharpoons H_2O_2(aq)$	+0.68	$\frac{1}{2}Cl_2(g) + e^- \rightleftharpoons Cl^-(aq)$	+1.36
$Pb^{4+}(aq) + 2e^- \rightleftharpoons Pb^{2+}(aq)$	+1.69	$MnO_4^-(aq) + 8H^+(aq) + 5e^- \rightleftharpoons Mn^{2+}(aq) + 4H_2O(l)$	+1.52
$Sn^{2+}(aq) + 2e^- \rightleftharpoons Sn(s)$	−0.14	$HOCl(aq) + H^+(aq) + e^- \rightleftharpoons \frac{1}{2}Cl_2(g) + H_2O(l)$	+1.64
$Sn^{4+}(aq) + 2e^- \rightleftharpoons Sn^{2+}(aq)$	+0.15	$Pb^{4+}(aq) + 2e^- \rightleftharpoons Pb^{2+}(aq)$	+1.69
$S(s) + 2H^+(aq) + 2e^- \rightleftharpoons H_2S(g)$	+0.14	$\frac{1}{2}H_2O_2(aq) + H^+(aq) + e^- \rightleftharpoons H_2O(l)$	+1.77
$Zn^{2+}(aq) + 2e^- \rightleftharpoons Zn(s)$	−0.76	$\frac{1}{2}F_2(g) + e^- \rightleftharpoons F^-(aq)$	+2.87

Change in pressure

A change in pressure affects gaseous reactants only. Oxygen acting as an oxidising agent has the redox half-equation:

$$O_2(g) + 2H_2O(l) + 4e^- \rightleftharpoons 4OH^-(aq) \quad E^\ominus = +0.40\,V$$

This assumes that the pressure of oxygen is 1.0 atm. In air, this is not the case. The partial pressure of oxygen in air is about 0.2 atm. This drives the redox equilibrium to the left, making $E < +0.40\,V$. Therefore, oxygen in the air is a less good oxidising agent than pure oxygen. Conversely, a scuba diver's air tank has oxygen at a partial pressure much greater than 1 atm. So, if damp air is pumped into the tank, internal rusting will occur more than it does with iron in normal air.

Change in temperature

The effect of a change in temperature depends on whether the redox half-equation is exothermic or endothermic. If it is exothermic, an increased temperature drives the position of equilibrium to the left (in the endothermic direction). This makes the value of the electrode potential less positive (or more negative).

Chlorine is reduced exothermically in aqueous solution. Therefore, an increase in temperature makes the new electrode potential less than +1.36 V.

Altering a reduction potential half-equation

Changing direction

If the electrode equation is reversed, its sign must also be reversed, for example:

$$Zn^{2+}(aq) + 2e^- \rightleftharpoons Zn(s) \qquad E^\ominus = -0.76\,V$$

$$Zn(s) \rightleftharpoons Zn^{2+}(aq) + 2e^- \qquad E^\ominus = -(-0.76) = +0.76\,V$$

$$\tfrac{1}{2}Cl_2(g) + e^- \rightleftharpoons Cl^-(aq) \qquad E^\ominus = +1.36\,V$$

$$Cl^-(aq) \rightleftharpoons \tfrac{1}{2}Cl_2(g) + e^- \qquad E^\ominus = -(+1.36) = -1.36\,V$$

Tip

This is similar to enthalpy calculations – if the equation of a reaction is reversed, the sign of ΔH has to be changed.

Multiplying by integers

The units of E are volts not volts per mole, so multiplying a redox half-equation has no effect on the value of E:

$$\tfrac{1}{2}Cl_2(g) + e^- \rightleftharpoons Cl^-(aq) \qquad E^\ominus = +1.36\,V$$

$$Cl_2(g) + 2e^- \rightleftharpoons 2Cl^-(aq) \qquad E^\ominus = +1.36\,V$$

Calculation of $E^\ominus_{cell}$ for a reaction

The standard cell potential, $E^\ominus_{cell}$, can be calculated from standard electrode potential data. Since these data are normally given as reduction potentials, the two reactants must be identified. One reactant will be on the left-hand side of one half-equation and the other on the right-hand side of the other half-equation.

Tip

This is *unlike* ΔH calculations, where the units are kJ mol^{-1} and the value depends on the number of moles in the equation as written.

The half-equation with the reactant on the right-hand side must be reversed. This alters the sign of its $E^\ominus$ value. If necessary, the two half-equations are multiplied by integers to give the same number of electrons in each equation, but this does not alter the $E^\ominus$ values. The overall equation is obtained by adding these half-equations together. The $E^\ominus$ value of the reversed half-equation is then added to the $E^\ominus$ value of the unchanged half-equation to give the value of $E^\ominus_{cell}$.

Worked example 1

Use the data below to calculate the value of $E^{\ominus}_{cell}$ for the reaction in which Fe^{3+} ions oxidise I^- ions in aqueous solution. Write the overall equation.

$$Fe^{3+}(aq) + e^- \rightleftharpoons Fe^{2+}(aq) \qquad E^{\ominus} = +0.77\,V$$

$$\frac{1}{2}I_2(s) + e^- \rightleftharpoons I^-(aq) \qquad E^{\ominus} = +0.54\,V$$

Answer

The reactants are Fe^{3+} and I^-, so the second equation has to be reversed and the sign of its $E^{\ominus}$ value changed.

Both equations have one electron, so no multiplying is needed.

$$Fe^{3+}(aq) + e^- \rightleftharpoons Fe^{2+}(aq) \qquad E^{\ominus} = +0.77\,V$$

$$I^-(aq) \rightleftharpoons \frac{1}{2}I_2(s) + e^- \qquad E^{\ominus} = -(+0.54) = -0.54\,V$$

These two equations and their $E^{\ominus}$ values are then added together:

$$Fe^{3+}(aq) + I^-(aq) \rightarrow Fe^{2+}(aq) + \frac{1}{2}I_2(s) \qquad E^{\ominus}_{cell} = +0.77 + (-0.54) = +0.23\,V$$

Worked example 2

Use the data below to calculate the value of $E^{\ominus}_{cell}$ for the reaction of dichromate(VI) ions in acidified potassium dichromate(VI) oxidising chloride ions in hydrochloric acid.

$$Cr_2O_7^{2-}(aq) + 14H^+(aq) + 6e^- \rightleftharpoons 2Cr^{3+}(aq) + 7H_2O(l) \qquad E^{\ominus} = +1.33\,V$$

$$\frac{1}{2}Cl_2(g) + e^- \rightleftharpoons Cl^-(aq) \qquad E^{\ominus} = +1.36\,V$$

Answer

The reactants are $Cr_2O_7^{2-}$ and Cl^-, so the second equation has to be reversed and the sign of its $E^{\ominus}$ value changed.

To get the overall equation, the number of electrons must be the same in both half-equations, so the second equation has to be multiplied by 6. This does not alter the $E^{\ominus}$ value. The half-equations are then added together.

$$Cr_2O_7^{2-}(aq) + 14H^+(aq) + 6e^- \rightleftharpoons 2Cr^{3+}(aq) + 7H_2O(l) \qquad E^{\ominus} = +1.33\,V$$

$$6Cl^-(aq) \rightleftharpoons 3Cl_2(g) + 6e^- \qquad E^{\ominus} = -1.36\,V$$

$$Cr_2O_7^{2-}(aq) + 14H^+(aq) + 6Cl^-(aq) \rightleftharpoons 2Cr^{3+}(aq) + 7H_2O(l) + 3Cl_2(g)$$

$$E^{\ominus}_{cell} = 1.33 + (-1.36) = -0.03\,V)$$

The value of $E^{\ominus}_{cell}$ is slightly negative, so the position of equilibrium is to the left under standard conditions.

This is the safest way to calculate the value of $E^{\ominus}$ of a redox reaction. It also generates the overall equation.

There are other methods, but they pose particular difficulties:

- The 'anticlockwise rule' works when the data are presented in increasing numerical order, with the most negative (least positive) $E^{\ominus}$ value on top. Each half-equation then occurs in an anticlockwise direction. For example, the direction of change for the combination of the $I_2\,|\,I^-$ and $Fe^{3+}\,|\,Fe^{2+}$ can be predicted using this rule (Figure 4.6).

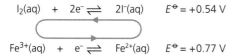

$I_2(aq) + 2e^- \rightleftharpoons 2I^-(aq) \qquad E^\ominus = +0.54\,V$

$Fe^{3+}(aq) + e^- \rightleftharpoons Fe^{2+}(aq) \qquad E^\ominus = +0.77\,V$

Figure 4.6

This shows that the top equation goes backwards and the bottom equation goes forwards. Fe^{3+} ions will oxidise I^- ions. As the top reaction is being reversed, its sign must also be reversed. So the value of $E^\ominus_{cell}$ is:

$$E^\ominus_{cell} = +0.77 - (+0.54) = +0.23\,V$$

- The rule '$E^\ominus_{cell} = E^\ominus_{oxidising\ agent} - E^\ominus_{reducing\ agent}$' or '$E^\ominus_{cathode} - E^\ominus_{anode}$' can be misremembered and also does not give the overall equation. In addition, it requires correct identification of the oxidising agent and the reducing agent. The reducing agent is found on the right of the reduction potential half-equation, and $E_{reducing\ agent}$ is the value of the reduction potential.

In worked example 2 above, the oxidising agent is dichromate(VI) and the reducing agent is the Cl^- ions.

Thus:

$$E^\ominus_{cell} = E^\ominus_{oxidising\ agent} - E^\ominus_{reducing\ agent} = +1.33 - (+1.36) = -0.03\,V$$

Test yourself

5 Use the data in Table 4.1 to calculate the cell potential for the reaction between iodide ions and Fe^{3+} ions, and write the equation for this redox reaction.

Cell diagrams

The cell diagram is a standard way of representing cells and redox processes. The diagram is written in the following order, from left to right:

- the formula of the metallic anode followed by a vertical line
- the ions present in the anode area followed by two vertical lines
- the ions present in the cathode area followed by a vertical line
- the formula of the metallic cathode

For the cell where zinc is oxidised (so is the anode) and copper ions reduced to copper (which is the cathode), the cell diagram is:

$$Zn(s) \mid Zn^{2+}(aq) \parallel Cu^{2+}(aq) \mid Cu(s)$$

For the cell where manganate(VII) ions oxidise iron(II) ions (so MnO_4^- is reduced and Fe^{2+} oxidised), the cell diagram is:

$$Pt(s) \mid MnO_4^-(aq),\ 8H^+(aq),\ Mn^{2+}(aq) \parallel Fe^{3+}(aq),\ Fe^{2+}(aq) \mid Pt(s)$$

Note that:

- if E_{cell} is positive, the reaction proceeds from left to right in the left-hand cell and from right to left in the right-hand cell
- electrons are not written in the diagram
- a single vertical line separates different states, such as solid and solution

- a pair of vertical lines represents the salt bridge
- a comma separates two different ions in the same solution

Feasibility of a redox reaction

A redox reaction is thermodynamically feasible if the value of the cell potential is positive.

Some books state that unless $E^{\ominus}_{cell}$ is more than $+0.03\,V$ or some other number, the reaction will not proceed very far. This is an oversimplification. As is shown below, the relationship between $E^{\ominus}_{cell}$ and ΔS_{total} and hence $\ln K$ also depends on the number of electrons transferred in the reaction.

Relationship between $E^{\ominus}_{cell}$, ΔS_{total}, $\Delta G^{\ominus}$ and K

The value of the total entropy change, ΔS_{total}, is directly proportional to the standard cell potential of a reaction. In turn, $\ln K$ is directly proportional to ΔS_{total}, where K is the equilibrium constant for the reaction.

This means that a positive $E^{\ominus}_{cell}$ results in a positive ΔS_{total} and hence a value of K greater than 1. The more positive the value of $E^{\ominus}_{cell}$, the larger is the value of the equilibrium constant.

A negative value of $E^{\ominus}_{cell}$ results in a negative ΔS_{total} and a value of K that is less than 1.

$$\Delta S_{total} = nE^{\ominus}_{cell}F/T$$

where n is the number of electrons transferred in the overall equation, F is the Faraday constant $(96\,500\,C\,mol^{-1})$ and T is the temperature in kelvin.

$$\ln K = \Delta S_{total}/R$$
$$= nE^{\ominus}_{cell}F/RT$$

where R is the gas constant $(8.31\,J\,K^{-1}\,mol^{-1})$.

Thus $\ln K$ is proportional to $E^{\ominus}_{cell}$. This means that a positive cell results in a value of K greater than 1 and a negative $E^{\ominus}_{cell}$ results in a value of K less than 1. A positive $E^{\ominus}_{cell}$ makes the reaction thermodynamically feasible.

The relationship between ΔG and $E^{\ominus}_{cell}$ is:

$$\Delta G = -nFE^{\ominus}_{cell}$$

So the more negative is ΔG, the more positive is the value of $E^{\ominus}_{cell}$.

But as $\Delta G = -RT\ln K$

$$\ln K = -\Delta G/RT = +nFE^{\ominus}_{cell}/RT$$

> **Tip**
>
> This relationship need not be learnt for A level chemistry, but the fact that $\ln K$ is directly proportional to $E^{\ominus}_{cell}$ is required.

Test yourself

6 Calculate the value of the equilibrium constant for the following reaction at 25°C ($F = 9.65 \times 10^4\,C\,mol^{-1}$; $R = 8.31\,J\,K^{-1}\,mol^{-1}$):

$$Cr_2O_7^{2-}(aq) + 14H^+(aq) + 6Cl^-(aq) \rightleftharpoons 2Cr^{3+}(aq) + 7H_2O(l) + 3Cl_2(g)$$
$$E^{\ominus}_{cell} = -0.03\,V$$

Extent of reaction

The relationship between ΔS_{total}, and K is shown above. In worked example 1 on p. 106, the cell potential for the oxidation of iodide ions by iron(III) ions is $+0.23\,V$. The value of $\Delta S^{\ominus}_{total} = +74\,J\,K^{-1}\,mol^{-1}$ and the numerical value of $K = 7.4 \times 10^3$. This value shows that the reaction significantly favours the products.

The oxidation of chloride ions by manganate(VII) ions in acid solution:

$$MnO_4^-(aq) + 5Cl^-(aq) + 8H^+(aq) \rightarrow Mn^{2+}(aq) + 2\tfrac{1}{2}Cl_2(g) + 4H_2O(l)$$

has $E^{\ominus}_{cell} = +0.16\,V$. This is a small value, but as there are five electrons transferred, the value of $K = 3 \times 10^{13}$. This is over a trillion times bigger than the K for the oxidation of I^- by Fe^{3+}, which involves just one electron and has the larger $E^{\ominus}_{cell} = +0.23\,V$.

The large value of K shows that a standard solution of manganate(VII) ions in acid solution almost completely oxidises a standard solution of chloride ions, despite $E^{\ominus}_{cell}$ being only $+0.16\,V$.

Remember:

- A positive cell potential means that the reaction is thermodynamically feasible.
- A negative cell potential means that the reaction is not thermodynamically feasible.

Summary

ΔS_{total} positive	$E^{\ominus}_{cell}$ positive	$K > 1$	ΔG negative	$E^{\ominus}_{cell}$ positive	$K > 1$
ΔS_{total} negative	$E^{\ominus}_{cell}$ negative	$K < 1$	ΔG positive	$E^{\ominus}_{cell}$ negative	$K < 1$

Actuality of reaction

A reaction may be thermodynamically feasible ($E^{\ominus}_{cell}$ positive) but might not take place. The reasons for this can be kinetic or connected with non-standard conditions.

Kinetic reasons

The sign of $E^{\ominus}_{cell}$ enables the prediction of whether a reaction is thermodynamically feasible. However, thermodynamic feasibility is no guarantee that the reaction will take place under standard conditions. The reaction may have such a high activation energy that it is too slow to be observed at room temperature. For example, $E^{\ominus}_{cell}$ for the reaction $H_2(g) + \tfrac{1}{2}O_2(g) \rightarrow H_2O(l)$ is $+1.23\,V$, but a mixture of hydrogen and oxygen will not react unless heated or unless a catalyst is present (see fuel cells on p. 113).

The reaction between persulfate ions, $S_2O_8^{2-}$, and iodide ions, I^-, is thermodynamically feasible as $E^{\ominus}_{cell} = +1.47\,V$. However, it does not occur unless a catalyst of iron ions (either Fe^{2+} or Fe^{3+}) is added. The activation energy is high because of the need for two negative ions to collide in the uncatalysed route.

The reactants are *kinetically* stable with respect to the products if the activation energy of the reaction is too high.

The reactants are *thermodynamically* stable with respect to the products if ΔS_{total} is negative, ΔG is positive or if $E^{\ominus}_{cell}$ is negative.

Non-standard conditions

The data provided in the data booklet or in an A level question are always standard electrode reduction potentials. If the concentration of a reactant or product is not $1.0\,mol\,dm^{-3}$, the value of E_{cell} will differ from that of $E^{\ominus}_{cell}$. This might result in a reaction taking place that is predicted to be unfeasible.

Worked example

Consider the redox reaction:

$$Cu^{2+}(aq) + 2I^-(aq) \rightarrow CuI(s) + \frac{1}{2}I_2(s)$$

Explain why this reaction will take place, given that:

$$Cu^{2+}(aq) + e^- \rightleftharpoons Cu^+(aq) \qquad E^{\ominus} = +0.15\,V$$

$$\frac{1}{2}I_2(s) + e^- \rightleftharpoons I^-(aq) \qquad E^{\ominus} = +0.54\,V$$

Answer

The reactants are Cu^{2+} and I^- ions. The feasibility is predicted by reversing the sign of the $E^{\ominus}$ value of the second equation and adding the two $E^{\ominus}$ values together.

$$E^{\ominus}_{cell} = +0.15 + (-0.54) = -0.39\,V$$

The negative value predicts that the reaction will not take place under standard conditions where the concentrations of $Cu^+(aq)$, $Cu^{2+}(aq)$ and I^- (aq) ions are all $1.0\,mol\,dm^{-3}$. However, this is not the case in this reaction because copper(I) iodide is precipitated and so $[Cu^+(aq)]$ is almost zero. This drives the equilibrium of the $Cu^{2+}|Cu^+$ reaction to the right, increasing its electrode potential and making the value of the non-standard cell potential positive. The reaction is now feasible and, as the activation energy is low, the reaction takes place rapidly.

Disproportionation reactions

> Disproportionation is where an element in a *single* species is simultaneously both oxidised and reduced.

If an element exists in three different oxidation states (which could include the zero state of the uncombined element), disproportionation becomes a possibility. The feasibility of such a reaction can be predicted from standard electrode potential data.

Worked example

Predict whether or not copper(I) ions will disproportionate into copper metal and copper(II) ions. If so, write the overall equation.

$$Cu^{2+}(aq) + e^- \rightleftharpoons Cu^+(aq) \qquad E^{\ominus} = +0.15\,V$$

$$Cu^+(aq) + e^- \rightleftharpoons Cu(s) \qquad E^{\ominus} = +0.52\,V$$

Answer

As this is a disproportionation reaction, a single species is both reduced and oxidised at the same time. In this example that species is the Cu^+ ion, so the first equation must be reversed and added to the second equation to give the overall equation:

$$Cu^+(aq) \rightleftharpoons Cu^{2+}(aq) + e^- \qquad E^\ominus = -0.15\,V$$

$$Cu^+(aq) + e^- \rightleftharpoons Cu(s) \qquad E^\ominus = +0.52\,V$$

$$2Cu^+(aq) \rightleftharpoons Cu^{2+}(aq) + Cu(s) \qquad E^\ominus_{cell} = -0.15 + (+0.52) = +0.37\,V$$

The value of $E^\ominus_{cell}$ is positive, so the disproportionation reaction is feasible.

This is a disproportionation reaction because copper in the +1 state is simultaneously oxidised to copper in the +2 state and reduced to copper in the zero state.

Practical aspects of electrochemistry

Electricity from chemical reactions

There are three ways in which useful amounts of electricity can be produced from chemical reactions. Chemical energy is converted directly into electrical energy, but the process is not 100% efficient as there are some heat losses.

Disposable batteries

Standard AA batteries consist of a zinc anode and a cathode of a carbon rod packed round with granules of manganese(IV) oxide. The electrolyte is a paste of ammonium chloride. The zinc loses electrons to form zinc ions. At the cathode, manganese(IV) oxide is reduced to a manganese(III) compound.

Alkaline batteries (Figure 4.7) are similar, except that the electrolyte is sodium hydroxide. Here, the anode reaction is:

$$Zn(s) + 2OH^-(aq) \rightarrow Zn(OH)_2(s) + 2e^-$$

The cathode reaction is:

$$2MnO_2(s) + 2H_2O(l) + 2e^- \rightarrow 2MnO(OH)(s) + 2OH^-(aq)$$

An AA alkaline battery

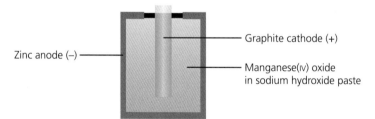

Graphite cathode (+)

Zinc anode (−)

Manganese(IV) oxide in sodium hydroxide paste

Figure 4.7 An alkaline battery

Since the OH⁻ ions used up at the anode are replaced by the OH⁻ ions formed at the cathode, the concentration of ions remains constant so the voltage does not fall until all the zinc has been used, at which point the battery becomes flat.

Mercury batteries (Figure 4.8) can be used in watches and heart pacemakers. The anode is zinc, the cathode is steel and the electrolyte is a paste of mercury(II) oxide in alkali.

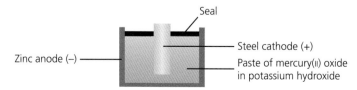

Seal

Steel cathode (+)

Zinc anode (−)

Paste of mercury(II) oxide in potassium hydroxide

Figure 4.8 A mercury button battery

Other button batteries are made of lithium and manganese(IV) oxide, or zinc and silver oxide with suitable electrolytes.

Rechargeable batteries

The lead–acid battery is used in cars. Each cell consists of two lead plates. The cathode is coated with solid lead(IV) oxide. The electrolyte is a fairly concentrated solution of sulfuric acid.

The anode reaction is:

$$Pb(s) + SO_4^{2-}(aq) \rightarrow PbSO_4(s) + 2e^-$$

The cathode reaction is:

$$PbO_2(s) + 4H^+(aq) + SO_4^{2-}(aq) + 2e^- \rightarrow PbSO_4(s) + 2H_2O(l)$$

The overall discharging reaction is:

$$Pb(s) + PbO_2(s) + 4H^+(aq) + 2SO_4^{2-}(aq) \rightarrow 2PbSO_4(s) + 2H_2O(l)$$

The potential of each cell is +2.0 V. Normally, six cells are arranged in series creating a battery with a potential of 12 V.

When all the lead(IV) oxide has been reduced, the battery is flat.

The discharging reaction is reversible. If an external potential greater than 12 V is applied, the reaction is driven backwards and the plates restored to their original composition.

The overall charging reaction is:

$$2PbSO_4(s) + 2H_2O(l) \rightarrow Pb(s) + PbO_2(s) + 4H^+(aq) + 2SO_4^{2-}(aq)$$

Hybrid cars have two engines. One is a conventional gasoline engine and the other is an electric engine powered by rechargeable batteries. When the driver applies the brakes, the kinetic energy of the car is converted to electric energy, which recharges the batteries.

Cars powered by batteries alone have a limited range, the average being 50 miles.

Digital cameras and mobile phones contain rechargeable lithium cells that use a solid polymer electrolyte. There are several types with different materials for the anode and cathode. One type of battery has a lithium anode and a titanium(IV) sulfide cathode. The reactions are:

$$Li \rightleftharpoons Li^+ + e^-$$

$$TiS_2 + e^- \rightleftharpoons TiS_2^-$$

The Li^+ and the TiS_2^- ions then form solid $LiTiS_2$.

The main principles of storage (rechargeable) cells are that:

- The chemical reactions at both electrodes must be able to be reversed when an electrical potential is applied.
- The oxidised and reduced forms of the anode and cathode must be solid.

The recharging process is electrolysis, where electrical energy causes a chemical reaction.

Fuel cells

Manned spacecraft are powered by hydrogen–oxygen fuel cells. These cells are also being developed for commercial use. Some London buses have such a fuel cell. The electricity it produces powers the electric motor of the bus. The buses are advertised as zero-emission buses because, when they are operating, only water and no carbon dioxide, is produced. Steam can be seen from the exhaust pipe near the roof on zero-emission buses. This is the water that has been produced by the reaction of the hydrogen fuel with oxygen.

A zero-emission London bus

Hydrogen gas is oxidised at the anode and the electrons released go round the external circuit powering the machinery to the cathode, where oxygen gas is reduced. The ions produced pass through the electrolyte. The only product is water, which must constantly be removed from the cell.

The electrodes are made of porous graphite embedded with the catalyst, which is usually platinum. Doped carbon nanotubes are being developed as a cheaper and more efficient catalyst.

There are two distinct types of hydrogen fuel cell.

Polymer electrolyte membrane (PEM) fuel cells

At the anode, hydrogen is oxidised and H^+ ions and electrons are formed. The H^+ ions then pass through the solid polymer electrolyte to the cathode. The electrons released pass round the external circuit to the cathode. Oxygen gas (from the air) is reduced at the cathode and water is formed. The half-equations are:

Anode $\quad 2H_2 \rightleftharpoons 4H^+ + 4e^-$

Cathode $\quad O_2 + 4H^+ + 4e^- \rightleftharpoons 2H_2O$

Overall $\quad 2H_2 + O_2 \rightarrow 2H_2O$

The basic design is shown in Figure 4.9.

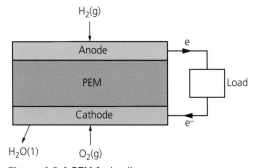

Figure 4.9 A PEM fuel cell

Alkaline fuel cells

The electrodes are porous platinum and the electrolyte is an aqueous solution of potassium hydroxide.

The principle is the same as with PEM cells. The hydrogen is oxidised at the anode:

$$2H_2(g) + 4OH^-(aq) \rightleftharpoons 4H_2O(l) + 4e^-$$

The electrons travel around the external circuit to the cathode, where oxygen is reduced:

$$O_2(g) + 2H_2O(l) + 42e^- \rightleftharpoons 4OH^-(aq)$$

Overall:

$$2H_2 + O_2 \rightarrow 2H_2O$$

The major disadvantages with alkaline fuel cells are that their efficiency is reduced by any carbon dioxide in the air and corrosive potassium hydroxide solution may leak out. However, they are more efficient than PEM cells and so are used in spacecraft, where pure oxygen rather than air is used.

Environmental issues

The statement that there are no emissions from hydrogen fuel cells (implying no CO_2) is misleading. The hydrogen could be produced by electrolysis, which consumes 96 million coulombs of electricity per tonne of hydrogen. This electricity will almost certainly have been produced by burning fossil fuels such as coal, oil or gas.

Another source of hydrogen is the endothermic reaction of methane with steam in a two-stage process, the overall reaction being:

$$CH_4 + 2H_2O \rightarrow CO_2 + 4H_2$$

The only way that a hydrogen–oxygen fuel cell could be rightly described as having zero emissions is if the electricity had been produced by nuclear power or some form of renewable energy. Therefore, although the bus itself does not produce carbon dioxide, it is created at the power station or at the plant making the hydrogen from methane.

Some prototype cars have been designed to run on fuel cells that use hydrogen. There are two, as yet, insurmountable problems:

- the storage of hydrogen gas in the car
- the problem of refuelling the vehicle at a garage forecourt

These pose dangers since gaseous hydrogen under pressure is highly flammable.

Research is being carried out into designing fuel cells that will use other fuels (e.g. ethanol), rather than hydrogen. The two half-equations for ethanol are:

$$C_2H_5OH(l) + H_2O(l) \rightleftharpoons CH_3COOH(aq) + 4H^+ + 4e^-$$

$$O_2(g) + 4H^+(aq) + 4e^- \rightleftharpoons 2H_2O(l)$$

Ethanol could be made by fermenting sugar or cereals, such as corn, wheat or rice. However, it is not a truly carbon-neutral process, because fossil fuels would have to be used during the harvesting of the crop and in the manufacture of ethanol. Another major drawback to the production of bioethanol is that it uses agricultural land. This means that food crops are not grown on that land, which results in a reduction in world food production.

China and India are developing economically and are increasing their demand for meat, which requires a considerable amount of grain to produce. This, combined with the drive to produce bioethanol, has pushed up the price of sugar and grain, and resulted in starvation in poor countries.

Methanol is another possibility for a fuel cell. However, methanol is made from carbon monoxide and hydrogen:

$$CO + 2H_2 \rightarrow CH_3OH$$

The carbon monoxide comes from coal or methane and the hydrogen itself has a significant carbon footprint.

Oxidising and reducing agents

Oxidising agents

An oxidising agent is a species that removes electrons from another species, thus oxidising it. It is itself reduced by the gain of electrons.

Some oxidising agents, the species produced when they react and their standard reduction potentials are given in Table 4.2.

Table 4.2 Common oxidising agents listed in order of decreasing power

Oxidising agent	Oxidising species	Reduced species	$E^{\ominus}/V$
Ozone	O_3 in $H^+(aq)$	O_2, H_2O	+2.07
Persulfate ions	$S_2O_8^{2-}$	SO_4^{2-}	+2.01
Hydrogen peroxide	H_2O_2 in $H^+(aq)$	H_2O	+1.77
Chloric(I) acid	HOCl in $H^+(aq)$	Cl_2, H_2O	+1.64
Manganate(VII) ions	MnO_4^- in $H^+(aq)$	Mn^{2+}, H_2O	+1.52
Lead(IV) oxide	PbO_2 in $H^+(aq)$	Pb^{2+}, H_2O	+1.47
Chlorine	Cl_2	Cl^-	+1.36
Dichromate(VI) ions	$Cr_2O_7^{2-}$ in $H^+(aq)$	Cr^{3+}, H_2O	+1.33
Manganese(IV) oxide	MnO_2 in $H^+(aq)$	Mn^{2+}, H_2O	+1.23
Oxygen	O_2 in $H^+(aq)$	H_2O	+1.23
Iodate(V) ions	IO_3^- in $H^+(aq)$	I_2, H_2O	+1.19
Bromine	Br_2	Br^-	+1.07
Iron(III) ions	Fe^{3+}	Fe^{2+}	+0.77
Iodine	I_2	I^-	+0.54
Tetrathionate ions	$S_4O_6^{2-}$	$S_2O_3^{2-}$	+0.09

> **Tip**
>
> The oxidation number of an element in the oxidising agent decreases (becomes less positive or more negative). The oxidation number of an element in the species being oxidised increases (becomes more positive or less negative).

All oxidising agents should oxidise the reduced form of any species below them in the table. For example, lead(IV) oxide will oxidise chloride ions to chlorine. A laboratory preparation of chlorine is to warm concentrated hydrochloric acid with lead(IV) oxide.

Worked example

Show that iodate(V) ions in acid solution should oxidise iodide ions and write the overall equation for the reaction.

Answer

The two reduction half-equations are:

$$\frac{1}{2}I_2(s) + e^- \rightleftharpoons I^-(aq) \qquad\qquad E^{\ominus} = +0.54\,V$$

$$IO_3^-(aq) + 6H^+(aq) + 5e^- \rightleftharpoons \frac{1}{2}I_2(s) + 3H_2O(l) \quad E^{\ominus} = +1.19\,V$$

Iodate(v) ions and iodide ions are the reactants. The overall equation is obtained by reversing the first equation, multiplying it by 5 and then adding it to the second equation:

$$IO_3^-(aq) + 6H^+(aq) + 5I^-(aq) \rightarrow 3I_2(s) + 3H_2O(l) \quad E^{\ominus}_{cell} = +1.19 + (-0.54) = 0.65\,V$$

$E^{\ominus}_{cell}$ is positive, so the redox reaction is feasible.

Redox titrations

Iodine titrations: estimation of the concentration of a solution of an oxidising agent

An oxidising agent is a species that receives electrons from another species, thus oxidising it. It is itself reduced by gain of electrons.

As can be seen from Table 4.2, all the oxidising agents (apart from tetrathionate ions) in the list should oxidise iodide ions to iodine. The method used here is to add an excess of iodide ions to a known volume of the solution of the oxidising agent. The liberated iodine is then titrated against standard sodium thiosulfate solution.

The reaction between iodine and thiosulfate ions can be used to find the concentration of a solution of an oxidising agent. The method is as follows:

- Pipette a known volume of the solution of the oxidising agent into a conical flask. Usually it is necessary to add some dilute acid at this stage, as H^+ ions are often present in their half-equations.
- Add excess potassium iodide solution (or solid potassium iodide) and swirl to mix the solution.
- Titrate the liberated iodine against standard sodium thiosulfate solution until the iodine colour fades to a pale straw colour.
- Add some starch indicator. The remaining unreacted iodine will react reversibly with the starch to form a blue-black complex.
- Continue adding sodium thiosulfate drop by drop until the blue-black colour disappears.
- Repeat the procedure until at least two concordant titres have been obtained.

The starch must not be added too early, as it will then irreversibly form a blue-black solid starch–iodine complex.

Worked example 1

1.00 g of an impure sample of potassium iodate(v), KIO_3, was dissolved in distilled water and the solution made up to 250 cm^3.

25.0 cm^3 portions of this solution were taken and about 25 cm^3 of dilute sulfuric acid and excess potassium iodide were added. Each was titrated with standard 0.100 mol dm^{-3} sodium thiosulfate solution. The mean titre was 23.75 cm^3.

The equations for the reactions are:

$$KIO_3 + 5KI + 3H_2SO_4 \rightarrow 3I_2 + 3K_2SO_4 + 3H_2O$$

$$I_2 + 2Na_2S_2O_3 \rightarrow 2NaI + Na_2S_4O_6$$

The ionic equations are:

$$IO_3^- + 5I^- + 6H^+ \rightarrow 3I_2 + 3H_2O$$

$$I_2 + 2S_2O_3^{2-} \rightarrow 2I^- + S_4O_6^{2-}$$

Calculate the purity of the potassium iodate(v).

Answer

amount (in moles) of sodium thiosulfate, $Na_2S_2O_3 = 0.100\,mol\,dm^{-3} \times 0.02375\,dm^3$

$= 2.375 \times 10^{-3}\,mol$

1 mol KIO_3 produces 3 mol I_2, which require 6 mol $Na_2S_2O_3$.

amount (in moles) of potassium iodate(v) in $25\,cm^3 = \dfrac{1}{6} \times 2.375 \times 10^{-3}$

$= 3.958 \times 10^{-4}\,mol$

amount (in moles) of potassium iodate(v) in $250\,cm^3 = 10 \times 3.958 \times 10^{-4}$

$= 3.958 \times 10^{-3}\,mol$

molar mass of $KIO_3 = 39.1 + 126.9 + (3 \times 16.0) = 214.0\,g\,mol^{-1}$

mass of pure KIO_3 in sample = moles × molar mass

$= 3.958 \times 10^{-3}\,mol \times 214.0\,g\,mol^{-1} = 0.847\,g$

purity of sample $= \dfrac{0.847\,g}{1.00\,g} \times 100 = 84.7\%$

Worked example 2

Brass is an alloy of copper and zinc, the proportions of which are varied to create a range of brasses with different properties. The percentage of copper in a small brass screw was determined as follows:

- The screw was weighed. Its mass was found to be 2.19 g.
- Some concentrated nitric acid was added to the screw. This was carried out in a fume cupboard. The copper and the zinc both reacted to form soluble nitrates, nitrogen dioxide and water.
- The solution was neutralised. It, and the washings, were transferred to a 250 cm³ standard flask and the volume made up to 250 cm³ with distilled water.
- 25.0 cm³ samples were measured by pipette into conical flasks and excess solid potassium iodide was added.
- The zinc ions did not react. Copper ions reacted according to the equation:

$2Cu^{2+} + 4I^- \rightarrow 2CuI + I_2$

- The liberated iodine was then titrated against a $0.106\,mol\,dm^{-3}$ solution of sodium thiosulfate, adding starch as the indicator near the end point.

$I_2 + 2Na_2S_2O_3 \rightarrow 2NaI + Na_2S_4O_6$

The mean titre was 23.75 cm³. Calculate the percentage of copper in the brass screw.

Answer

amount (in moles) of sodium thiosulfate $= 0.106\,mol\,dm^{-3} \times 0.02375\,dm^3$

$= 0.0025175\,mol$

2 mol $Na_2S_2O_3^{2-}$ react with 1 mol I_2, which comes from 2 mol Cu^{2+}, so:

amount of Cu^{2+} in pipetted sample = amount of $S_2O_3^{2-}$ in titre $= 0.0025175\,mol$

amount of Cu^{2+} in $250\,cm^3 = 10 \times 0.0025175 = 0.025175\,mol$

mass of copper in brass screw $= 63.5\,g\,mol^{-1} \times 0.025175\,mol = 1.599\,g$

% of copper in brass screw $= 1.599 \times 100/2.19 = 73.0\%$

Potassium manganate(VII) titrations: estimation of the concentration of a reducing agent

A reducing agent is a species that gives electrons to another species, thus reducing it. It is itself oxidised by loss of electrons.

A list of some reducing agents, the species produced when they react, and their standard *reduction* potentials are given in Table 4.3.

Table 4.3 Common reducing agents

Reducing agent	Oxidised form	$E^{\ominus}/V$	
$(COO)_2^{2-}$	$2CO_2$	-0.49	
H_2S	S	$+0.14$	
Sn^{2+}	Sn^{4+}	$+0.15$	
I^-	$\frac{1}{2}I_2$	$+0.54$	Decreasing strength as a reducing agent
H_2O_2	O_2	$+0.68$	
Fe^{2+}	Fe^{3+}	$+0.77$	
Br^-	$\frac{1}{2}Br_2$	$+1.07$	
Pb^{2+}	PbO_2 (Pb^{4+})	$+1.47$	

Reducing agents become oxidised and the oxidation number of an element in the reducing agent increases (becomes more positive or less negative). The oxidation number of an element in the species being reduced decreases.

$$\frac{1}{2}I_2(s) + e^- \rightleftharpoons I^-(aq) \qquad E^{\ominus} = +0.54\,V$$

So:

$$I^-(aq) \rightleftharpoons \frac{1}{2}I_2(s) + e^- \qquad E^{\ominus} = -0.54\,V$$

> The reducing agent is on the *right-hand* side of the standard reduction potential half-equation.

The method is to titrate a standard solution of potassium manganate(VII) with the solution of the reducing agent. As can be seen from Table 4.3 and from the $E^{\ominus}$ value of the MnO_4^-, H^+, Mn^{2+} system ($E^{\ominus}_{cell} = +1.52\,V$), all the reducing agents in the table will reduce manganate(VII) ions in acidic solution.

Worked example

Show that hydrogen peroxide should reduce manganate(VII) ions in acid solution. Write the overall equation for the reaction.

Answer

$$O_2(g) + 2H^+(aq) + 2e^- \rightleftharpoons H_2O_2(aq) \qquad\qquad E^{\ominus} = +0.68\,V$$

$$MnO_4^-(aq) + 8H^+(aq) + 5e^- \rightleftharpoons Mn^{2+}(aq) + 4H_2O(l) \qquad E^{\ominus} = +1.52\,V$$

The reactants are H_2O_2 and MnO_4^-, so the first equation has to be reversed. To achieve the same number of electrons in each equation, multiply the first equation by 5 and the second equation by 2. This gives ten electrons in each equation, which will cancel when the equations are added.

> **Tip**
>
> Be careful when selecting the correct redox half-equation for hydrogen peroxide. In this example it is acting as a reducing agent and so it will be on the *right* in the half-equation.

$$5H_2O_2(aq) \rightleftharpoons 5O_2(g) + 10H^+(aq) + 10e^- \qquad E^\ominus = -0.68\,V$$

$$2MnO_4^-(aq) + 16H^+(aq) + 10e^- \rightleftharpoons 2Mn^{2+}(aq) + 8H_2O(l) \qquad E^\ominus = +1.52\,V$$

$$5H_2O_2(aq) + 2MnO_4^-(aq) + 6H^+(aq) \rightleftharpoons 5O_2(g) + 2Mn^{2+}(aq) + 8H_2O(l)$$

$$E^\ominus_{reaction} = (-0.68) + (+1.52) = 0.84\,V$$

The value of $E^\ominus_{reaction}$ is positive, so hydrogen peroxide should reduce manganate(VII) ions in acid solution.

The general method for titrating the standard solution of potassium manganate(VII) with a reducing agent is as follows:

- A sample of known volume, usually $25.0\,cm^3$, of the reducing agent is pipetted into a conical flask.
- Approximately $25\,cm^3$ of dilute sulfuric acid is added.
- A burette is filled with a standard solution of potassium manganate(VII).
- Potassium manganate(VII) solution is added steadily, with swirling, until the purple colour disappears slowly.
- The potassium manganate(VII) is then added dropwise, until the solution becomes slightly pink.
- The titration is repeated until at least two consistent titres are obtained. There is no need to add an indicator because the manganate(VII) solution is so intensely coloured. The titration is stopped when the smallest excess of MnO_4^- ions causes a faint pink colour to be visible.

Titration of Fe(II) with manganate(VII)

Worked example

Iron tablets contain hydrated iron(II) sulfate mixed with a filler. Some tablets were crushed and $7.17\,g$ of the powdered tablets were dissolved in water. The solution was made up to $250\,cm^3$. $25.0\,cm^3$ of this solution was pipetted into a conical flask and $25\,cm^3$ of dilute sulfuric acid was added from a measuring cylinder. This mixture was then titrated with a $0.0205\,mol\,dm^{-3}$ solution of potassium manganate(VII) until a faint pink colour remained. The titration was repeated and the mean titre was found to be $23.40\,cm^3$. Calculate the percentage of iron in the iron tablets.

Answer

$$amount\ (moles)\ of\ MnO_4^-\ in\ titre = 0.0205\,mol\,dm^{-3} \times 0.02340\,dm^3$$

$$= 0.0004797\,mol$$

The equation for the reaction is:

$$5Fe^{2+}(aq) + MnO_4^-(aq) + 8H^+(aq) \rightarrow 5Fe^{3+}(aq) + Mn^{2+}(aq) + 8H_2O(l)$$

$$amount\ (moles)\ of\ Fe^{2+}\ in\ 25\,cm^3\ of\ solution = 0.0004797\,mol\ MnO_4^- \times 5/1$$

$$= 0.002399\,mol$$

$$amount\ (moles)\ of\ Fe^{2+}\ in\ 250\,cm^3\ of\ solution = 10 \times 0.002399 = 0.02399\,mol$$

$$mass\ of\ iron\ in\ sample = 55.8\,g\,mol^{-1} \times 0.02399\,mol = 1.338\,g$$

$$\%\ of\ iron\ in\ tablet = \frac{mass\ of\ iron \times 100}{mass\ of\ powdered\ tablet} = \frac{1.338 \times 100}{7.17} = 18.7\%$$

Uncertainty of measurements

The accuracy of a pipette depends on a number of factors, such as its quality, and the temperature and viscosity of the solution being used. Most $25.0 \, cm^3$ school pipettes are accurate to $\pm 0.05 \, cm^3$ and so have a percentage error of $0.05 \times 100/25.0 = 0.2\%$. The error in a burette is $\pm 0.05 \, cm^3$ for each reading and so the maximum error in a titre is $\pm 0.1 \, cm^3$.

The concentrations of standard solutions are chosen so that the titre will be between $20 \, cm^3$ and $30 \, cm^3$. Suppose the titre is $24.00 \, cm^3$. The percentage error in the use of the burette is:

$$\frac{error \times 100}{titre} = \frac{0.1 \times 100}{24.00} = 0.4\%$$

If the titre had been $12.00 \, cm^3$, the error would still have been $\pm 0.1 \, cm^3$, but the percentage error would be $0.1 \times 100/12.00 = 0.8\%$.

A chemical balance that weighs to two decimal places has an error of $\pm 0.01 \, g$ for each reading (including the zero reading if the balance is tared). Thus the error in the mass is $0.02 \, g$.

In the worked example on p. 119 about iron tablets:

- the percentage error due to weighing is $0.02 \times 100/7.17 = 0.28\%$
- the pipette has a percentage error of 0.2%
- the burette has a percentage error of $0.1 \times 100/23.4 = 0.43\%$
- the total percentage error is $0.28\% + 0.2\% + 0.43\% = 0.91\%$

This means that the actual percentage of iron in the tablets is between 17.79% and 19.61%.

Worked example

A sample of mass $1.30 \, g$ of a *d*-block metal sulfate, $M_2(SO_4)_3$, was dissolved in water. Excess potassium iodide was added and the iodine liberated was titrated against standard sodium thiosulfate solution. The titre showed that $0.00325 \, mol$ of the transition metal sulfate was present in the $1.30 \, g$.

a) Calculate the molar mass of the $M_2(SO_4)_3$.

b) Hence calculate the atomic mass of the element M. Suggest its identity.

c) Assuming that the error in each weighing is $\pm 0.01 \, g$, calculate the percentage error in the mass of $M_2(SO_4)_3$ taken.

d) Assuming that there are no other significant errors, calculate the maximum and minimum values of the molar mass and hence of the atomic mass of the element M.

e) What does this indicate about the reliability of the identification of M?

Answer

a) molar mass = mass/moles = $\dfrac{130 \, g}{0.00325 \, mol^{-1}} = 400 \, g \, mol^{-1}$

b) mass of the sulfate group = $3 \times (32.1 + 4 \times 16.0) = 288.3$

mass due to 2 atoms of M = $400 - 288.3 = 117.7$

relative atomic mass of M $= \frac{1}{2} \times 117.7 = 55.85$

So, the element M is iron, as the r.a.m. of iron in the periodic table is 55.8.

c) total weighing error is $\pm 0.02\,g$

percentage error in weighing the solid $= \dfrac{0.02 \times 100}{1.32} = 1.52\%$

d) $\pm 1.52\%$ in $400\,g\,mol^{-1}$ is $\pm \dfrac{1.52 \times 400}{100}$

$= \pm 6.1\,g\,mol^{-1}$ in the molar mass

So, the maximum molar mass is $406.1\,g\,mol^{-1}$

minimum molar mass is $393.9\,g\,mol^{-1}$

maximum relative atomic mass is $\frac{1}{2} \times (406.1 - 288.3) = 58.9$

minimum relative atomic mass is $\frac{1}{2} \times (393.9 - 288.3) = 52.8$

e) These values suggest that the metal M could be manganese ($A_r = 54.9$), iron ($A_r = 55.8$) or chromium ($A_r = 58.9$) and so the validity of the identification of M as iron is poor.

Summary tasks

Make sure that you can:

- work out oxidation numbers
- explain oxidation or reduction in terms of change in oxidation number or electron transfer
- write ionic half-equations and hence overall redox equations
- describe the design and working of electrochemical cells including batteries and hydrogen fuel cells
- calculate $E^{\ominus}_{cell}$ given standard reduction potentials
- recall standard conditions
- explain why non-standard conditions can affect feasibility
- draw cell diagrams

Check that you:

- understand that a positive value of E_{cell} means that the redox reaction is feasible
- can define oxidising agents and reducing agents
- understand the concept of disproportionation
- can describe how the concentration of oxidising and reducing agents can be found by titration
- are able to use titration data to calculate concentrations

Questions

Refer to Table 4.1 on p. 104 for standard reduction potential values.

1 Write the half-equations for:

   a) the reduction of chlorine to chloride ions

   b) the oxidation of Fe^{2+} ions to Fe^{3+} ions

2 Use your answers to question 1 to write overall equations for the reaction between chlorine and Fe^{2+} ions.

3 a) Calculate the cell potential for each of the following reactions and suggest whether or not the reaction is feasible:

   i) a reaction between lead(iv) ions and chloride ions

   ii) a reaction between tin(iv) ions and Fe^{2+} ions

   b) Write equations for any of the reactions in (a) (i)–(ii) that are feasible.

4 Both potassium manganate(vii) and potassium dichromate(vi) are used in acid solution as oxidising agents. Use the data in Table 4.1 to explain why hydrochloric acid must *not* be used in the oxidation of an organic substance by potassium manganate(vii) but can be used when potassium dichromate(vi) is the oxidising agent.

5 a) Define the term **disproportionation**.

   b) Explain why an element must have at least three different oxidation states to be able to undergo a disproportionation reaction.

   c) Use the $E^\ominus$ values in Table 4.1 to predict whether manganate(vi) ions, MnO_4^{2-}, will disproportionate into manganate(vii) ions, MnO_4^-, and manganese(iv) oxide, MnO_2.

   d) Predict the effect of increasing the pH of the solution on the feasibility of this disproportionation.

6 Calculate $E^\ominus_{cell}$ for the oxidation by oxygen of iron in aqueous solution. Write the overall equation for this reaction.

7 Explain why iron corrodes to a lesser extent in oxygenated water if the pH of the water is increased by the addition of alkali.

8 a) Predict whether ferrate(vi) ions, FeO_4^{2-}, will be reduced to Fe^{3+} or to Fe^{2+} ions by hydrogen peroxide in an acidic solution.

$$FeO_4^{2-}(aq) + 8H^+(aq) + 3e^- \rightleftharpoons Fe^{3+}(aq) + 4H_2O(l) \quad E^\ominus = +2.20V$$

$$Fe^{3+}(aq) + e^- \rightleftharpoons Fe^{2+}(aq) \quad E^\ominus = +0.77V$$

$$O_2(g) + 2H^+(aq) + 2e^- \rightleftharpoons H_2O_2(aq) \quad E^\ominus = +0.68V$$

   b) Write the overall equation for the reaction that takes place.

9 $25.00\,cm^3$ of a solution of potassium iodate(v) was pipetted into a conical flask. $25\,cm^3$ of dilute sulfuric acid and 2 g of potassium iodide (an excess) were added. The iodine liberated was titrated with $0.104\,mol\,dm^{-3}$ sodium thiosulfate solution using starch as an indicator. The mean titre was $23.20\,cm^3$. Calculate the concentration of the potassium iodate(v) solution.

10 Describe how the concentration of a solution of sodium chlorate(i), NaClO, could be found experimentally.

11 What are the advantages and disadvantages of running a motor vehicle using a fuel cell that is powered by hydrogen?

12 Explain why the strong O—H bond stretching vibration in ethanol cannot be used in infrared breathalysers.

13 Iron(ii) sulfate contains water of crystallisation and its formula can be written as $FeSO_4.xH_2O$. Describe an experiment that would enable you to find the value of x. The method must involve a titration. Your answer should include what you would do and what measurements you would make, and show how you would use your measurements to calculate the value of x. (Heating the hydrated solid would decompose the iron(ii) sulfate, so this is not an acceptable method.)

Exam practice questions

1 a) A spot of water containing some phenolphthalein is placed on a piece of steel and observed after an hour. The outside edge of the drop was coloured pink and there was a faint precipitate in the middle. Explain how the rusting of the steel produced these results. Illustrate your answer with ionic half-equations. (4)

b) The oxidation of iodide ions, I^-, by persulfate ions, $S_2O_8^{2-}$, is very slow at room temperature, but the reaction is catalysed by Fe^{3+} ions.

i) Suggest why the reaction is slow in the absence of the catalyst. (1)

ii) Use the data below to explain how Fe^{3+} ions catalyse this redox reaction. (4)

$$I_2 + 2e^- \rightleftharpoons 2I^- \qquad E^\ominus = +0.54V$$

$$Fe^{3+} + e^- \rightleftharpoons Fe^{2+} \qquad E^\ominus = +0.77V$$

$$S_2O_8^{2-} + 2e^- \rightleftharpoons 2SO_4^{2-} \ E^\ominus = +2.01V$$

c) 10.00 g of impure iron(III) chloride, $FeCl_3$, was dissolved in water and the solution made up to 250 cm^3 in a volumetric flask. Excess potassium iodide was added to 25.0 cm^3 portions and the iodine liberated was then titrated against a 0.200 mol dm^{-3} solution of sodium thiosulfate. The mean titre was 28.60 cm^3.

i) The oxidation number of sulfur in $S_2O_3^{2-}$ ions is:

A +2   **C** +4

B +3   **D** +8   (1)

ii) Calculate the percentage purity by mass of the iron(III) chloride.

$$Fe^{3+} + I^- \rightarrow Fe^{2+} + \tfrac{1}{2}I_2$$

$$I_2 + 2S_2O_3^{2-} \rightarrow 2I^- + S_4O_6^{2-} \qquad (5)$$

iii) Starch indicator must not be added until the iodine solution goes very pale. Explain why this is necessary and the effect on the percentage purity if it were added too early. (1)

(Total 16 marks)

2 a) The oxidation number of

i) oxygen in KO_2 is (1)

A 0   **B** $-\frac{1}{2}$ **C** -1 **D** -2

ii) carbon in $C_2O_4^{2-}$ is (1)

A +4   **B** +3   **C** +2   **D** +1

b) Calculate the standard cell potential and hence the thermodynamic feasibility of a reaction in which manganate(vii) ions in acid solution oxidise ethanedioate ions to carbon dioxide, under standard conditions at 25°C. (3)

$$2CO_2(g) + 2e^- \rightleftharpoons C_2O_4^{2-}(aq) \quad E^\ominus = -0.49V$$

$$MnO_4^-(aq) + 8H^+(aq) + 5e^-$$
$$\rightleftharpoons Mn^{2+}(aq) + 4H_2O(l)$$
$$E^\ominus = +1.52V$$

c) Suggest why, in practice, the reaction does not occur under standard conditions at 25°C. (1)

d) Draw a labelled diagram of the apparatus that you would use to measure the standard reduction potential of acidified potassium manganate(vii). (6)

e) Which of the following would **not** alter the value of the measured potential? (1)

A   Increasing the temperature

B   Increasing the pH

C   Using $NaNO_3$ rather than KNO_3 in the salt bridge

D   Using a calomel electrode rather than a standard hydrogen electrode

(Total 13 marks)

Transition metals (Topic 15)

Principles of transition metal chemistry

The d-block elements lie between the s-block metals and the p-block non-metals in the periodic table. Those in period 4 are shown in Table 5.1.

Table 5.1 The d-block elements in period 4

Sc	Ti	V	Cr	Mn	Fe	Co	Ni	Cu	Zn
Scandium	Titanium	Vanadium	Chromium	Manganese	Iron	Cobalt	Nickel	Copper	Zinc

Electron configuration

Neutral atoms

Argon has the electron configuration $1s^2\ 2s^2\ 2p^6\ 3s^2\ 3p^6$. The next lowest energy level is the $4s$-orbital, so it fills before the $3d$. Therefore, potassium has the electron configuration [Ar] $3d^0\ 4s^1$ and calcium [Ar] $3d^0\ 4s^2$.

After calcium, the d-block starts and the $3d$-orbitals begin to be filled. The general configuration for a d-block element is [Ar] $3d^x\ 4s^2$ where x is the number of the column along the d-block. Scandium is the first d-block element, so its configuration is [Ar] $3d^1\ 4s^2$, vanadium is the third, so its configuration is [Ar] $3d^3\ 4s^2$ and iron is the sixth so its configuration is [Ar] $3d^6\ 4s^2$.

In the fourth period, Sc to Zn, there are two exceptions to this rule. There is a slight gain in stability in having a full or half-full set of d-orbitals. Thus chromium, the fourth d-block element, has the electron configuration [Ar] $3d^5\ 4s^1$ *not* [Ar] $3d^4\ 4s^2$; copper has the configuration [Ar] $3d^{10}\ 4s^1$ *not* [Ar] $3d^9\ 4s^2$ (Table 5.2).

Positive ions

When a d-block element in period 4 loses electrons and forms a positive ion, the outer s-electrons are always lost before any d-electrons. Losing all the $4s$-electrons makes the ionic radius smaller than if it had lost its $3d$-electrons. This means that the lattice energy and the hydration energy are more exothermic. Therefore, in a reaction the overall ΔH is energetically more favourable than if just the $3d$-electrons had been lost. The electron configurations of d-block elements in period 4 and their 2+ and 3+ ions are shown in Table 5.2.

Table 5.2 Period 4 d-block elements

Element	Electron configuration		
	Atom	M^{2+} ion	M^{3+} ion
Sc	[Ar] $3d^1 4s^2$	Does not exist	[Ar] $3d^0 4s^0$
Ti	[Ar] $3d^2 4s^2$	[Ar] $3d^2 4s^0$	[Ar] $3d^1 4s^0$
V	[Ar] $3d^3 4s^2$	[Ar] $3d^3 4s^0$	[Ar] $3d^2 4s^0$
Cr	[Ar] $3d^5 4s^1$	[Ar] $3d^4 4s^0$	[Ar] $3d^3 4s^0$
Mn	[Ar] $3d^5 4s^2$	[Ar] $3d^5 4s^0$	[Ar] $3d^4 4s^0$
Fe	[Ar] $3d^6 4s^2$	[Ar] $3d^6 4s^0$	[Ar] $3d^5 4s^0$
Co	[Ar] $3d^7 4s^2$	[Ar] $3d^7 4s^0$	[Ar] $3d^6 4s^0$
Ni	[Ar] $3d^8 4s^2$	[Ar] $3d^8 4s^0$	[Ar] $3d^7 4s^0$
Cu	[Ar] $3d^{10} 4s^1$	[Ar] $3d^9 4s^0$	Does not exist
Zn	[Ar] $3d^{10} 4s^2$	[Ar] $3d^{10} 4s^0$	Does not exist

The Cu^+ ion has the electronic configuration [Ar] $3d^{10} 4s^0$.

Transition metals

The d-block elements are those between the s-block and the p-block. All d-block elements have an outer electron configuration of nd^x, $(n + 1)s^y$, where x is any number from 1 to 10, y is 1 or 2 and n is the orbit number.

Transition metals are defined differently:

> **A transition metal has one or more unpaired d-electrons in one of its ions.**

or

> **One of its ions has a partially filled d-shell or has at least one unpaired electron in its d-orbitals.**

- Scandium forms Sc^{3+} as its only ion. This has no d-electrons and so scandium is not a transition metal.
- Titanium forms a Ti^{3+} ion, which has one unpaired d-electron. Therefore, titanium is a transition metal.
- Iron has a partially filled d-shell in a Fe^{2+} ion. Therefore, iron is a transition metal.
- Zinc does not form either a Zn^+ or a Zn^{3+} ion. Zn^{2+} has 10 d-electrons that are all paired in five full d-orbitals. Therefore, zinc is not a transition metal.

The arrangements of electrons in Fe^{2+} and Zn^{2+} ions are shown in Figure 5.1.

Figure 5.1 Electron configurations of Fe^{2+} and Zn^{2+} ions

---

Test yourself

1 Write the electron configurations of vanadium and the V^{3+} ion.

Ionisation energies

First ionisation energies

In period 3, the first ionisation energies follow a general upward trend from sodium across to argon. This is caused by an increase in the nuclear charge without an increase in the number of shielding electrons in the inner orbits. The effective nuclear charge increases considerably, and this causes a large increase in the first ionisation energies. The first ionisation energy of sodium is $494\,\text{kJ}\,\text{mol}^{-1}$ and that of argon is $1520\,\text{kJ}\,\text{mol}^{-1}$.

The pattern is different across the d-block. The outer electron that is removed in the reaction:

$$M(g) \rightarrow M^+(g) + e^-$$

is a $4s$-electron, and it is shielded by the inner $3d$-electrons (as well as by the $1s$-, $2s$-, $2p$-, $3s$- and $3p$-electrons). Although the nuclear charge increases across the block from scandium to zinc, the number of inner shielding $3d$-electrons increases as well. This means that the first ionisation energies of the d-block elements in period 4 are fairly similar. This is shown in Figure 5.2.

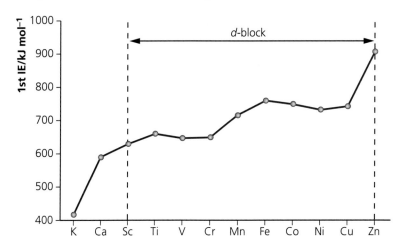

Figure 5.2 First ionisation energies of period 4 elements from potassium to zinc

Successive ionisation energies

There is normally a big jump between successive ionisation energies as a new quantum shell loses an electron. For example, there is a big jump between the second and third ionisation energies of magnesium (electron structure: $1s^2\,2s^2\,2p^6\,3s^2$) because the third electron has to come from the second orbit. This electron is subjected to a much stronger pull from the nucleus as it is much less shielded.

The energy levels of the $3d$- and the $4s$-electrons are very similar in d-block elements and so the big jump comes after all the $4s$- and all the $3d$-electrons have been removed. This is shown in Table 5.3 and in Figure 5.3.

The numbers in blue in Table 5.3 refer to the first $3p$-electron being removed.

It can be seen clearly that there is a much larger difference in energy between $3p$- and $3d$-electrons, as there is a large jump when the first $3p$-electron is being removed. This is shown graphically in Figure 5.3.

Table 5.3 Difference in successive ionisation energies in kJ mol^{-1}

	Titanium ([Ar] 3d^2 4s^2)	Vanadium ([Ar] 3d^3 4s^2)	Chromium ([Ar] 3d^5 4s^1)	Manganese ([Ar] 3d^5 4s^2)
1st and 2nd	649	720	937*	794
2nd and 3rd	1410*	1500*	1400	1740*
3rd and 4th	1450	1730	1780	1940
4th and 5th	**5450**	1680	2300	2170
5th and 6th		**6120**	1630	2390
6th and 7th			**7900**	1750
7th and 8th				**7300**

The * refers to the first 3d-electron being removed.

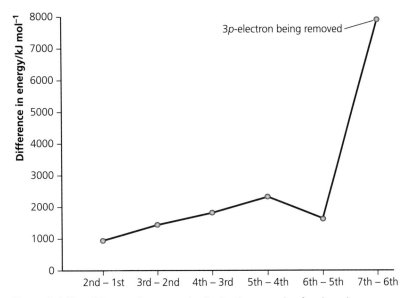

Figure 5.3 The difference in successive ionisation energies for chromium

Common chemical properties of transition metals

Variable oxidation states

The metals in the s-block exist in only one oxidation state in their compounds — for example, sodium is always +1 and magnesium is always +2.

The non-transition d-block metals also have a single oxidation state. Zinc is always +2 in its compounds and scandium is always +3.

The transition metals exist in several different oxidation states. For example, manganese has stable compounds such as $MnSO_4$ (+2), MnO_2 (+4), K_2MnO_4 (+6) and $KMnO_4$ (+7). It also forms compounds in the +3 and +5 states.

Table 5.4 Oxidation states of the d-block metals

Sc	Ti	V	Cr	Mn	Fe	Co	Ni	Cu	Zn
				+7					
			+6	+6	+6				
		+5		+5					
	+4	+4	+4	+4					
+3	+3	+3	+3	+3	+3	+3	+3		
	+2	+2	+2	+2	+2	+2	+2	+2	+2
								+1	

In Table 5.4 oxidation states in red are the stable states; those in blue are less stable.

The reason for variable oxidation states is that the successive ionisation energies increase steadily, as was shown in Figure 5.3. For example, the extra energy required to remove a third electron from chromium is regained in the stronger ionic bonding involving the Cr^{3+} ion compared with the weaker ionic bonding by the less charged Cr^{2+} ion.

Test yourself

2 Give the name and formula of a copper compound in:
  a) the +1 oxidation state
  b) the +2 oxidation state

Redox reactions

It is because transition metals have variable oxidation states that redox reactions are common. A transition metal in a higher oxidation state will be an oxidising agent. One in a lower oxidation state will be a reducing agent.

The ease with which a transition metal ion is oxidised or reduced is given by its standard reduction potential, $E^{\ominus}$.

- The more negative this potential, the worse the ion on the left-hand side of the half-equation is as an oxidising agent and the better the ion on the right-hand side of the half-equation is as a reducing agent.
- The more positive the value of $E^{\ominus}$, the better the ion on the left-hand side of the half-equation is as an oxidising agent and the worse the ion on the right-hand side is as a reducing agent.

For example:

$$V^{3+} + e^- \rightleftharpoons V^{2+} \qquad\qquad E^{\ominus} = -0.26\,V$$

$$Fe^{3+} + e^- \rightleftharpoons Fe^{2+} \qquad\qquad E^{\ominus} = +0.77\,V$$

$$\frac{1}{2}Cr_2O_7^{2-} + 7H^+ + 3e^- \rightleftharpoons Cr^{3+} + 3\frac{1}{2}H_2O \quad E^{\ominus} = +1.33\,V$$

Tip

The half-equation for a reduction potential has electrons on the left.

- Dichromate(VI) ions are the best oxidising agent and vanadium(III) ions are the worst.
- Chromium(III) ions are the worst reducing agent and vanadium(II) ions are the best.

The feasibility of a redox reaction is indicated by the value of the standard potential of the cell, $E^{\ominus}_{cell}$.

Feasibility is worked out by first reversing the half-equation that has one of the reactants on the right-hand side and changing the sign of its $E^{\ominus}$ value. This half-equation is then added to the half-equation that has the other reactant on the left-hand side. The sum of the $E^{\ominus}$ values for the two half-equations gives $E^{\ominus}_{cell}$. If the value is positive, the reaction is thermodynamically feasible and will take place providing that the activation energy is not too high.

Worked example

Will dichromate(VI) ions oxidise Fe^{2+} ions? If so, write the ionic equation for the reaction.

Answer

$$Cr_2O_7{}^{2-} + 14H^+ + 6e^- \rightleftharpoons 2Cr^{3+} + 7H_2O \quad E^{\ominus} = +1.33\text{ V}$$

$$Fe^{3+} + e^- \rightleftharpoons Fe^{2+} \qquad\qquad\qquad E^{\ominus} = +0.77\text{ V}$$

Reverse the second half-equation, multiply it by six and add it to the first half-equation.

$$6Fe^{2+} \rightleftharpoons 6Fe^{3+} + 6e^- \qquad\qquad E^{\ominus} = -(+0.77) = -0.77\text{ V}$$

$$Cr_2O_7{}^{2-} + 14H^+ + 6e^- \rightleftharpoons 2Cr^{3+} + 7H_2O \qquad E^{\ominus} = +1.33\text{ V}$$

$$Cr_2O_7{}^{2-} + 14H^+ + 6Fe^{2+} \rightleftharpoons 2Cr^{3+} + 7H_2O + 6Fe^{3+} \quad E^{\ominus}_{cell} = -0.77 + (+1.33) = +0.56\text{ V}$$

$E^{\ominus}_{cell}$ is positive, so the reaction is feasible and the reactants are thermodynamically unstable relative to the products.

In some cases the activation energy of the reaction could be too high for the reaction to take place rapidly enough to be observed at room temperature. The reactants are then said to be **kinetically stable** relative to the products.

Consider the reaction:

$$C_2O_4{}^{2-}(aq) + S_2O_8{}^{2-}(aq) \rightleftharpoons 2CO_2(g) + 2SO_4{}^{2-}(aq) \qquad E^{\ominus}_{cell} = +1.31\text{ V}$$

This is thermodynamically feasible but does not take place because it requires the reaction between two negative ions and so has a high activation energy. The reaction is catalysed by Co^{3+} ions. When added to the mixture, rapid evolution of gas (carbon dioxide) is seen. The Co^{3+} ions, which are pink, oxidise the $C_2O_4{}^{2-}$ ions and are reduced to blue Co^{2+} ions. These then reduce the $S_2O_8{}^{2-}$ ions and the pink colour due to Co^{3+} ions is then seen again.

The standard reduction potentials of some transition metal ions, arranged in order of increasing oxidising power, are given in Table 5.5. The ion on the top right (Cr^{2+}) is the best reducing agent in the list and that at the bottom right (Fe^{3+}) is the worst reducing agent.

Table 5.5 Standard reduction potentials for some transition metal ions

Half-equation	$E^{\ominus}/V$
$Cr^{3+} + e^- \rightarrow Cr^{2+}$	−0.41
$V^{3+} + e^- \rightarrow V^{2+}$	−0.26
$CrO_4^{2-} + 4H_2O + 3e^- \rightarrow Cr(OH)_3 + 5OH^-$	−0.13
$[Co(NH_3)_6]^{3+} + e^- \rightarrow [Co(NH_3)_6]^{2+}$	+0.10
$Cu^{2+} + e^- \rightarrow Cu^+$	+0.15
$VO^{2+} + 2H^+ + e^- \rightarrow V^{3+} + H_2O$	+0.34
$[Fe(CN)_6]^{3-} + e^- \rightarrow [Fe(CN)_6]^{4-}$	+0.36
$Cu^+ + e^- \rightarrow Cu$	+0.52
$MnO_4^{2-} + 2H_2O + 2e^- \rightarrow MnO_2 + 4OH^-$	+0.59
$Fe^{3+} + e^- \rightarrow Fe^{2+}$	+0.77
$VO_2^+ + 2H^+ + e^- \rightarrow VO^{2+} + H_2O$	+1.00
$MnO_2 + 4H^+ + 2e^- \rightarrow Mn^{2+} + 2H_2O$	+1.23
$Cr_2O_7^{2-} + 14H^+ + 6e^- \rightarrow 2Cr^{3+} + 7H_2O$	+1.33
$MnO_4^- + 8H^+ + 5e^- \rightarrow Mn^{2+} + 4H_2O$	+1.51
$Co^{3+} + e^- \rightarrow Co^{2+}$	+1.81
$FeO_4^{2-} + 8H^+ + 3e^- \rightarrow Fe^{3+} + 4H_2O$	+2.20

In Table 5.5, the water ligands have been omitted to simplify the equations. Ligands other than H_2O are included in the formulae.

Notice the effect of the ligand on the value of $E^{\ominus}$:

- The reduction potential of the hydrated iron(III) ion is more positive than that of the hexacyanoferrate(III) ion. This means that the +3 oxidation state becomes stabilised relative to the +2 state by the change to the strong cyanide ligand. Therefore, hydrated iron(III) is a stronger oxidising agent than hexacyanoferrate(III).
- This is even more noticeable with cobalt(III). Almost nothing will oxidise hydrated Co^{2+} ions to hydrated Co^{3+} ions, but if the Co^{2+} is complexed with ammonia, the oxidation can take place.

> **Tip**
>
> A reduction potential measures the ease of reduction of a substance. The more positive the reduction potential, the more likely it is that the substance will be reduced and, therefore, the stronger it is as an oxidising agent.

> **Test yourself**
>
> 3 a) Use the table above and the reduction potentials on p. 104 to predict whether hydrogen sulfide will reduce VO_2^+ ions to VO^{2+} or to V^{3+} ions.
>
> b) Write the overall equation for the reaction that takes place.

Bonding

In most compounds, in the +2 and +3 oxidation states, the transition metals are ionically bonded. For example, iron(II) sulfate, $FeSO_4$, is ionic, as is chromium(III) sulfate, $Cr_2(SO_4)_3$. Anhydrous chlorides, bromides and iodides are usually covalent, but are ionic when hydrated.

When the transition metal is in an oxidation state of +4 or higher, it is covalently bonded, often in an anion. For example, the manganese atom in a MnO_4^- ion is covalently bonded to the four oxygen atoms by one single and three double bonds (Figure 5.4).

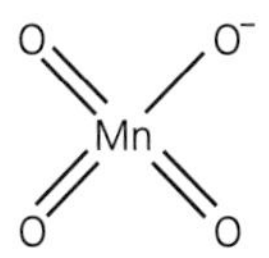

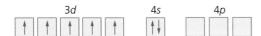

Figure 5.4

Different cation charges

The extra energy required to remove a third electron from an Fe^{2+} ion (the third ionisation energy) to form Fe^{3+} is only $+2960\,kJ\,mol^{-1}$. This can be recovered either from lattice energy, if it forms a solid, or from hydration energy of the cation, if it is in solution.

This is not the case with calcium, where removal of a third electron would have to be from an inner shell. The third ionisation energy of calcium is $+4940\,kJ\,mol^{-1}$, which is too large to be recovered from lattice or hydration energy.

Tip

Never state that there are Mn^{7+} ions. An oxidation state of +7 is different from an Mn^{7+} ion.

Number of covalent bonds

For each covalent bond to be formed, the element must have an unpaired electron in its valence shell. For transition metals, the valence shell consists of the occupied 4*s*- and 3*d*-orbitals and the unoccupied 4*p*-orbitals. All these are at a similar energy level and so can be used for bonding. For example, the valence electron configuration of manganese is shown in Figure 5.5.

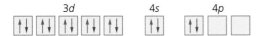

Figure 5.5

When it forms seven covalent bonds, as in the MnO_4^- ion, it has to have seven unpaired electrons. This is achieved by promoting an electron from the 4*s*-orbital into an empty 4*p*-orbital. These seven unpaired electrons are then used to form seven covalent bonds (Figure 5.6).

Figure 5.6

↑ represents an Mn electron; ↓ represents an O electron

As the energy levels of the 3*d*-, 4*s*- and 4*p*-orbitals are similar, little energy is required for promotion and this is recouped from the bond energy released. This means that the overall energy change through losing electrons followed by hydration of the ions (or placing ions into a lattice) and the *overall* energy change for promotion of electrons followed by covalent bond formation are both exothermic and, therefore, likely to be thermodynamically feasible.

Zinc has a stable d^{10} configuration. The energy needed to promote any of these electrons would not be regained from the energy released by covalent bond formation. Therefore, zinc does not show variable oxidation states.

Tip

A ligand is an ion or molecule that is bonded via a dative covalent bond to a metal ion. An atom in that ligand must have a lone pair of electrons.

Formation of complex ions

The accepted A level theory is that a dative covalent bond forms between an atom in the ligand, which donates a pair of electrons, and the central metal ion.

Aqua ions

When *d*-block cations are dissolved in water they become hydrated. The oxygen atom in a water molecule has a lone pair of electrons that forms a dative covalent bond with an empty 3*d*- or 4*p*-orbital in the metal ion. Most transition metals form complex aqua ions with six water ligands $[M(H_2O)_6]^{2\text{ or }3+}$.

An example of an aqua ion is the hydrated chromium(III) ion, which has the formula $[Cr(H_2O)_6]^{3+}$.

Tip

The formulae of complex ions are always written between square brackets.

- The water molecules are called **ligands**.
- One of the lone pairs of electrons on the oxygen atom of each water molecule forms a dative covalent bond with an empty orbital in the Cr^{3+} ion.
- Six dative bonds form, so the hydrated ion has the **coordination number** 6.
- The ion, with its water molecules bonded to the central metal ion, is called a **complex ion**.

The coordination number is the number of near neighbouring atoms that are bonded to the central ion.

In the example of the $[Cr(H_2O)_6]^{3+}$ ion, the Cr^{3+} ion has six oxygen atoms (one from each of the six water ligands) as near neighbours.

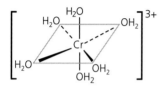

Figure 5.7

The shape of this complex ion can be predicted using valence-shell electron-pair repulsion (VSEPR) theory. There are six dative bonds, each containing a pair of electrons. These six pairs of bonding electrons repel each other to the position of minimum repulsion, which is also the position of maximum separation. The shape is, therefore, octahedral. All complex ions with coordination number 6 are octahedral (Figure 5.7).

Other complex ions
Monodentate ligands
There are many molecules and anions that can form complex ions with transition metal cations:

Tip

When drawing hydrated ions make sure that the dative bonds all start from the O of the H_2O and not from the H.

- Ammonia, NH_3, and organic amines such as ethylamine, $C_2H_5NH_2$, form complexes. An example is the complex of Cu^{2+} and ammonia, which has the formula $[Cu(NH_3)_4(H_2O)_2]^{2+}$.
- Anions such as Cl^- and CN^- also form complexes:
  - $[Fe(CN)_6]^{4-}$ is a complex between an Fe^{2+} ion and six CN^- ions.
  - $[CrCl_4]^-$ is a complex between a Cr^{3+} ion and four Cl^- ions.

It is energetically unfavourable to fit six large ligands around a small cation. The Cl^- ion is much larger than a Cr^{3+} ion and the complex formed has a coordination number of 4. The shape of this ion is tetrahedral, with a bond angle of 109.5°.

The $[CuCl_2]^-$ complex ion has two Cl^- ligands around a central Cu^+ ion. This complex ion is linear with a 180° bond angle.

These examples of complexing species, and also water, are **monodentate ligands**, in which the ion or molecule uses one lone pair of electrons to form a dative bond with the *d*-block ion.

Test yourself

4 Draw a diagram of the $[Fe(CN)_6]^{3-}$ ion to show its shape. Mark on your diagram the bond angles.

Platinum complexes as chemotherapy drugs

A platinum(II) ion, Pt^{2+}, can form a complex with two ammonia molecules and two chloride ions. This is a neutral complex, platin, with formula $[Pt(NH_3)_2Cl_2]$. Its shape is planar and the two chlorine ions can be arranged *cis* or *trans* to each other (Figure 5.8).

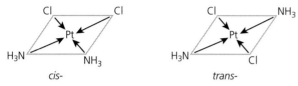

cis-   *trans-*

Figure 5.8

The platinum complex bonds to adjacent guanine molecules in one strand of DNA in cancer cells by a ligand exchange reaction. Each of the chloride ligands is replaced by one of the nitrogen atoms in guanine. This prevents replication of the DNA. The damaged cancer cell is then destroyed by the body's immune system. Unfortunately, *cis*-platin has a number of side effects including kidney damage and the inhibition of hair growth. The latter results in patients, who are undergoing chemotherapy, losing their hair temporarily.

A newer anti-cancer drug is the *E*-isomer of a complex that contains two platinum ions. This complex bonds to two guanine molecules in different strands of the DNA in a cancer cell, completely blocking its replication (Figure 5.9).

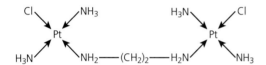

Figure 5.9

Bidentate ligands

Some more complex molecules or ions have two lone pairs on different atoms and so can form two dative bonds with the central metal ion. The geometry has to be correct for this to happen, as a ring is formed. Such ligands are called **bidentate ligands**. Two examples are 1,2-diaminoethane, $NH_2CH_2CH_2NH_2$, and ethanedioate ions, $^-OOCCOO^-$ (Figure 5.10).

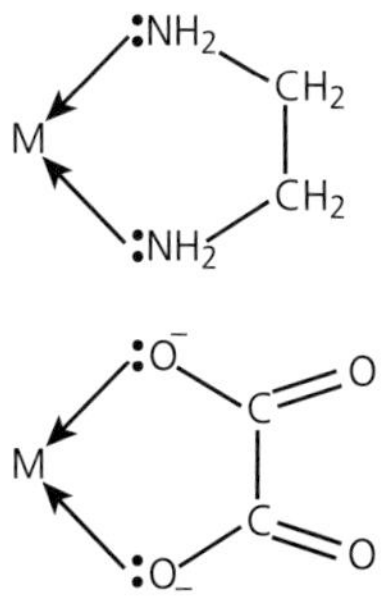

The ring involving the bidentate ligand contains five atoms. Five-membered rings, such as in glucose, are stable stereo structures with no bond strain.

Polydentate ligands

Other species can form five or six dative bonds with the central metal ion. These are called **polydentate ligands**. One of the best reagents for forming complexes of this type is the disodium salt of EDTA. EDTA loses two further H^+ ions to give an ion with two amine groups and four carboxylate groups (Figure 5.11).

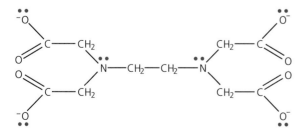

Figure 5.11

Figure 5.10

Dimethylamine cannot act as a bidentate ligand as, if it did, it would form a four-membered ring with the metal ion. The bond strain would be too great for this to be stable.

EDTA stands for ethylenediamine-tetraacetic acid.

Therefore, EDTA has six sites containing a lone pair (marked in red) and so can form six dative bonds.

Some common ligands are listed in Table 5.6.

Table 5.6 Common ligands

Ligand type	Name	Formula
Neutral	Water	H_2O
	Ammonia	NH_3
	Methylamine	CH_3NH_2
Negative ions	Fluoride	F^-
	Chloride	Cl^-
	Cyanide	CN^-*
	Thiocyanate	SCN^-
	Hydroxide	OH^-
	Sulfate	SO_4^{2-}
Bidentate	1,2-diaminoethane	$NH_2CH_2CH_2NH_2$
	Ethanedioate	$^-OOCCOO^-$
Polydentate	EDTA	$^{-2}(OOCCH_2)_2N(CH_2)_2N(CH_2COO)_2^{2-}$

* The cyanide ion normally bonds through the carbon atom.

In the haemoglobin molecule (Figure 5.12), the iron ions are complexed with an organic species that can form five bonds to the metal. The sixth position is taken up either by an oxygen molecule (arterial blood) or by a water molecule (venous blood).

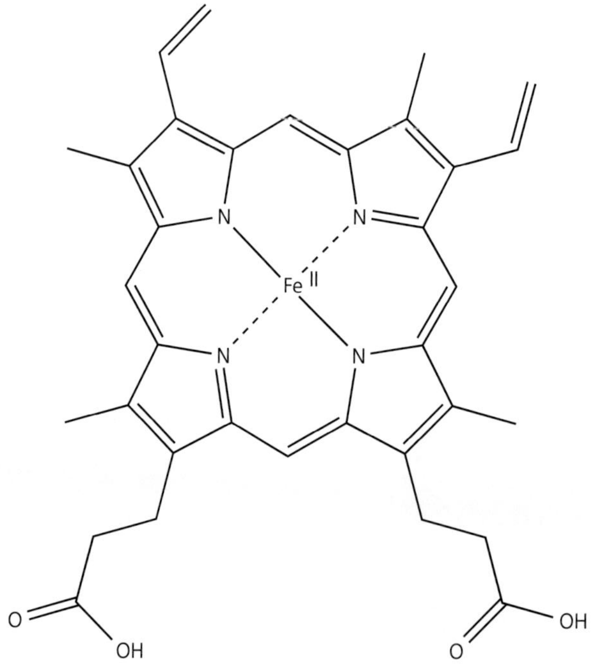

Tip

The formula of haemoglobin need not be remembered for A level.

Figure 5.12 The structure of haemoglobin

The four nitrogen atoms act as ligands with the central Fe^{2+} ion forming a planar structure. The iron is also bound strongly to a globular protein below the ring (not shown in the diagram). A sixth position, which is above the ring, can reversibly bind oxygen by a dative covalent bond, thus completing the octahedral group of six ligands. When oxygen is removed, a very weakly bonded water molecule fills the site, forming a distorted octahedron. Carbon monoxide can bind irreversibly in the position where oxygen is normally bound. This prevents haemoglobin carrying oxygen to cells and, if enough carbon monoxide has been inhaled, the person dies.

Test yourself

5 Give the formula of:

   a) a chromium(III) complex ion   **b)** a copper(II) complex ion

---

Common physical properties of transition metal ions

Coloured ions

The d-orbitals in a transition metal ion are all at the same energy level, but they point in different directions. Three of the orbitals point between the x-, y- and z-axes and two point along these axes (Figure 5.13).

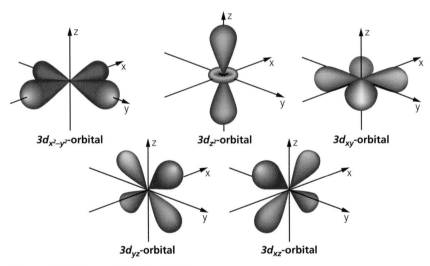

Figure 5.13 Shapes of the d-orbitals

When six ligands approach the ion, they do so along the x-, y- and z-axes. This causes greater repulsion with the two d-orbitals that point along the x-, y- and z-axes than with the three that point between the axes. The energy levels of the d-orbitals are split into a lower group of three and an upper group of two (Figure 5.14).

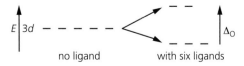

Figure 5.14 Splitting of d-orbitals by six ligands

The energy difference Δ_O between these two sets of d-orbitals in a typical octahedral complex ion is equal to the energy of a photon in the visible region of the spectrum.

When white light shines through a solution of a complex ion of a transition metal, photons of a particular frequency are absorbed and their energy promotes an electron from the lower energy level to the upper energy level. This is called a d–d transition. A colour is *removed* from the white light and the solution has the complementary colour to the light absorbed (Figure 5.15). Within a fraction of a second the ion with an electron in the upper level collides with another ion. The electron drops down and energy is released as heat. The complex ion is once again in the ground state, able to absorb more light energy.

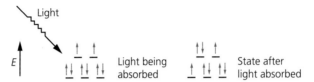

Figure 5.15 Absorption of light energy

Ions with no d-electrons are not coloured simply because they do not have any d-electrons to promote. Therefore, Sc^{3+} and Ti^{4+} are colourless, as both have the electron configuration of [Ar] $3d^0\ 4s^0$.

Ions with 10 d-electrons are also not coloured. Even though the energy levels of the d-orbitals are split by the ligands, they are full, so promotion from a lower d- to a higher d-level is not possible. Therefore Cu^+ ions, electronic configuration [Ar] $3d^{10}\ 4s^0$, form colourless complexes such as such as $[Cu(NH_3)_2]^+$. Likewise Zn^{2+} ions, electronic configuration [Ar] $3d^{10}\ 4s^0$, also forms colourless complexes such as $[Zn(H_2O)_6]^{2+}$.

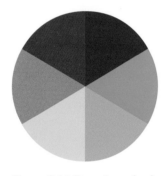

Figure 5.16 The colour wheel

The colour wheel shown in Figure 5.16 shows the relationship between the colour of the light absorbed and the complementary colour of the complex ion. These colours are diametrically opposite each other.

The $[Cu(H_2O)_6]^{2+}$ ion absorbs orange light, so it is blue. The $[Ni(H_2O)_6]^{2+}$ ion absorbs red light, so it is green.

The sequence of events for the colour of transition metal complexes is as follows:

- energy levels of the d-orbitals already split by ligands
- light energy absorbed, removing colour from white light → electron promoted to higher level
- transmitted light has complementary colour of absorbed light

With flame colours, the opposite takes place:

- heat from Bunsen → electron promoted
- electron falls back, emitting coloured light

These two processes must not be confused.

Solutions of some complex metal ions (left to right: $[Ti(H_2O)_6]^{3+}$, $[Co(H_2O)_6]^{2+}$, $[Ni(H_2O)_6]^{2+}$ and $[Cu(H_2O)_6]^{2+}$)

Test yourself

6 What colour of light is absorbed by:

a) $[Cr(H_2O)_4Cl_2]^+$, which is green? b) $[Fe(H_2O)_5NCS]^{2+}$, which is red?

Effect of ligand on colour

Some ligands interact more strongly than others with the *d*-electrons and so cause a greater splitting. The relative strength of ligands is shown in Figure 5.17.

Strong ligands
CN⁻
$NH_2CH_2CH_2NH_2$
NH_3
H_2O
⁻OOCCOO⁻ (ethanedioate)
OH⁻
F⁻
SCN⁻
Cl⁻
Weak ligands
SO_4^{2-}

Figure 5.17 Relative strength of ligands

A strong ligand splits the *d*-orbitals in the complex ion to a greater extent than a weak ligand does (Figure 5.18).

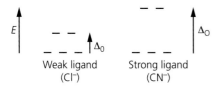

Weak ligand Strong ligand
(Cl⁻)   (CN⁻)

Figure 5.18 Splitting of *d*-orbitals by different ligands

If a stronger ligand replaces a weaker ligand, the colour absorbed moves towards the high-energy (violet) end of the spectrum. This can be shown by the addition of excess ammonia solution to aqueous copper sulfate. The reaction is:

$$[Cu(H_2O)_6]^{2+}(aq) + 4NH_3(aq) \rightarrow [Cu(NH_3)_4(H_2O)_2]^{2+}(aq) + 4H_2O(l)$$

Relatively weaker H_2O ligands have been replaced by stronger NH_3 ligands. The absorption moves from orange towards yellow and the colour of the complex changes from blue to violet-blue (see Figure 5.16).

Oxidation number of the transition metal ion

An ion with a high charge density will attract a ligand strongly, so the splitting of the d-orbitals will be greater. The $[Fe(H_2O)_6]^{2+}$ ion absorbs red light, which means that it is green. The $[Fe(H_2O)_6]^{3+}$ ion absorbs yellow light and is amethyst (pale purple–violet).

Change in coordination number

The d-/d- splitting differs between that caused by an octahedral field and that caused by a tetrahedral or planar field.

> **The coordination number of a complex ion is the number of atoms bonded directly to the central metal ion.**

Thus if the coordination number changes, the colour will change.

When concentrated HCl is added to a solution of copper(II) chloride, the equilibrium:

$$[Cu(H_2O)_6]^{2+}(aq) + 4Cl^-(aq) \rightleftharpoons [CuCl_4]^{2-}(aq) + 6H_2O(l)$$
 blue   yellow

is driven to the right. The colour changes from blue via green to yellow. The green colour occurs when both $[Cu(H_2O)_6]^{2+}$ and $[CuCl_4]^{2-}$ are present. The light absorbed changes from orange (causing the ion to be blue) to violet (causing the ion to be yellow). The coordination number in $[Cu(H_2O)_6]^{2+}$ is six and in $[CuCl_4]^{2-}$ it is 4.

Summary

The colour of transition metal complexes is caused by the ligand splitting the d-orbitals into two different sets of energy levels. Light is absorbed and an electron promoted. The colour of the complex is the complementary colour to that absorbed.

The d-orbital splitting of the transition metal, and hence the colour of the complex, depends on the nature of the ligand and on the oxidation state of the transition metal and the coordination number of the complex.

Stereoisomerism

Some octahedral complexes exhibit geometric (*cis-*/*trans-*) isomerism and some exhibit optical isomerism.

Cis–trans isomerism occurs in octahedral and square planar complexes (but not tetrahedral). When two ligands are adjacent they are said to be *cis*, when opposite each other, *trans*.

The geometric isomerism of the planar complex $[Pt(NH_3)_2Cl_2]$ was shown on p. 133. The two geometric isomers of the octahedral complex $[Co(NH_3)_4Cl_2]^+$ are shown in Figure 5.19.

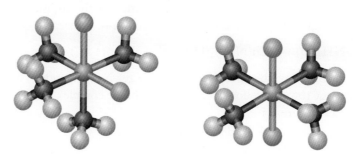

Figure 5.19 (a) *cis*-$[Co(NH_3)_4Cl_2]^+$ (b) *trans*-$[Co(NH_3)_4Cl_2]^+$

Optical isomerism occurs with bidentate ligands such as 1-2-diethylamine, $NH_2CH_2CH_2NH_2$, and the ethanedioate ion, $^-OOCCOO^-$. The isomers of the iron(III) complex $[Fe(OOCCOO)_3]^{3-}$ are shown in Figure 5.20. One is the mirror image of the other and so they rotate the plane of plane polarised light in opposite directions (see p. 191).

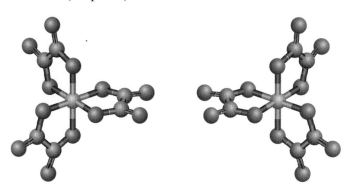

Figure 5.20 Optical isomerism

Test yourself

7 Draw the two optical isomers of the complex $[Cr(en)_3]^{3+}$ where en stand for the bidentate ligand 1,2-diaminoethane.

Reactions of transition metal elements

Vanadium

Vanadium forms compounds in the +2, +3, +4 and +5 oxidation states (Table 5.7). The colour of the ions depends on the oxidation state of vanadium.

Table 5.7 Oxidation states of vanadium and colours of the ions

Oxidation state	Formula of the ion	Colour
+2	V^{2+}	Lavender
+3	V^{3+}	Green
+4	VO^{2+}	Blue
+5	VO_2^+ VO_3^-	Yellow Colourless

Solutions of vanadium in the +2, +3, +4 and +5 oxidation states

Ammonium vanadate(V), NH_4VO_3, is a colourless solid, but when added to water, the solution is yellow. This is because of the reaction:

$$VO_3^- + H_2O \rightleftharpoons VO_2^+ + 2OH^-$$

Addition of acid drives the equilibrium to the right and the yellow colour becomes more intense.

This is not a redox reaction because vanadium is in the +5 oxidation state in both VO_3^- and VO_2^+.

The standard reduction potentials for the redox changes of vanadium are shown in Table 5.8.

Table 5.8 Standard reduction potentials for vanadium

Reduction half-equation	Change in oxidation state	$E^\ominus$/V
$VO_2^+ + 2H^+ + e^- \rightleftharpoons VO^{2+} + H_2O$	+5 to +4	+1.00
$VO^{2+} + 2H^+ + e^- \rightleftharpoons V^{3+} + H_2O$	+4 to +3	+0.34
$V^{3+} + e^- \rightleftharpoons V^{2+}$	+3 to +2	−0.26

Worked example

When $Fe^{2+}(aq)$ and $Sn^{2+}(aq)$ ions are added to separate solutions of vanadium(v) ions, $VO_2^+(aq)$, what will be the final colour of each solution?

$$Fe^{3+}(aq) + e^- \rightleftharpoons Fe^{2+}(aq) \qquad E^\ominus = +0.77\,V$$

$$Sn^{4+}(aq) + 2e^- \rightleftharpoons Sn^{2+}(aq) \qquad E^\ominus = +0.15\,V$$

Answer

1 Iron(ii) ions as the reducing agent

a) Reduction of vanadium(v) to vanadium (iv):

$$VO_2^+ + 2H^+ + e^- \rightleftharpoons VO^{2+} + H_2O \qquad E^\ominus = +1.00\,V$$

$$Fe^{2+} \rightleftharpoons Fe^{3+} + e^- \qquad E^\ominus = -0.77\,V$$

Overall:

$$VO_2^+ + 2H^+ + Fe^{2+} \rightleftharpoons VO^{2+} + H_2O + Fe^{3+} \quad E^\ominus_{cell} = +1.00 + (-0.77) = +0.23\,V$$

$E^\ominus_{cell}$ for the reaction is positive so the reduction is feasible.

b) Subsequent reduction to vanadium(iii)

$$VO^{2+} + 2H^+ + e^- \rightleftharpoons V^{3+} + H_2O \qquad E^\ominus = +0.34\,V$$

$$Fe^{2+} \rightleftharpoons Fe^{3+} + e^- \qquad E^\ominus = -0.77\,V$$

Overall:

$$VO^{2+} + 2H^+ + Fe^{2+} \rightleftharpoons V^{3+} + H_2O + Fe^{3+} \qquad E^\ominus_{cell} = +0.34 + (-0.77) = -0.43\,V$$

$E^\ominus_{cell}$ for the reaction is negative, so the reduction is not feasible.

The conclusion is that iron(ii) ions will reduce vanadium(v) to vanadium(iv) but not to vanadium(iii), and so the colour will change from yellow to blue.

2 Tin(ii) ions as the reducing agent

a) Reduction of vanadium(v) to vanadium (iv):

$$VO_2^+ + 2H^+ + e^- \rightleftharpoons VO^{2+} + H_2O \qquad E^\ominus = +1.00\,V$$

$$Sn^{2+} \rightleftharpoons Sn^{4+} + 2e^- \qquad E^\ominus = -0.15\,V$$

Overall:

$$2VO_2^+ + 4H^+ + Sn^{2+} \rightleftharpoons 2VO^{2+} + 2H_2O + Sn^{4+} \quad E^\ominus_{cell} = +1.00 + (-0.15) = +0.85\,V$$

$E^\ominus_{cell}$ for the reaction is positive, so the reduction is feasible.

The colour change is actually yellow to green to blue. The green colour is when equal amounts of VO_2^+ ions (yellow) and V^{3+} ions (blue) are present.

b) Subsequent reduction to vanadium(III)

$$VO^{2+} + 2H^+ + e^- \rightleftharpoons V^{3+} + H_2O \qquad E^\ominus = +0.34\,V$$

$$Sn^{2+} \rightleftharpoons Sn^{4+} + 2e^- \qquad E^\ominus = -0.15\,V$$

Overall:

$$2VO^{2+} + 4H^+ + Sn^{2+} \rightleftharpoons 2V^{3+} + 2H_2O + Sn^{4+} \quad E^\ominus_{cell} = +0.34 + (-0.15) = +0.19\,V$$

$E^\ominus_{cell}$ for the reaction is positive and so the reduction is feasible.

The conclusion is that tin(II) ions will reduce vanadium(V) first to vanadium(IV) and then to vanadium(III).

The value of $E^\ominus_{cell}$ for the reduction of vanadium(III) to vanadium(II) by tin(II) is −0.41 V and so that reaction does not take place.

The conclusion is that tin(II) ions will reduce vanadium(V) first to vanadium(IV) and then to vanadium(III) and so the colour changes from yellow (via green and blue) to green.

The predictions made in the worked example above can be checked experimentally:

- Mix together equal volumes of dilute hydrochloric acid and iron(II) sulfate solution.
- Add a few drops of ammonium vanadate(v) solution
- Observe the final colour. (Warm if necessary.)

Repeat the experiment using a solution of tin(II) chloride instead of iron(II) sulfate.

Check that the final colours obtained agree with the predictions.

> $E^\ominus_{cell}$ values predict that sulfur dioxide should reduce vanadium(v) to vanadium(III). But, as the activation energy for reduction to V^{3+} is too high, the reaction stops at vanadium(IV).

Test yourself

8 a) Use Table 5.8 to predict the oxidation state of vanadium when oxygen gas is blown through an acidified solution of V^{2+} ions:

$$\frac{1}{2}O_2(g) + 2H^+(aq) + 2e^- \rightarrow H_2O(l) \quad E^\ominus = +1.23\,V$$

b) Write the equation for the overall reaction that takes place.

Reduction to vanadium(II)

This can be achieved by warming a solution of powdered zinc with ammonium vanadate(v) in the presence of 50% hydrochloric acid solution. The experiment is carried out in a conical flask fitted with a Bunsen valve in order to exclude air. The VO_2^+ ions are steadily reduced and the final colour is lavender, due to V^{2+} ions.

The solution containing yellow VO_2^+ ions first turns green. This is caused by a mixture of yellow VO_2^+ ions and blue VO^{2+} ions. The solution turns blue when all the VO_2^+ ions have been reduced to blue VO^{2+} ions, then green again as V^{3+} ions are formed and finally lavender when reduction to V^{2+} is complete.

Chromium

The oxidation states of chromium

The colours of chromium ions in different oxidation states are shown in Table 5.9. The standard reduction potentials for chromium are shown in Table 5.10.

Table 5.9 Oxidation states of chromium and colours of the ions

Oxidation state	Formula of the ion	Colour
+2	Cr^{2+}	Blue
+3	Cr^{3+}	Green
+6	CrO_4^{2-} $Cr_2O_7^{2-}$	Yellow Orange

Table 5.10 The standard reduction potentials for chromium

Reduction half-equation	Change in oxidation state	$E^{\ominus}$
$Cr_2O_7^{2-}(aq) + 14H^+(aq) + 6e^- \rightleftharpoons 2Cr^{3+}(aq) + 7H_2O$	+6 to +3	+1.33 V
$Cr^{3+}(aq) + e^- \rightleftharpoons Cr^{2+}(aq)$	+3 to +2	−0.41 V

The +6 state

Potassium dichromate(VI) contains the $Cr_2O_7^{2-}$ ions. These are in equilibrium with chromate(VI) ions.

$$Cr_2O_7^{2-} + H_2O \rightleftharpoons 2CrO_4^{2-} + 2H^+$$
orange   yellow

> This is not a redox reaction as the chromium in both species is in the +6 oxidation state.

Addition of alkali drives the equilibrium to the right by removal of H^+ ions. This will cause the solution to change from orange to yellow. Conversely addition of acid to an aqueous solution of CrO_4^{2-} ions drives the equilibrium to the left, turning the solution from yellow to orange.

Reduction from +6 to +3

Potassium dichromate(VI) in acid solution is a good oxidising agent, so it will be reduced by many reducing agents.

Worked example

Use Table 4.1 on p. 104 to calculate whether acidified potassium dichromate(VI) will oxidise hydrogen peroxide under standard conditions. If so, write the ionic equation for the redox reaction.

Answer

The half-equations and their standard reduction potentials are:

$$O_2(g) + 2H^+(aq) + 2e^- \rightleftharpoons H_2O_2(aq) \qquad E^{\ominus} = +0.68\,V$$

$$Cr_2O_7^{2-}(aq) + 14H^+(aq) + 6e^- \rightleftharpoons 2Cr^{3+}(aq) + 7H_2O(l) \quad E^{\ominus} = +1.33\,V$$

Multiplying the top equation by 3 and then reversing it, gives:

$$3H_2O_2(l) + Cr_2O_7^{2-}(aq) + 14H^+(aq) \rightleftharpoons 2Cr^{3+}(aq) + 7H_2O(l) + 3O_2(g) + 6H^+(aq)$$

$$E^{\ominus}_{cell} = -(+0.68) + 1.33V = +0.65\,V$$

This is positive, so the reaction is feasible.

The overall equation must not have H^+ ions on both sides. Cancelling them results in:

$$3H_2O_2(l) + Cr_2O_7^{2-}(aq) + 8H^+(aq) \rightleftharpoons 2Cr^{3+}(aq) + 7H_2O(l) + 3O_2(g)$$

> **Tip**
> Make sure that you choose a half-equation with hydrogen peroxide on the right.

> **Tip**
> You must always cancel electrons when writing an overall equation from half-equations.

Oxidation from +3 to +6

Hydrogen peroxide in alkaline solution is a powerful enough oxidising agent to oxidise Cr^{3+} ions to CrO_4^{2-} ions:

$$CrO_4^{2-}(aq) + 4H_2O(l) + 3e^- \rightleftharpoons Cr(OH)_3(s) + 5OH^-(aq) \quad E^\ominus = -0.13\,V$$

$$H_2O_2(aq) + 2e^- \rightleftharpoons 2OH^-(aq) \quad\quad\quad\quad\quad\quad\quad E^\ominus = +1.24\,V$$

To get the overall equation and the $E^\ominus_{cell}$ value, the top equation has to be reversed and multiplied by 2 and added to the bottom equation multiplied by 3.

$$3H_2O_2(aq) + 2Cr(OH)_3(s) + 4OH^-(aq) \rightleftharpoons 8H_2O(l) + 2CrO_4^{2-}(aq)$$

$$E^\ominus_{cell} = +1.24 - (-0.13) = +1.37\,V$$

The +3 state

The most common compounds of chromium(III) contain the hydrated ion.

Hydrated chromium(III) chloride exists in several forms with different numbers of chloride ions within the coordination sphere:

Form I: $[Cr(H_2O)_6]Cl_3$ is grey-blue

Form II: $[Cr(H_2O)_5Cl]Cl_2$ is pale green

Form III: $[Cr(H_2O)_4Cl_2]Cl$ is green

1 mol of form I reacts with excess silver nitrate solution to form a precipitate of 3 mol of silver chloride; 1 mol of form II gives rise to a precipitate of 2 mol of silver chloride; 1 mol of form III gives only 1 mol of precipitate.

Reduction to +2

When a solution of $Cr_2O_7^{2-}$ (or of Cr^{3+}) ions is reduced by zinc and acid, the solution eventually goes blue as the $Cr^{2+}(aq)$ ions form. These ions are very easily oxidised, but if they are reacted with ethanoate ions, a stable complex is formed.

A solution of potassium dichromate(VI) (or of chromium(III) sulfate) is placed in a flask with some zinc and 50% concentrated hydrochloric acid. A delivery tube is fitted with the bottom end below the surface of the acidified potassium dichromate(VI) solution and the other end below the surface of a solution of sodium ethanoate (Figure 5.21).

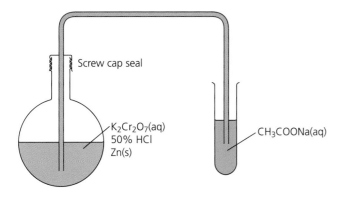

Figure 5.21 Preparation of the chromium(II) ethanoate complex

The seal at the top is loose to let hydrogen escape. The orange solution first turns green as Cr^{3+} ions are formed and then blue as these are reduced to Cr^{2+} ions.

At this stage, the cap of the seal is screwed shut and the pressure of hydrogen forces the solution out into the test tube containing ethanoate ions.

The hydrated chromium(II) ions undergo ligand exchange and a precipitate of the neutral red chromium(II) ethanoate complex is formed:

$$2[Cr(H_2O)_6]^{2+}(aq) + 4CH_3COO^-(aq) \rightarrow [Cr_2(CH_3COO)_4(H_2O)_2](s) + 10H_2O(l)$$

One interesting feature of this complex is that the two oxygen atoms in each ethanoate ion form dative bonds with different Cr^{2+} ions.

The $E^{\ominus}_{cell}$ for this reaction can be calculated from the half-equations:

$$Zn^{2+}(aq) + 2e^- \rightleftharpoons Zn(aq) \qquad E^{\ominus} = -0.76\,V$$

$$Cr^{3+}(aq) + e^- \rightleftharpoons Cr^{2+}(aq) \qquad E^{\ominus} = -0.41\,V$$

Overall equation:

$$2Cr^{3+}(aq) + Zn(s) \rightleftharpoons 2Cr^{2+}(aq) + Zn^{2+}(aq)$$

$$E^{\ominus}_{cell} = -(-0.76) + (-0.41) = +0.35\,V$$

Test yourself

9 Give the formula of a compound of chromium in the following oxidation states:

   a) +2   b) +3   c) +6

Deprotonation of hydrated transition metal ions

When a base is added to a solution of hydrated d-block ions, **deprotonation** takes place to a greater or lesser extent depending on the strength of the base.

Deprotonation is a reaction in which a base removes a proton (H^+ ion) from the species.

By water

Water is a very weak base and only significantly deprotonates 3+ aqua ions such as $[Cr(H_2O)_6]^{3+}$.

$$[Cr(H_2O)_6]^{3+}(aq) + H_2O(l) \rightleftharpoons [Cr(H_2O)_5(OH)]^{2+}(aq) + H_3O^+(aq)$$

The formation of the H_3O^+ ion makes a solution of a chromium(III) compound acidic, with a pH of less than 7. Further deprotonation is not extensive.

A similar reaction takes place with hydrated iron(III) ions:

$$\underset{\text{amethyst}}{Fe(H_2O)_6]^{3+}(aq)} + H_2O(l) \rightleftharpoons \underset{\text{yellow-brown}}{[Fe(H_2O)_5(OH)]^{2+}(aq)} + H_3O^+(aq)$$

The charge density on a divalent ion such as Cu^{2+} is lower, so it attracts the ligand electrons less and the hydrogen atoms in the water ligands are less $\delta+$. This means that very little deprotonation takes place with hydrated copper(II) ions and water and so the solution is only slightly acidic.

By stronger bases

All hydrated *d*-block ions are deprotonated when other bases, such as the strong base sodium hydroxide or the weak base ammonia, are added. The deprotonation is so extensive that an uncharged and hence insoluble species is produced. For example:

$$[Cr(H_2O)_6]^{3+}(aq) + 3OH^-(aq) \rightarrow [Cr(H_2O)_3(OH)_3](s) + 3H_2O(l)$$

$$[Cr(H_2O)_6]^{3+}(aq) + 3NH_3(aq) \rightarrow [Cr(H_2O)_3(OH)_3](s) + 3NH_4^+(aq)$$

$$[Fe(H_2O)_6]^{3+}(aq) + 3OH^-(aq) \rightarrow [Fe(H_2O)_3(OH)_3](s) + 3H_2O(l)$$

$$[Fe(H_2O)_6]^{3+}(aq) + 3NH_3(aq) \rightarrow [Fe(H_2O)_3(OH)_3](s) + 3NH_4^+(aq)$$

Metals in the +2 oxidation state also form precipitates of the hydrated hydroxides, for example:

$$[Fe(H_2O)_6]^{2+}(aq) + 2OH^-(aq) \rightarrow [Fe(H_2O)_4(OH)_2](s) + 2H_2O(l)$$

$$[Fe(H_2O)_6]^{2+}(aq) + 2NH_3(aq) \rightarrow [Fe(H_2O)_4(OH)_2](s) + 2NH_4^+(aq)$$

$$[Co(H_2O)_6]^{2+}(aq) + 2OH^-(aq) \rightarrow [Co(H_2O)_4(OH)_2](s) + 2H_2O(l)$$

$$[Co(H_2O)_6]^{2+}(aq) + 2NH_3(aq) \rightarrow [Co(H_2O)_4(OH)_2](s) + 2NH_4^+(aq)$$

$$[Cu(H_2O)_6]^{2+}(aq) + 2OH^-(aq) \rightarrow [Cu(H_2O)_4(OH)_2](s) + 2H_2O(l)$$

$$[Cu(H_2O)_6]^{2+}(aq) + 2NH_3(aq) \rightarrow [Cu(H_2O)_4(OH)_2](s) + 2NH_4^+(aq)$$

> The formulae of the hydroxide precipitates are sometimes written without the coordinated water, e.g. $Cu(OH)_2$ for copper(II) hydroxide.

Amphoteric hydroxides

With some *d*-block metal ions, if an excess of a strong base is added, further deprotonation can take place. These are the amphoteric hydroxides that dissolve in excess sodium hydroxide solution. For example:

$$[Cr(H_2O)_3(OH)_3](s) + 3OH^-(aq) \rightarrow [Cr(OH)_6]^{3-}(aq) + 3H_2O(l)$$

$$[Zn(H_2O)_2(OH)_2](s) + 2OH^-(aq) \rightarrow [Zn(OH)_4]^{2-}(aq) + 2H_2O(l)$$

An amphoteric hydroxide is one that can act as either an acid or a base, so chromium(III) hydroxide also reacts with acids:

$$Cr(OH)_3(s) + 3H^+(aq) \rightarrow Cr^{3+}(aq) + 3H_2O(l)$$

> The formula of a metal hydroxide can be written with or without the water ligands. Thus both $Cr(OH)_3$ and $[Cr(OH)_3(H_2O)_3]$ are acceptable as the formula of chromium(III) hydroxide.

The colour of the hydrated hydroxide formed with sodium hydroxide solution and whether or not the precipitate dissolves in excess can be used to identify a transition metal and its oxidation state. The colours are listed in Table 5.11 on p. 146.

Hydroxides of, from left: iron(II), iron(III), copper(II) and nickel(II)

Table 5.11 Effect of adding sodium hydroxide solution to some hydrated ions

Ion	Colour of precipitate	Effect of adding excess NaOH
Cr^{3+} in $[Cr(H_2O)_6]^{3+}$	Green	Forms green solution
Mn^{2+} in $[Mn(H_2O)_6]^{2+}$	Off-white*	None
Fe^{2+} in $[Fe(H_2O)_6]^{2+}$	Green†	None
Fe^{3+} in $[Fe(H_2O)_6]^{3+}$	Red-brown	None
Co^{2+} in $[Co(H_2O)_6]^{2+}$	Blue‡	None
Ni^{2+} in $[Ni(H_2O)_6]^{2+}$	Green	None
Cu^{2+} in $[Cu(H_2O)_6]^{2+}$	Blue	None
Zn^{2+} in $[Zn(H_2O)_6]^{2+}$	White	Forms colourless solution

* The precipitate with Mn(II) salts darkens on exposure to air as it is slowly oxidised to manganese(IV) oxide. Darkening is much more rapid if an oxidising agent (e.g. H_2O_2) is added to the precipitate.

† The precipitate with Fe(II) salts goes brown on exposure to air as it is oxidised to iron(III) hydroxide. Darkening is much more rapid if an oxidising agent (e.g. H_2O_2) is added to the precipitate. Very pure solutions of Fe^{2+} ions give a pale green (almost white) precipitate of hydrated iron(II) hydroxide.

‡ The precipitate of $Co(OH)_2$ turns pink on standing as it loses water.

When sodium hydroxide is added to a solution of a silver salt, deprotonation of the $[Ag(H_2O)_2]^+$ ions takes place, followed by dehydration of the hydroxide to form a brown precipitate of silver oxide:

$$2[Ag(H_2O)_2]^+(aq) + 2OH^-(aq) \rightarrow Ag_2O(s) + 5H_2O(l)$$

Ligand exchange reactions

In complex ions, the ligands are not irreversibly bound and can be replaced by other ligands in a **ligand exchange reaction**. In most cases, it is water ligands that are replaced. The extent to which this happens is measured by the **stability constant**.

For the ligand exchange reaction:

$$M(H_2O)_6^{2+} + 4L \rightarrow ML_4^{2+} + 6H_2O$$

or for:

$$M(H_2O)_6^{2+} + 6L \rightarrow ML_6^{2+} + 6H_2O$$

The equilibrium constant is given by:

$[H_2O]^6$ is omitted from the expression for K because it is the solvent and therefore its concentration is constant.

$$K = \frac{[ML_4]^{2+}}{[M(H_2O)_6]^{2+}[L]^4} \quad \text{or} \quad K = \frac{[ML_6]^{2+}}{[M(H_2O)_6]^{2+}[L]^6}$$

and the stability constant as:

$$\text{stability constant} = \log K$$

The value of K depends upon:

- the relative strengths of the bond between the metal ion and the ligand
- entropy factors (p. 72)

Stability constants for some copper(II) complexes are given in Table 5.12.

Addition of monodentate ligands to *d*-block ions

Addition of ammonia

The addition of excess ammonia solution to some ions results in ligand exchange. These are the ions that dissolve in excess ammonia to form an ammine. All transition metal ions are first deprotonated by basic ammonia, forming precipitates of hydrated hydroxides. The hydroxides of cobalt(II), nickel(II), copper(II), zinc(II) and silver(I) readily form an ammine by ligand exchange. The precipitate of chromium(III) hydroxide reacts very slowly to form an ammonia complex.

The blue precipitate of hydrated copper(II) hydroxide redissolves in excess ammonia solution:

$$[Cu(H_2O)_4(OH)_2](s) + 4NH_3(aq) \rightarrow [Cu(NH_3)_4(H_2O)_2]^{2+} + 2OH^-(aq) + 2H_2O(l)$$

The overall reaction between hydrated copper(II) ions and ammonia solution is the exchange of four water ligands by ammonia ligands:

$$[Cu(H_2O)_6]^{2+}(aq) + 4NH_3(aq) \rightarrow [Cu(NH_3)_4(H_2O)_2]^{2+}(aq) + 4H_2O(l)$$

The results of gradually adding ammonia solution to hydrated ions of some *d*-block elements until it is in excess are shown in Table 5.13.

Table 5.12 Stability constants for some copper(II) complexes

Complex	log K
$[CuCl_4]^{2-}$	5.6
$[Cu(NH_3)_4]^{2+}$	13.1
$[Cu(EDTA)]^{2-}$	18.8

Table 5.13 Effect of adding ammonia solution

Ion	Colour of precipitate when a small amount is added	Effect of adding excess ammonia
Cr^{3+} in $[Cr(H_2O)_6]^{3+}$	Green	† Dissolves slightly to form a green solution
Mn^{2+} in $[Mn(H_2O)_6]^{2+}$	Off-white*	None
Fe^{2+} in $[Fe(H_2O)_6]^{2+}$	Green*	None
Fe^{3+} in $[Fe(H_2O)_6]^{3+}$	Red-brown	None
Co^{2+} in $[Co(H_2O)_6]^{2+}$	Blue	Dissolves to form a brown solution
Ni^{2+} in $[Ni(H_2O)_6]^{2+}$	Green	Dissolves to form a pale blue solution
Cu^{2+} in $[Cu(H_2O)_6]^{2+}$	Blue	Dissolves to form a deep blue solution
Zn^{2+} in $[Zn(H_2O)_6]^{2+}$	White	Dissolves to form a colourless solution
Ag^+ in $[Ag(H_2O)_2]^+$	Brown‡	Dissolves to form a colourless solution

* The precipitates of $Mn(OH)_2$ and $Fe(OH)_2$ darken as they oxidise in air.

† The ammonia complex with chromium hydroxide forms very slowly. If liquid ammonia is added to solid hydrated chromium(III) chloride, the ammonia molecules take the place of water molecules around the chromium ion:

$$[Cr(H_2O)_6]Cl_3 + 6NH_3 \rightarrow [Cr(NH_3)_6]Cl_3 + 6H_2O$$

‡ The brown precipitate of silver oxide is often not seen because the ammonia complex forms so easily. Adding ammonia solution to a precipitate of AgCl or AgBr also makes this silver complex:

$$AgCl(s) + 2NH_3(aq) \rightarrow [Ag(NH_3)_2]^+(aq) + Cl^-(aq)$$

AgBr is so insoluble that concentrated ammonia is required. AgI is even more insoluble and the complex does not form, even with concentrated ammonia.

Addition of chloride ions

The dative covalent bond between a metal ion and chloride ions is stronger than that with water. However the chloride ion is much bigger and two or four ligands only will fit around the metal ion. When concentrated hydrochloric acid is added to aqueous copper(II) sulfate the solution turns yellow as $[CuCl_4]^{2-}$ complex ions are formed.

$$[Cu(H_2O)_6]^{2+}(aq) + 4Cl^-(aq) \rightarrow [CuCl_4]^{2-}(aq) + 6H_2O(l)$$

A similar reaction takes place with hydrated cobalt(II) ions forming $[CoCl_4]^{2-}(aq)$ ions.

In both reactions the coordination number changes from 6 to 4.

Addition of cyanide ions

Cyanide ions form strong ligands with many hydrated transition metal ions in a ligand exchange reaction. The test for iron(III) ions is to get a deep blue precipitate (Prussian blue) when a solution of potassium hexacyanoferrate(II) is added. It can be made in a ligand exchange reaction with cyanide ions.

$$[Fe(H_2O)_6]^{2+}(aq) + 6CN^-(aq) \rightarrow [Fe(CN)_6]^{4-}(aq) + 6H_2O(l)$$

The precipitation reaction is:

$$Fe^{3+}(aq) + K^+(aq) + [Fe(CN)_6]^{4-}(aq) \rightarrow KFe[Fe(CN)_6](s)$$

Addition of bidentate and polydentate ligands to *d*-block ions

Transition metal ions, such as $[Cr(H_2O)_6]^{3+}$, react with 1,2-diaminoethane, $H_2NCH_2CH_2NH_2$, which can be represented by 'en':

$$[Cr(H_2O)_6]^{3+} + 3en \rightarrow [Cr(en)_3]^{3+} + 6H_2O$$
4 particles   7 particles

Both the nitrogen atoms in 1, 2-diaminoethane form dative covalent bonds with the central chromium ion, forming a five-membered ring.

Diaminomethane cannot act as a bidentate ligand as the resulting bond angle would have to be 90° and this would result in too much strain.

Transition metal ions also react with EDTA:

$$[Cr(H_2O)_6]^{3+} + EDTA^{4-} \rightarrow [Cr(EDTA)]^- + 6H_2O$$
2 particles   7 particles

The driving force of these ligand exchange reactions is the considerable increase in ΔS_{system}. This is caused by the increase in number of particles as the exchange reaction takes place.

Copper(II) complexes

Copper forms a number of complexes.

Hydrated copper(II) ions *in solution* consist of an octahedral arrangement of six water molecules around the central Cu^{2+} ion, $[Cu(H_2O)_6]^{2+}$. Two of the water molecules opposite each other are further away from the copper ion than the other four, which are in the same plane as the copper ion. The splitting of the *d*-orbitals is such that the ion is turquoise-blue.

Solid hydrated copper(II) sulfate has the formula $[Cu(H_2O)_4)]SO_4.H_2O$ and is the familiar turquoise blue. Each copper ion is surrounded by four water molecules. The fifth molecule of water of crystallisation is bonded to the sulfate ion (Figure 5.22).

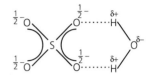

Figure 5.22

The two π-bonds in the $SO_4{}^{2-}$ ion are delocalised around the four oxygen atoms, which share the 2⁻ charge.

When solid blue hydrated copper(II) sulfate is heated, it loses its water ligands. As there are now no ligands, there is no splitting of the *d*-orbitals and so it does not absorb visible light. Therefore, anhydrous copper(II) sulfate is white.

Solid hydrated copper(II) chloride, $CuCl_2.2H_2O$, is green because it is in fact the complex ion pair made up of one blue complex ion and one yellow one. Its formula is $[Cu(H_2O)_4]^{2+}.[CuCl_4]^{2-}$.

Copper(II) ions also form complexes with:

- ammonia

$$[Cu(H_2O)_6]^{2+} + 4NH_3 \rightarrow [Cu(NH_3)_4(H_2O)_2]^{2+} + 4H_2O$$

- amines such as ethylamine

$$[Cu(H_2O)_6]^{2+} + 4C_2H_5NH_2 \rightarrow [Cu(C_2H_5NH_2)_4(H_2O)_2]^{2+} + 4H_2O$$

- 1, 2-diaminoethane (en)

$$[Cu(H_2O)_6]^{2+} + 3en \rightarrow [Cu(en)_3]^{2+} + 6H_2O$$

- ethanediaminetetraacetate ($EDTA^{4-}$)

$$[Cu(H_2O)_6]^{2+} + EDTA^{4-} \rightarrow [Cu(EDTA)]^{2-} + 6H_2O$$

The relative change in ΔS_{system} in these ligand exchange reactions is shown by the following experiments:

1. Take a solution of copper(II) sulfate and add concentrated ammonia until a clear blue solution is formed. Note the colour and divide the solution into two portions.

2. To one portion, add excess 1,2-diaminoethane solution; to the other portion, add excess of a solution of the disodium salt of EDTA. Note the colours in each case.

3. To the solution of the 1,2-diaminoethane complex add a solution of the disodium salt of EDTA. Note any colour change.

Complexes of Cu^{2+} ions with water, ammonia, EDTA and 1,2-diaminoethane

4 Relate the reactions to the stability constants given in Table 5.12 (p. 147) and suggest a value for the stability constant for $[Cu(en)_3]^{2+}$.

Fehling's and Benedict's solutions are complexes of copper(II) ions with tartrate ions. These complexes are reduced to a red precipitate of copper(I) oxide by aldehydes, but not by ketones.

Copper(I) complexes

Hydrated copper(I) ions are unstable in water and disproportionate spontaneously:

$$2Cu^+(aq) \rightarrow Cu(s) + Cu^{2+}(aq)$$

$$Cu^+ + e^- \rightleftharpoons Cu \qquad E^\ominus = +0.52\,V$$

$$\frac{Cu^+ \rightleftharpoons Cu^{2+} + e^- \qquad E^\ominus = -(+0.15)\,V = -0.15\ V}{2Cu^+ \rightleftharpoons Cu + Cu^{2+} \qquad E^\ominus_{cell} = +0.52 + (-0.15) = +0.37\,V}$$

However, they can be stabilised by complexation. Copper(I) chloride is a white solid and reacts with ammonia to form a colourless solution of a copper(I) ammine complex:

$$CuCl(s) + 2NH_3(aq) \rightleftharpoons [Cu(NH_3)_2]^+(aq) + Cl^-(aq)$$

Solid copper(I) chloride also dissolves in concentrated hydrochloric acid, forming the colourless linear complex ion, $[CuCl_2]^-$:

$$CuCl(s) + HCl(aq) \rightleftharpoons [CuCl_2]^-(aq) + H^+(aq)$$

Copper(I) iodide is precipitated when iodide ions reduce copper(II) ions:

$$2Cu^{2+}(aq) + 4I^-(aq) \rightleftharpoons 2CuI(s) + I_2(s)$$

The addition of ammonia solution to this precipitate produces a colourless solution of the copper(I) ammonia complex:

$$CuI(s) + 2NH_3(aq) \rightleftharpoons [Cu(NH_3)_2]^+(aq) + I^-(aq)$$

A blue colour begins to form on the surface of this colourless solution as the copper(I) complex is slowly oxidised by the oxygen in the air to form the copper(II) complex. This blue colour gradually spreads through the whole solution.

Copper(I) complex ions are colourless because the electronic structure of the ion is $[Ar]\ 3d^{10}\ 4s^0$. All the d-orbitals in the d-shell are full. Therefore, even though the energy levels of the d-orbitals are split, promotion of an electron from one of the lower split d-orbitals to a higher one cannot take place.

Catalytic activity

Transition metals and their compounds are good catalysts. This is particularly true of the elements at the right-hand side of the d-block.

Heterogeneous catalysts

A heterogeneous catalyst is in a different phase from the reactants and the reaction occurs on the surface of the catalyst. Many industrial processes use transition metals or their compounds as heterogeneous catalysts. For example, in the Haber process, iron in the solid state is used to catalyse the reaction between hydrogen and nitrogen gases.

Metal catalysts work by providing active sites onto which the reactant molecules can bond (adsorb). The sequence of reaction is:

Step 1 (fast): gaseous reactants + active site → adsorbed reactants

Step 2 (slow): adsorbed reactants → adsorbed product

Step 3 (fast): adsorbed product → gaseous product + empty active site

The cycle is then repeated.

A transition metal can act as a catalyst because its energetically available d-orbitals can accept electrons from a reactant molecule or its d-electrons can form a bond with a reactant molecule. This can be illustrated by the catalytic hydrogenation of an alkene. The alkene bonds to an active site by its π-electrons becoming involved with an empty d-orbital in the catalyst. The σ-bond in the hydrogen molecule breaks and each hydrogen atom forms a bond with a d-electron on an atom in the catalyst. The two hydrogen atoms then bond with the partially broken π-bond in the alkene and the alkane formed is released from the surface of the catalyst.

Some heterogeneous catalysts work because of the variable oxidation state of the transition metal. For example, vanadium(v) oxide is used as the catalyst in the oxidation of sulfur dioxide to sulfur trioxide in the manufacture of sulfuric acid by the contact process. The sulfur dioxide is oxidised by the vanadium(v) oxide, which is reduced to vanadium(IV) oxide:

$$SO_2(g) + V_2O_5(s) \rightarrow SO_3(g) + 2VO_2(s)$$

The oxygen then oxidises the vanadium(IV) oxide back to vanadium(v) oxide:

$$\frac{1}{2}O_2(g) + 2VO_2(s) \rightarrow V_2O_5(s)$$

The overall equation is:

$$SO_2(g) + \frac{1}{2}O_2(g) \rightarrow SO_3(g)$$

Catalytic converters

A petrol-driven car produces a number of pollutants, especially carbon monoxide and oxides of nitrogen such as NO. These can be removed by passing the hot exhaust gases through a catalytic converter. The catalyst is a thin layer of platinum (with some rhodium) coated on a ceramic base. The platinum adsorbs the gases, which then react on the catalyst's surface to form carbon dioxide and nitrogen:

$$CO(g) + NO(g) \rightarrow CO_2(g) + \frac{1}{2}N_2(g)$$

Finally the product gases are desorbed, allowing the surface to adsorb more carbon monoxide and nitrogen monoxide.

Homogeneous catalysts

Homogeneous catalysts are in the same phase as the reactants. They always work via an intermediate compound or ion. For example, Fe^{2+} ions catalyse the oxidation of iodide ions by persulfate ions in aqueous solution:

$$2I^-(aq) + S_2O_8^{2-}(aq) \rightarrow I_2(s) + 2SO_4^{2-}(aq)$$

The two reactants are negative ions and so repel each other, making the reaction very slow. When positively charged Fe^{2+} ions are added, they are oxidised by the negatively charged persulfate ions:

$$S_2O_8^{2-}(aq) + 2Fe^{2+}(aq) \rightarrow 2SO_4^{2-}(aq) + 2Fe^{3+}(aq)$$

The Fe^{3+} ions are then reduced by iodide ions, regenerating the Fe^{2+} catalyst:

$$2Fe^{3+}(aq) + 2I^-(aq) \rightarrow 2Fe^{2+}(aq) + I_2(s)$$

An interesting example of autocatalysis is the reaction between manganate(VII) ions and ethanedioate ions:

$$2MnO_4^- + 16H^+ + 5C_2O_4^{2-} \rightarrow 2Mn^{2+} + 10CO_2 + 8H_2O$$

The Mn^{2+} ions produced act as a catalyst in this reaction between the two negative ions. The consequence is that the rate of reaction speeds up as the catalyst Mn^{2+} is formed and finally slows down as the concentrations of the reactants become very small.

Summary tasks

Make sure that you can:

- write the electronic configuration of *d*-block metals and their ions
- define transition metal and *d*-block element
- define the term ligand

Can you explain:

- why transition metals have variable valency?
- why most transition metal ions are coloured and why some are colourless?
- why the colour of complex ions changes with change in ligand, coordination number and oxidation state?
- the bonding in complex ions and their shape?
- ligand exchange reactions involving bidentate and polydentate ligands in terms of entropy?

Check that you:

- know the colours of vanadium ions in its different oxidation states
- can calculate $E^{\ominus}_{cell}$ and the overall redox equation given suitable data
- are able to predict the final oxidation state in a redox reaction given $E^{\ominus}$ data
- can write ionic equations for the reactions of sodium hydroxide and of ammonia with *d*-block ions
- understand the difference between deprotonation and ligand exchange

Make sure that you:

- know the difference between homogeneous and heterogeneous catalysts
- can explain how V_2O_5 acts as a catalyst in the contact process
- can write equations to show how Fe^{2+} ions catalyse the reaction between I^- ions and $S_2O_8^{2-}$ ions
- understand what is meant by autocatalysis, and give an example of it

Questions

1 Explain why molybdenum has the electron configuration $[Kr]\, 4d^5\, 5s^1$.

2 Explain why the first ionisation energies of the *p*-block elements increase considerably from left to right whereas those of the *d*-block elements hardly alter.

3 Draw a dot-and-cross diagram, showing the outer electrons only, for:

a) $CrO_4{}^{2-}$

b) $VO_2{}^+$

4 Explain why titanium can form both 2+ and 3+ ions whereas calcium and zinc do not form 3+ ions.

5 Explain why hydrated Ti^{4+} ions are colourless, but hydrated Ti^{3+} ions are coloured.

6 Explain why, when excess ammonia is added to copper(II) sulfate solution, the colour changes from turquoise (blue-green) to violet-blue.

7 Why is anhydrous copper(II) sulfate white and why are copper(I) complexes also white?

8 Hydrated chromium(III) ions can be deprotonated. Write equations to show the deprotonation that takes place when:

a) the hydrated ions are dissolved in water

b) sodium hydroxide is added to the hydrated ions, slowly and then in excess

9 A $25.0\,cm^3$ sample of a $0.100\,mol\,dm^{-3}$ solution of V^{3+} ions was placed in a conical flask and excess dilute sulfuric acid added. Potassium manganate(VII) of concentration $0.0500\,mol\,dm^{-3}$ was added from a burette until a faint pink colour was seen. The titre was $20.0\,cm^3$.

a) Calculate the amount (moles) of potassium manganate(VII) ions in the titre.

b) Calculate the number of moles of electrons that the manganate(VII) has received from the vanadium(III) ions.

c) Calculate the amount (moles) of vanadium(III) ions in the sample.

d) Calculate the oxidation state of the vanadium after reaction with potassium manganate(VII).

10 Predict whether chloride and bromide ions will be oxidised by manganese(IV) oxide, MnO_2, in acid solution. Use the *E* values in Table 4.1 on p. 104 to answer this question.

11 The reduction potential for Cr^{2+} ions being reduced to chromium metal is $-0.91\,V$ and that for Cr^{3+} ions being reduced to Cr^{2+} ions is $-0.41\,V$:

$$Cr^{2+} + e^- \rightleftharpoons Cr \qquad E^\ominus = -0.91V$$
$$Cr^{3+} + e^- \rightleftharpoons Cr^{2+} \qquad E^\ominus = -0.41V$$

Predict whether Cr^{2+} ions will disproportionate in aqueous solution to Cr metal and Cr^{3+} ions. If so, write the equation for the reaction that takes place.

12 Describe how you would prepare, from a solution of chromium(III) sulfate:

a) a solution of a chromium(III) complex

b) a solution containing chromate(VI) ions

c) a solution containing chromium(II) ions

13 What do you understand by the following terms? Give an example of each.

a) ligand exchange

b) heterogeneous catalyst

Exam practice questions

1 a) Explain why the electronic configuration of copper is $[Ar] 4s^1 3d^{10}$. (2)

b) When sodium hydroxide is added to a solution containing $[Cu(H_2O)_6]^{2+}$ a precipitate is formed of $[Cu(OH)_2(H_2O)_4]$. When aqueous ammonia is added to this precipitate, a dark blue solution is formed.

   i) Identify the ion causing the deep blue solution. (1)

   ii) Use these two reactions to explain the difference between deprotonation and ligand exchange. (2)

c) Water, ammonia and 1-2-diaminoethane (en) all form complex ions with Cu^{2+} ions.

   i) Explain why $[Cu(NH_3)_4(H_2O)_2]^{2+}$ ions and $[Cu(H_2O)_6]^{2+}$ ions are different colours. (3)

   ii) When a solution of 1,2-diaminoethane (en) is added to a solution containing $[Cu(NH_3)_4(H_2O)_2]^{2+}$ ions, a ligand exchange reaction takes place. Write the equation for this reaction and use it to explain why this reaction takes place. (3)

d) Bordeaux mixture is used in France as a fungicide on grapes. It contains both copper(II) sulfate and calcium hydroxide. Excess dilute hydrochloric acid was added to 8.42 g of Bordeaux mixture and the resulting solution made up to $250\,cm^3$ in a standard flask. Excess potassium iodide was added to $25.0\,cm^3$ portions and the liberated iodine was titrated against a $0.104\,mol\,dm^{-3}$ solution of sodium thiosulfate. The mean titre was $23.65\,cm^3$. Calculate the percentage by mass of copper in the Bordeaux mixture. (5)

$$Cu^{2+}(aq) + 2I^-(aq) \rightarrow CuI(s) + \frac{1}{2}I_2(aq)$$

$$I_2(aq) + 2S_2O_3^{2-}(aq) \rightarrow 2I^-(aq) + S_4O_6^{2-}(aq)$$

(Total 16 marks)

2 a) The oxidation states of vanadium in VO_3^-, VO_2^+ and VO^{2+} are: (1)

	VO_3^-	VO_2^+	VO^{2+}
A	6	4	5
B	6	5	5
C	5	4	4
D	5	5	4

b) A solution of iodine is added to a solution of V^{3+} ions.

   i) Use the data below and the electrode potentials in the A level data book to show to what oxidation state the V^{3+} ions will be oxidised. Justify your choice. (4)

   ii) Write the equation for the reaction and state the colour change that would be noticed. (2)

c) Vanadium(V) oxide, V_2O_5, is the catalyst in the contact process for the manufacture of sulfuric acid. It catalyses the reaction:

$$2SO_2(g) + O_2(g) \rightarrow 2SO_3(g)$$

Which of the following statements are the most accurate? (1)

1 It is a homogeneous catalyst.

2 It is a heterogeneous catalyst.

3 It lowers the activation energy for the reaction between SO_2 and O_2.

4 It provides an alternative route with a lower activation energy.

	Statements
A	1 and 3
B	1 and 4
C	2 and 3
D	2 and 4

(Total 8 marks)

6 Kinetics II (Topic 16)

The main purpose of investigating the rate of a reaction is to provide evidence for the mechanism of that reaction.

The rate of a chemical reaction is the rate of change of concentration of a reactant or product with time.

Its units are $mol\,dm^{-3}\,s^{-1}$.

The *average* rate of reaction is defined as:

$$rate = \frac{\Delta concentration}{\Delta time}$$

where $\Delta concentration$ is the change in concentration of a reactant or product and $\Delta time$ is the time over which this change takes place.

This is only a reasonable assumption if the concentration of a reactant has fallen by less than 10% during the time elapsed.

> **Tip**
>
> The value of Δ[reactant] is negative because its concentration decreases with time. Therefore, a more correct definition of rate is:
>
> $$rate = \frac{-\Delta[reactant]}{\Delta time}$$
>
> or
>
> $$rate = \frac{+\Delta[product]}{\Delta time}$$
>
> This gives a positive value for the rate in both cases.

> **Test yourself**
>
> 1 Hydrogen peroxide slowly oxidises ethanol in acid solution. In an experiment, the amount of hydrogen peroxide in $50\,cm^3$ of solution had fallen from 1.46×10^{-3} moles to 1.32×10^{-3} moles in $45\,s$. Calculate the rate of the reaction.

Required year 1 knowledge

Collision theory

For a reaction to take place, reactant molecules must collide:

- with kinetic energy greater than or equal to the activation energy of the reaction
- with the correct orientation

Maxwell–Boltzmann distribution of energy

The molecules in a gas or liquid and the molecules or ions in a solution move at different speeds. They possess different amounts of kinetic energy. This is shown by the blue line in Figure 6.1.

The fraction of molecules with energy equal to or greater than a particular energy value is given by the area under the graph to the right of that energy. Thus the blue area to the right of the **activation energy, E_a**, is the fraction of molecules that have sufficient energy (at temperature T_1) to react on collision, providing that the orientation of collision is correct. The fraction of the molecules that have energy greater than or equal to E_a is $e^{-E_a/RT}$ and hence the rate of reaction is proportional to $e^{-E_a/RT}$.

Effect of physical conditions on rate

Temperature

When the temperature is increased, the molecules or ions gain kinetic energy. They have a greater range of energies (greater entropy) and the average energy is increased. This means that the peak of the Maxwell–Boltzmann distribution is lowered and moved to the right. This is shown by the red line (at temperature T_2) in Figure 6.1. The red area to the right of the activation energy is greatly increased because a much greater *proportion* of the colliding molecules has energy greater than or equal to the activation energy. Therefore, a greater proportion of collisions will result in reaction.

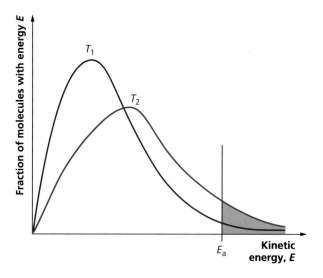

Figure 6.1 Maxwell–Boltzmann distribution of kinetic energy

A reaction that takes place fairly quickly at room temperature has an activation energy of about $60\,kJ\,mol^{-1}$. This means that less than one in a billion collisions will have the necessary energy for a reaction to take place.

An approximate guide is that the rate doubles for a $10\,K$ increase in temperature. The magnitude of the effect of increasing temperature depends on the value of the activation energy. A rise from $298\,K$ to $308\,K$ will cause the rate to increase by a factor of:

$$\frac{e^{(-E_a/308R)}}{e^{(-E_a/298R)}}$$

where R is the gas constant ($8.13\,JK^{-1}\,mol^{-1}$) and E_a is the activation energy for the reaction.

> **Worked example**
>
> If $E_a = 60\,kJ\,mol^{-1}$, calculate by how much the rate increases as the temperature rises from 298 K to 308 K.
>
> **Answer**
>
> $$\frac{rate_{308}}{rate_{298}} = \frac{e^{-60\,000/(308 \times 8.13)}}{e^{-60\,000/(298 \times 8.13)}} = \frac{e^{-23.96}}{e^{-24.77}} = \frac{392 \times 10^{-11}}{1.75 \times 10^{-11}} = 2.2$$
>
> Thus the rate increases by a factor of *approximately* 2 or by 100%.

An increase in temperature also increases the average speed of the molecules and so increases the collision *frequency*. For a 10 K rise from 298 K, this increases the rate by a factor of 1.02 (2%). This is negligible compared with the increase in rate caused by the increased proportion of collisions that result in reaction.

Pressure: for a gaseous reaction

If the pressure on a gaseous system is increased at constant temperature, the molecules become packed more closely together. There is no change in their speed or energy, but the collision *frequency* increases. The same proportion of the collisions results in reaction. However, because the frequency of collisions increases, the rate of reaction also goes up.

The situation is different if a gas is reacting with a solid, such as a catalyst. The surface area of the solid is usually the limiting factor, so the rate is independent of the pressure of the gas (p. 177).

Concentration: for a reaction in solution

An increase in concentration will increase the chance of the reacting species (molecules or ions) colliding. This will cause the rate of successful collisions to increase.

Year 2 kinetics

Rate equations

The purpose of the experimental methods described below is to find the order of the reaction with respect to each reactant and also to evaluate the rate equation. Consider the reaction:

$$nA + mB \rightarrow products$$

The rate equation for this reaction is of the form:

$$rate = k[A]^p[B]^q$$

where n and m are the stoichiometries in the chemical equation, k is the rate constant and p and q are the powers of the concentrations of the substances in the rate equation.

The quantity k is called the **rate constant** and varies with the nature of the reaction, the temperature and the presence of any catalyst.

> **Tip**
>
> The rate constant is always represented by a *lower-case k*. An upper-case *K* is the symbol for equilibrium constant.

The general formula given for the rate equation is not always correct. Some reversible reactions have much more complex rate equations, often containing fractional partial orders. These are beyond the scope of A level.

The order of reaction is $p + q$. The order with respect to substance A (also called the partial order) is p. The order with respect to substance B is q.

The order of a reaction is the *sum* of the powers to which the concentrations of the reactants are raised in the *experimentally* determined rate equation.

The partial order of one reactant is the power to which the concentration of that reactant is raised in the rate equation.

The rate constant, k, is the constant of proportionality that connects the rate of reaction with the concentration of the reactants.

The values of p and q cannot be predicted from the chemical equation. They depend on both the stoichiometry *and* the mechanism of the reaction. Therefore, they have to be found by experiment.

Test yourself

2 Consider the reaction:

    A + 2B + 3C → products

It was found to be first order in A and B and second order in C. Write the rate equation for this reaction.

Experimental methods

The rate of a reaction cannot be measured directly. It can only be determined from concentration and time data. There are a number of methods for 'following' a reaction that enable these data to be measured.

Titration

If the concentration of a reactant or product can be estimated by a titration, the reaction can be followed using this technique:

- Measure out samples of the reactants with known concentration.
- Mix them together, start a clock and stir the mixture thoroughly.
- At regular time intervals, withdraw samples using a pipette and quench (stop) the reaction. Quenching can usually be achieved either by adding the solution from the pipette to ice-cold water or to a solution that reacts with one of the reactants, to prevent further reaction from taking place. The time at which half the contents of the pipette have been added to the quenching solution is noted.
- The quenched solution is then titrated against a suitable standard solution.

The titre is proportional to the concentration of the reactant or product being titrated.

This method can be used when an acid, alkali or iodine is a reactant or product. Acids can be titrated with a standard alkali, alkalis with a standard acid and iodine with a standard solution of sodium thiosulfate.

Tip

Care must be taken that the quenching reagent does not react with one of the reagents to give the same product that is being measured. For example, the acid hydrolysis of an ester cannot be quenched by adding alkali because this would react with the ester and increase the amount of product. Sodium hydrogencarbonate will remove acid without making the solution alkaline.

In the presence of an acid catalyst, aqueous solutions of iodine and propanone react according to the equation:

$$CH_3COCH_3 + I_2 \rightarrow CH_2ICOCH_3 + HI$$

Describe a method to find how the concentration of iodine varies with time in this reaction.

Answer

- Place $25\,cm^3$ of propanone solution in a beaker, followed by $25\,cm^3$ of dilute sulfuric acid.
- Place $25\,cm^3$ of iodine solution of known concentration in a second beaker.
- Simultaneously, mix the two solutions and start a clock.
- Stir the mixture thoroughly. After 5 minutes remove $10\,cm^3$ of the solution in a pipette and run it into a cold sodium hydrogencarbonate solution. Note the time when half the liquid in the pipette has run into the sodium hydrogencarbonate solution.
- Titrate the iodine present with standard sodium thiosulfate solution, adding starch when the iodine colour has faded to a straw colour.
- Stop when the blue–black colour of the starch–iodine complex has vanished. Read the burette volume.
- Repeat the process every 5 minutes until there is no solution left.

The concentration of iodine is proportional to the volume of sodium thiosulfate solution required to decolorise the iodine.

In the experiment described in the worked example above, in order to reduce the number of variables, it is usual to have the concentrations of the acid and the propanone about ten times greater than the concentration of iodine. Then, the only two variables are time and the concentration of iodine. The concentrations of the acid and the propanone remain approximately constant during the experiment.

Colorimetry

If a reactant or product is coloured, the concentration of the coloured species can be measured using a spectrophotometer (Figure 6.2). The amount of light of a particular frequency that is absorbed depends on the concentration of the coloured substance.

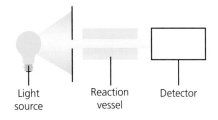

Light source   Reaction vessel   Detector

Figure 6.2 A spectrophotometer

The reactants are mixed and a clock started. The light absorbed is measured at set time intervals.

A suitable example is the reaction between bromine and methanoic acid:

$$Br_2(aq) + HCOOH(aq) \rightarrow 2Br^-(aq) + CO_2(g) + 2H^+(aq)$$

If this reaction is done in a beaker, the colour of bromine can be seen to fade gradually. A spectrophotometer is used to follow the absorption of light by bromine.

The fading colour of bromine as it reacts with methanoic acid

Change of mass of reaction mixture

If a gas is evolved during a reaction, the rate can be calculated by measuring either when a fixed mass of gas has been given off:

$$\text{average rate} = \frac{\text{mass lost}}{\text{time elapsed}}$$

or by measuring the mass at intervals of time and plotting a graph of mass against time:

rate at a time $t = -$ the gradient at time t

The initial rate of reaction is the gradient at $t = 0$.

A conical flask containing the reaction mixture is placed on a balance and the mass is measured at intervals of time.

This is not a very accurate method for two reasons:

● Some liquid may be lost from the flask as spray. This can be overcome by putting a plug of cotton wool in the mouth of the flask.
● The mass change is very small. If excess acid is added to 1.0 g of zinc, the total mass will only decrease by 0.03 g.

Volume of gas evolved

If the reaction produces a gas, the volume of gas produced can be measured at regular time intervals. The volume of gas is proportional to the moles of gas and can, therefore, be used to measure the concentration of the product.

The rate of the reaction of an acid with a solid carbonate can be studied this way. The acid is added to the carbonate and the volume of carbon dioxide noted every 30 seconds (Figure 6.3).

$$CaCO_3(s) + 2H^+(aq) \rightarrow Ca^{2+}(aq) + H_2O(l) + CO_2(g)$$

The assumption is often made that the rate of reaction is proportional to 1/time for a certain volume of gas to be produced. This is only an acceptable approximation if less than 10% of the acid is used up.

Test yourself

3 In a reaction A → B + C, the value of [A] fell from 0.12 mol dm⁻³ to 0.012 mol dm⁻³ in 60 s. Explain why it is inaccurate to state that the rate of the reaction is 0.0018 mol dm⁻ s⁻¹.

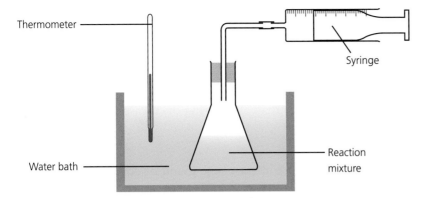

Thermometer

Syringe

Water bath

Reaction
mixture

Figure 6.3 Measuring the volume of carbon dioxide produced in a reaction

Infrared spectroscopy

Infrared spectroscopy can be used in a similar way to colorimetry. The spectrometer is set at a particular frequency and the amount of infrared radiation absorbed at that frequency is measured at regular time intervals. The oxidation of propan-2-ol to propanone by acidified potassium dichromate(VI) can be followed by setting the spectrometer at $1700 \, cm^{-1}$ (the absorption frequency due to the stretching of the C=O bond) and measuring the increase in absorption as the CHOH group is oxidised to the C=O group.

Electrical measurements

pH

If one of the reactants or one of the products in a reaction is an acid or an alkali and the reaction takes place in aqueous solution, the change in pH with time can be measured.

The problem with this technique is that pH is a logarithmic quantity. If a strong acid is a reactant and the starting concentration is $1.0 \, mol \, dm^{-3}$ with a pH = 0, the pH only changes to 1 when 90% of the acid has reacted. The pH rises to 2 when 99% of the acid has reacted. This method requires a very accurate, and hence expensive, pH meter to monitor the change in acid concentration. This makes the method unsuitable for school laboratory use.

Electrical conductivity

If ions are produced in a reaction, the rate can be followed by measuring the change in electrical conductivity at intervals of time.

The enzyme in saliva hydrolyses aspirin, releasing ethanoic acid. This is partially ionised into H^+ and CH_3COO^- ions and the rate can be followed by the increase in conductivity due to the production of ions. Another example would be the hydrolysis of a halogenoalkane by water:

$$CH_3CHBrCH_3(l) + H_2O(l) \rightarrow CH_3CH(OH)CH_3(aq) + H^+(aq) + Br^-(aq)$$

Time for the reaction to finish

An approximate method is to add the two reactants and time how long it takes for the reaction to stop. An example would be to add a strip of magnesium to an excess of dilute sulfuric acid and time how long it takes for the production of hydrogen bubbles to stop. The experiment is repeated with either a different concentration of the acid or at a different temperature.

The assumption is then made that the rate is proportional to 1/time. However, this is only valid if the concentration of the acid has fallen by less than 10–15% and if the temperature did not change by more than 5°C during the measurement.

Initial rate experiments

The initial rate is the rate of reaction at the moment when the reactants are mixed.

Theoretically the initial rate is the gradient of the graph of concentration against time at zero time. In practice the easiest way to measure the initial rate is to measure the change in concentration over a period of time during which the concentration of the reactants has decreased by 10% or less. The initial rate approximates to change in concentration/time taken. 'Clock' reactions are a way of determining initial rates.

'Clock' reactions

In a 'clock' reaction, the reactants are mixed and the time taken to produce a fixed amount of product is measured. The experiment is then repeated several times using different starting concentrations.

This gives several initial rates of reaction at different concentrations.

The iodine 'clock'

The oxidation of iodide ions by hydrogen peroxide in acid solution can be followed as a 'clock' reaction:

$$H_2O_2(aq) + 2I^-(aq) + 2H^+(aq) \rightarrow I_2(s) + 2H_2O(l)$$

- $25\,cm^3$ of hydrogen peroxide solution is mixed in a beaker with $25\,cm^3$ of water and a few drops of starch solution are added.
- $25\,cm^3$ of potassium iodide solution and $5\,cm^3$ of a dilute solution of sodium thiosulfate are placed in a second beaker.
- The contents of the two beakers are mixed and the time taken for the solution to go blue is measured.
- The experiment is repeated with the same volumes of potassium iodide and sodium thiosulfate but with $20\,cm^3$ of hydrogen peroxide and $30\,cm^3$ of water, and then with other relative amounts of hydrogen peroxide and water, totalling $50\,cm^3$.

If the number of moles of thiosulfate ions is much less than the number of moles of the hydrogen peroxide and iodide ions, the average rate measured is almost identical to the initial rate.

The reaction produces iodine, which reacts with the sodium thiosulfate. When all the sodium thiosulfate has been used up, the next iodine that is produced reacts with the starch to give an intense blue-black colour.

The amount of iodine produced in the measured time is proportional to the volume of sodium thiosulfate solution taken. Therefore, the average rate of reaction for each experiment is proportional to 1/time.

The sulfur 'clock'

Sodium thiosulfate is decomposed by acid, producing a precipitate of sulfur:

$$S_2O_3{}^{2-}(aq) + 2H^+(aq) \rightarrow S(s) + SO_2(aq) + H_2O(l)$$

Instead of varying the concentration of sodium thiosulfate, the temperature could be altered. This would enable the activation energy to be calculated.

- A large X is drawn on a white tile with a marker pen.
- $2\,cm^3$ of sodium thiosulfate solution is mixed with $25\,cm^3$ of water in a beaker.
- $25\,cm^3$ of dilute nitric acid is placed in a second beaker.
- The first beaker is placed on top of the X and the contents of the second one are added.
- The mixture is stirred and the time (t) taken for sufficient sulfur to be produced to hide the X when looking down through the beaker is measured.
- The experiment is repeated with different relative amounts of sodium thiosulfate and water, totalling $50\,cm^3$.

The number of moles of sulfur produced is the same in all experiments. Therefore, the average rate of reaction for each experiment is proportional to $1/t$.

Deduction of order of reaction

From concentration–time graphs: using half-lives

This is done by measuring several half-lives.

Half-life is the time taken for the concentration of a reactant to halve.

For a *first*-order reaction, the half-life is constant at a fixed temperature. This means, for example, that if it takes 25 s for the concentration of any reactant to fall from 8 units to 4 units, then it also takes 25 s for it to fall from 4 units to 2 units or from 6 units to 3 units.

For a *second*-order reaction, the half-life increases in a regular geometric manner. This means, for example, that if it takes 25 s for the concentration of any reactant to fall from 8 units to 4 units, then it will take 50 s for it to fall from 4 units to 2 units.

If a graph of the concentration of a reactant is plotted against time and the concentration falls during the experiment to less than 25% of its initial value, two consecutive half-lives can be measured. If the fall is less than this, two non-consecutive half-lives can still be measured, but the fall must be greater than 66% to be certain that the half-lives are accurate within experimental error.

> **Tip**
>
> The symbol for half-life is $t_{1/2}$.

Worked example

Consider the reaction:

$$A + B \rightarrow products$$

Use the data here to plot a graph of [A] against time. Measure two consecutive half-lives and hence deduce the order of reaction.

[A]/mol dm^{-3}	Time/s
1.00	0
0.90	5
0.75	12
0.42	38
0.30	52
0.20	70
0.15	82

Answer

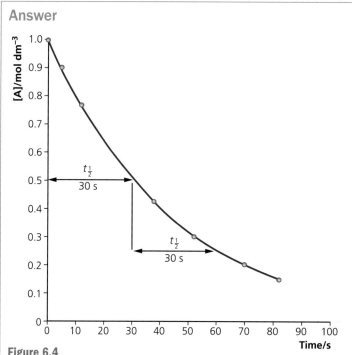

Figure 6.4

See Figure 6.4.

half-life from [A] = 1.0 mol dm^{-3} to [A] = 0.50 mol dm^{-3} = 30 s

half-life from [A] = 0.50 mol dm^{-3} to [A] = 0.25 mol dm^{-3} = 30 s

The half-life is constant, so the reaction is first order.

Tip

All kinetic experiments should be carried out at constant temperature and for most reactions the laboratory itself acts as a constant-temperature medium. However, most reactions are exothermic, so the temperature may rise spontaneously. This can cause the half-life to be slightly shorter.

In the worked example above, note that the second half-life is not 60 s. This is the sum of the two consecutive half-lives and represents the concentration falling to one-quarter of the original value.

Note also that the two half-lives need not be consecutive. If the time for the concentration of A to fall from 0.40 mol dm^{-3} to 0.20 mol dm^{-3} had been measured from the graph, it would also have been 30 s. Likewise, the time for the concentration of A to fall from 0.60 mol dm^{-3} to 0.30 mol dm^{-3} would also be 30 s.

Test yourself

4 In a reaction A → B + C, the concentration of A fell from 0.24 mol dm^{-3} to 0.12 mol dm^{-3} in 64 s and to 0.06 mol^{-3} in 2 minutes 8 seconds. State the order of reaction.

Worked example

for those doing A level maths

For a reaction $A + 2B \rightarrow C + 3D$, the expression:

$$\text{rate} = \frac{-\Delta[A]}{\Delta t}$$

is an approximation that measures the average rate during this period. The instantaneous rate is the differential of this:

$$\text{rate} = \frac{-d[A]}{dt} \left(\text{or} - \frac{1}{2}\frac{d[B]}{dt} \text{ or } + \frac{d[C]}{dt} \text{ or } + \frac{1}{3}\frac{d[D]}{dt} \right)$$

For a first-order reaction this becomes:

$$\text{rate} = \frac{-d[A]}{dt} = k[A]$$

which on integration becomes:

$$kt = \ln [A]_0 - \ln[A]_t = \ln\left(\frac{[A]_0}{[A]_t} \right)$$

where $[A]_0$ is the initial concentration of A and $[A]_t$ is its concentration at time t. After one half-life the initial concentration of A has halved:

$$[A]_{t_{1/2}} = \frac{1}{2}[A]_0$$

Therefore:

$$kt_{1/2} = \ln \left\{ [A]_0 / \frac{1}{2}[A]_0 \right\} = \ln 2$$

$$t_{1/2} = \frac{\ln 2}{k} \text{ or } k = \frac{\ln 2}{t_{1/2}}$$

This proves that the half-life of a first-order reaction is constant at a given temperature and that its value can be used to calculate the rate constant, k.

In the worked example above, the half-life is 30 s, so $k = \ln 2 / 30 = 0.023\,\text{s}^{-1}$.

From concentration–time graphs: form of the graph

When a graph of [A] is plotted against time, the shape of the graph depends on the order of reaction.

The numerical value of the slope of the graph at any value of [A] is the rate of reaction at that concentration.

- If it is a horizontal line, it means that the reaction is not taking place (rate of reaction = 0).
- If a *straight* line sloping downwards is obtained, the slope is constant. This means that the rate is constant. This only occurs when the reaction is zero order (Figure 6.5).

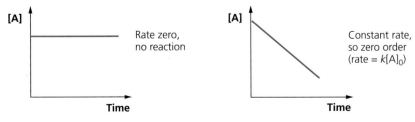

Figure 6.5

The half-lives on the graph in Figure 6.6(a) are constant. Therefore, this reaction is first order.

The half-lives on the graph in Figure 6.6(b) increase rapidly, doubling as the concentration is halved. Therefore, this reaction is not first order.

This method only works if the concentrations of the other reactants are effectively constant. This is done by having them in about four times excess.

If the experiment is repeated with double the amount of propanone, a straight line of negative slope will still be obtained, but its slope will also be doubled. This shows that the reaction is first order with respect to propanone.

- If a downward *curve* is obtained, with a numerically decreasing slope, the rate is decreasing as [A] falls. Therefore, the reaction is first order or greater (Figure 6.6).

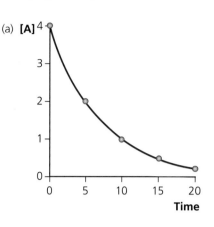
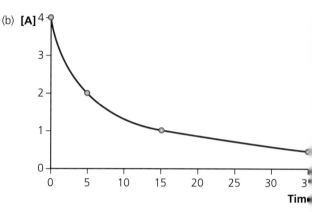

Figure 6.6 Determining reaction order from concentration–time curves. (a) A first-order reaction (b) greater than first-order reaction

Worked example

The iodination of propanone in acid solution was studied with the acid and propanone at ten times the concentration of the iodine (p. 159). The volume of sodium thiosulfate is proportional to the concentration of iodine.

The graph of volume of sodium thiosulfate against time was plotted. It was found to be a straight line with a negative slope. Evaluate the order of this reaction with respect to iodine.

Answer

As the slope of the graph is constant, the rate of the reaction is constant. Thus it is zero order with respect to iodine.

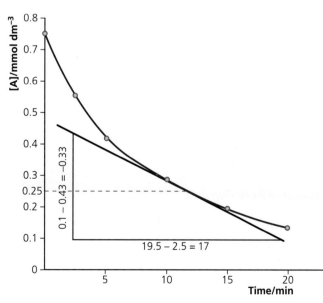

Figure 6.7 Calculating the rate of a second-order reaction by drawing a tangent

Drawing tangents

The rate at any particular concentration can be calculated by drawing a tangent to the curve at that point and measuring the slope of the tangent.

For a plot of concentration of reactant against time, the rate of reaction is equal to minus the slope of the graph (Figure 6.7).

It is difficult to draw a tangent accurately. The tangential line must be long enough for the coordinates at the top and the bottom of the line to be read from the graph without a large error.

By drawing tangents at two points, or by comparing the initial rate with the rate measured by the tangent, the order of reaction can be deduced.

Worked example 1

The reaction $NO_2(g) + CO(g) \rightarrow NO(g) + CO_2(g)$ was studied, using a large excess of CO, and the graph of $[NO_2]$ as a function of time was drawn, as in Figure 6.7, where [A] represents $[NO_2]$.

a) Draw the tangent at [A] = 0.25 mmol dm^{-3} and measure its slope (gradient). Hence deduce the rate of reaction when [A] = 0.25 mmol dm^{-3}.

b) The initial rate, when [A] was 0.75 mmol dm^{-3}, was 0.17 mmol dm^{-3} min^{-1}. Deduce the order of the reaction.

c) The experiment was repeated with the same concentration of NO_2 but twice as much CO, but the rate remained the same. Suggest the rate equation that fits these data.

Answer

a) gradient of the graph at [A] = 0.25 mmol dm^{-3}

$$= \frac{(0.1 - 0.43)}{(19.5 - 2.5)} = \frac{-0.33}{17} = -0.019 \, \text{mmol dm}^{-3} \, \text{min}^{-1}$$

rate of reaction when [A] = 0.25 mol dm^{-3} = +0.019 mmol dm^{-3} s^{-1}

b) initial rate when [A] = 0.75 mol dm^{-3} = +0.17 mmol dm^{-3} min^{-1}

The concentration of [A] was decreased by a factor of 3 and the rate decreased by a factor of $0.17/0.019 = 8.9 \approx 9$ (or 3^2), so the reaction is second order in NO_2.

c) The second experiment shows that the concentration of CO does not affect the rate, so the reaction is zero order with respect to CO.

The rate equation is:

$$\text{rate} = k[NO_2]^2$$

The partial orders of this reaction provide evidence for its mechanism — see p. 172.

From the slope of rate–concentration graphs

If the rate of a reaction, or some quantity that is proportional to the rate, is plotted against the concentration of one reactant, the order with respect to that reactant can be found.

The experiment must be such that the concentrations of the other reactants must not alter significantly during the experiment. This is done by having them in at least a four times excess over the reagent whose concentration is being altered.

The reciprocal of the time for the reaction to proceed to a certain point (1/time) is often used as a measure of the rate.

- If the graph of rate (or 1/time) against [reactant] is a *horizontal* straight line, the reaction is zero order with respect to that reagent.
- If the graph of rate (or 1/time) against [reactant] is a *rising* straight line, the reaction is first order with respect to that reactant.
- If the graph of rate (or 1/time) against [reactant]^2 is a *rising* straight line, the reaction is second order with respect to that reactant.

Worked example

Colourless nitrogen monoxide reacts with excess oxygen to form the brown gas nitrogen dioxide:

$$2NO(g) + O_2(g) \rightarrow 2NO_2(g)$$

The time taken for a certain depth of brown colour to appear was measured. The data obtained are shown in the table:

Time/s	1/time (proportional to rate)/s^{-1}	[NO]/mol dm^{-3}	[NO]^2/mol2 dm^{-6}
60	0.017	0.045	2.0×10^{-3}
100	0.010	0.035	1.2×10^{-3}
200	10.005	0.024	0.60×10^{-3}

a) Plot:

   i) a graph of 1/time against [NO]

   ii) a graph of 1/time against [NO]^2

   Use these graphs to determine the order of reaction with respect to nitrogen monoxide.

b) A new series of readings was obtained using twice the initial concentration of oxygen. The gradient of the graph of 1/time against [NO]^2 doubled. Determine the order of reaction with respect to oxygen.

Answer

a) See Figure 6.8.

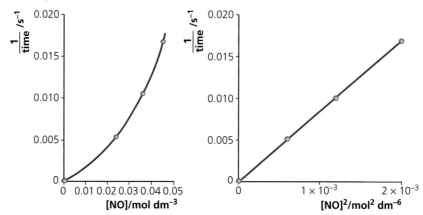

> The answer would have been the same had the data been about partial pressures of the two gases rather than about their concentrations.

> The origin must be plotted as one point. The rate is zero when [A] = 0.

Figure 6.8

The graph of 1/time against [NO] is a curve. So the reaction is *not* first order with respect to nitrogen monoxide, as the rate is *not* proportional to [NO].

The graph of 1/time against [NO]^2 is a straight line, so the rate is proportional to [NO]^2. Therefore the reaction is second order with respect to nitrogen monoxide.

b) The gradient of the line is proportional to $k[O_2]^x$. The gradient doubles as $[O_2]$ doubles, so the reaction is first order with respect to oxygen.

From initial rates

The initial rate of a reaction is the rate at the instant that the chemicals are mixed. This is normally found by measuring the time taken for the concentration of a reactant or product to change by a known amount, which must be less than 10% of the initial concentration of the reactant. The experiment is then repeated, changing the concentration of one of the reactants but keeping the concentration of all the others constant. A clock reaction, as described above, is a way of measuring approximate initial rates.

Consider a reaction:

$A + B + C \rightarrow$ products

The experimental method is as follows:

- The initial rate is measured when all three reactants have the same concentration, for example, $1.0 \, mol \, dm^{-3}$.
- The experiment is repeated with $[A] = 2.0 \, mol \, dm^{-3}$ and $[B]$ and $[C]$ unchanged at $1.0 \, mol \, dm^{-3}$.
  - If the rate does not alter, the reaction is zero order with respect to substance A.
  - If the rate doubles (increases by a factor of 2^1), it is first order in A.
  - If the rate increases by a factor of 4 (2^2) it is second order in A.
- A third experiment is performed with $[A]$ and $[C]$ equal to $1.0 \, mol \, dm^{-3}$ and $[B] = 2.0 \, mol \, dm^{-3}$. This enables the partial order with respect to B to be deduced.
- A fourth experiment is carried out in which $[C]$ is altered but $[A]$ and $[B]$ are kept the same as in one of the previous experiments. This enables the order with respect to C to be deduced.

The overall order is the *sum* of all the partial orders.

The change in concentration can usually be measured by one of the procedures described earlier in this chapter.

Worked example

The reaction between nitrogen(II) oxide and hydrogen at 1000°C is:

$2NO(g) + 2H_2(g) \rightarrow N_2(g) + 2H_2O(g)$

Use the data below to deduce the order of reaction with respect to hydrogen and nitrogen(II) oxide. Calculate the overall order of the reaction. Write the rate equation and calculate the value of the rate constant.

Experiment	[NO]/mol dm⁻³	[H₂]/mol dm⁻³	Initial rate/mol dm⁻³ s⁻¹
1	4.0×10^{-3}	1.0×10^{-3}	1.2×10^{-5}
2	8.0×10^{-3}	1.0×10^{-3}	4.8×10^{-5}
3	8.0×10^{-3}	4.0×10^{-3}	1.92×10^{-4}

Answer

Consider experiments 1 and 2:

- $[NO]$ is increased by a factor of 2. $[H_2]$ is unchanged.
- The rate increases by a factor of 2^2. Therefore, the reaction is second order in nitrogen(II) oxide.

Consider experiments 2 and 3:

- $[H_2]$ goes up by a factor of 4. [NO] is unchanged.
- The rate increases by a factor of 4^1. Therefore, the reaction is first order with respect to hydrogen (even though there are two hydrogen molecules in the chemical equation for the reaction).

overall order $= 2 + 1 = 3$

rate $= k[NO]^2[H_2]^1$

rate constant, $k = \dfrac{\text{rate}}{[NO]^2[H_2]^1}$

Using the data from experiment 1:

$$k = \frac{1.2 \times 10^{-5}}{(4.0 \times 10^{-3}) \times (1.0 \times 10^{-3})} = 750\,\text{dm}^6\,\text{mol}^{-2}\,\text{s}^{-1}$$

The units can be worked out using dimensions:

$$\text{units} = \frac{\text{concentration} \times \text{time}^{-1}}{\text{concentration}^2 \times \text{concentration}} = \text{concentration}^{-2} \times \text{time}^{-1} = \text{dm}^6\,\text{mol}^{-2}\,\text{s}^{-1}$$

Note that if the reaction were second order in hydrogen, when $[H_2]$ was increased by a factor of 4, the rate would increase by a factor of 4^2 or 16 times. This was not the case in this reaction.

You must either indicate the experiments that you are comparing or state which concentrations remain constant and how the other changes. Both are indicated in the worked example.

Test yourself

5 The rate equation for the reaction A + 2B + 3C → products was found to be rate $= k[A][B][C]^2$.

By what factor would the initial rate increase if [A] and [C] were both doubled?

Units of rate constants

For a first-order reaction, the rate equation is rate $= k[A]^1$. Therefore, $k = \text{rate}/[A]$. The units of the rate constant are:

$$\frac{\text{concentration} \times \text{time}^{-1}}{\text{concentration}} = \text{time}^{-1}\ (\text{e.g. s}^{-1}\text{ or min}^{-1})$$

For a second-order reaction, rate $= k[A]^2$ or rate $= k[A][B]$:

$$k = \text{rate}/[A]^2 \text{ or } k = \text{rate}/[A][B]$$

The units of the rate constant are:

$$\frac{\text{concentration} \times \text{time}^{-1}}{\text{concentration}^2} = \text{concentration}^{-1}\text{time}^{-1}\ (\text{e.g. dm}^3\,\text{mol}^{-1}\,\text{s}^{-1})$$

The units of the rate constant for other orders can be worked out in a similar way.

Tip

The units of the rate constant, k, vary according to the total order of reaction.

Test yourself

6 Calculate the units of the rate constant, where rate $= k[A][B]^2$.

Mechanisms and the rate-determining step

Single-step reactions

Some reactions take place in a single step. For example, the reaction between aqueous hydroxide ions and a primary halogenoalkane is a one-step reaction that is thought to involve a collision between the two species.

During the collision, the C–halogen bond begins to break as a new O–C bond forms. At this halfway point, the system is said to have reached a position of maximum potential energy. This is the **transition state** between the reactants and the products — for example, with CH_3CH_2Br (Figure 6.9).

Tip

Don't forget to include the negative charge on the transition state.

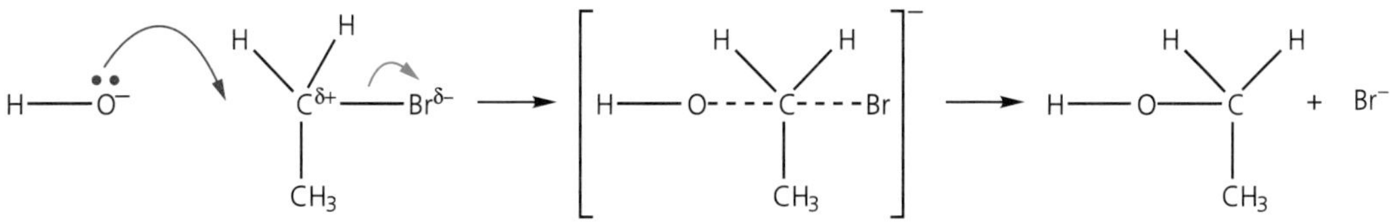

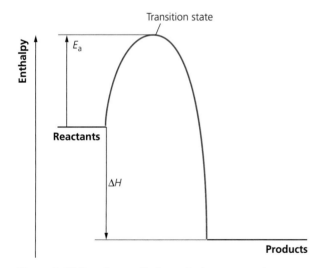

Figure 6.9

Transition state

The red curly arrow shows the movement of a lone pair of electrons from the oxygen to the carbon as a covalent bond forms. The green arrow represents the electrons in the C–Br σ-bond moving to the bromine atom as the bond breaks.

A curly arrow represents the movement of a pair of electrons.

The transition state occurs when the new O–C bond is half-formed and the C–Br bond is half-broken.

The reaction energy profile for a single-step reaction is shown in Figure 6.10.

Transition state

E_a

Reactants

ΔH

Products

Figure 6.10 Reaction profile for a single-step reaction

As this is a single-step reaction between two species, the reaction is second order and the rate equation is:

rate $= k[\text{A}][\text{B}]$

In this example:

rate $= k[\text{OH}^-][CH_3CH_2Br]$

Tip

The powers to which the concentrations are raised in the rate equation for a *single*-step reaction are the same as the stoichiometry.

Multi-step reactions

Many reactions take place in more than one step, via intermediate compounds, ions or radicals.

The hydrolysis of a tertiary halogenoalkane, for example 2-chloro-2-methylpropane, with aqueous hydroxide ions is an example of a two-step reaction.

Step 1: the C—Cl bond breaks heterolytically, forming a carbocation and a chloride anion:

$$(CH_3)_3CCl \rightarrow (CH_3)_3C^+ + Cl^-$$

The rate equation for step 1 is:

$$\text{rate} = k_1[(CH_3)_3CCl]$$

Step 2: the lone pair of electrons on the oxygen of the OH^- ion forms a new bond with the positive carbon atom:

$$(CH_3)_3C^+ + OH^- \rightarrow (CH_3)_3COH$$

The rate equation for step 2 is:

$$\text{rate} = k_2[(CH_3)_3C^+][OH^-]$$

The overall rate is controlled by the rate of the slowest step in the mechanism. This step is called the **rate-determining step.**

> **The rate-determining step is the slowest step in a multi-step mechanism.**

For the hydrolysis of 2-chloro-2-methylpropane, the first step is the slower step and is therefore rate determining. As OH^- enters the mechanism *after* the rate-determining step, $[OH^-]$ does not appear in the rate equation which, for this reaction, is:

$$\text{rate} = k_1[(CH_3)_3CCl]$$

Evidence for a mechanism

Order of reaction

The main evidence for a mechanism is the order of reaction with respect to each reactant.

The hydrolysis of halogenoalkanes can take place by two mechanisms. Both are nucleophilic substitutions, but in one the rate of reaction depends only on the concentration of the halogenoalkane and not on the nucleophile. This is called an S_N1 reaction (S = substitution, N = nucleophilic and 1 = first order). As there are two reactants and the reaction is zero order with respect to the nucleophile, the reaction must take place in at least two steps with the nucleophile entering the reaction *after* the rate-determining step.

In the other type of mechanism, the rate equation is:

$$\text{rate} = k[\text{halogenoalkane}][\text{nucleophile}]$$

This is called an S_N2 reaction and is thought to take place in a single step, going via a transition state.

Halogenoalkanes react with nucleophiles such as OH^-, H_2O, NH_3 and CN^- in substitution reactions. This is because the carbon atom joined to the halogen is slightly $\delta+$ and is, therefore, attacked by nucleophiles.

Which mechanism is followed depends on whether the halogenoalkane is primary, secondary or tertiary.

Primary halogenoalkanes

These react in an **S_N2 reaction**. The mechanism is a single step that goes through a **transition state**. An example of an S_N2 mechanism involving a transition state is the reaction between hydroxide ions and bromoethane, which is shown in Figure 6.9 (p. 171). Remember to include the lone pair of electrons on the nucleophile and the partial charges on the halogenoalkane.

Tip

A transition state is not a species that can be isolated. It changes immediately into the product.

The energy released in the formation of the O—C bond is enough to provide the energy to break the C—halogen bond. The weaker the C—halogen bond, the faster is the rate of the reaction. Therefore, since the C—Cl bond is the strongest and the C—I bond is the weakest, the rate order is:

C—I > C—Br > C—Cl

Further evidence comes from the optical activity of the product compared with that of the reactant (p. 191).

Tertiary halogenoalkanes

Tertiary halogenoalkanes react by an S_N1 mechanism. This type of reaction takes place in two steps.

Step 1: the carbon–halogen bond breaks, an intermediate carbocation is formed and a halide ion is released. This is the slow rate-determining step (Figure 6.11).

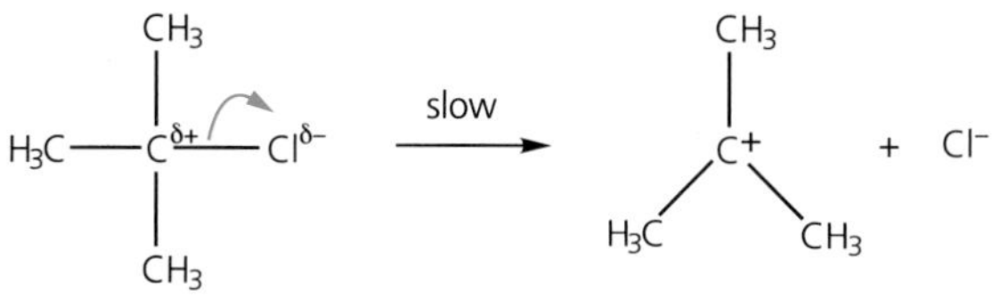

A carbocation is an ion in which there is a positive charge on a carbon atom.

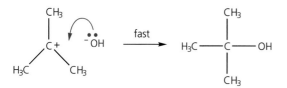

Figure 6.11

Step 2: the carbocation is attacked by the nucleophile in a fast reaction (Figure 6.12).

Tip

Remember to include the partial charges on the carbon and the halogen and the lone pair of electrons on the nucleophile.

Figure 6.12

As with the S_N2 mechanism, additional evidence for the S_N1 mechanism can come from optical activity if the halogenoalkane is chiral.

Secondary halogenoalkanes

- The rate of reactions with S_N2 mechanisms decreases in the order primary > secondary > tertiary halogenoalkane. This is because of the increasing steric hindrance by the alkyl groups on the attacking nucleophile.
- The rate of reactions with S_N1 mechanisms increases in the order primary < secondary < tertiary halogenoalkane. This is because the intermediate carbocation is increasingly stabilised by the electron-pushing effect of the alkyl groups.

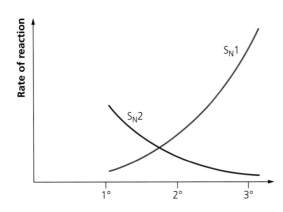

Figure 6.13 Different rates of S_N1 and S_N2 reactions

These relationships are shown graphically in Figure 6.13.

Figure 6.13 shows that primary halogenoalkanes react almost entirely by an S_N2 mechanism and that tertiary halogenoalkanes react by an S_N1 mechanism.

Secondary halogenoalkanes react by both mechanisms.

The overall rate is fastest with a tertiary halogenoalkane and slowest with a primary. For example, 2-chloro-2-methylpropane, $(CH_3)_3CCl$, produces an instant precipitate of silver chloride with aqueous silver nitrate, whereas 1-chloropropane gives a precipitate only after heating for a long period.

First step is rate determining

If the rate-determining step is the first step, then the rate equation for the overall reaction is the same as that for the rate-determining step.

For the alkaline hydrolysis of 2-chloro-2-methylpropane, the rate equation is:

$$rate = k[(CH_3)_3CCl]$$

This means that if a substance enters the mechanism *after* the rate-determining step, its partial order is zero. In this example the partial order of the alkali is zero.

Worked example

The reaction:

$$NO_2(g) + CO(g) \rightarrow NO(g) + CO_2(g)$$

is 2nd order with respect to NO_2 and zero order with respect to CO. Suggest a mechanism that is consistent with these data.

Answer

1st step (slower): this must have 2 mol of NO_2 on the left so that it will be 2nd order in NO_2:

$$2NO_2(g) \rightarrow NO(g) + NO_3(g)$$

2nd step (faster):

$$NO_3(g) + CO(g) \rightarrow NO_2(g) + CO_2$$

Overall equation:

$$2NO_2(g) + NO_3(g) + CO(g) \rightarrow NO(g) + NO_3(g) + NO_2(g) + CO_2(g)$$

Which simplifies to:

$$NO_2(g) + CO(g) \rightarrow NO(g) + CO_2(g)$$

Tip

The steps in a mechanism must add up to the overall equation.

Test yourself

7 Bromine reacts with propanone in the presence of OH^- ions. The first step is the slowest and involves the removal of a proton from the CH_3 group. Write the rate equation for this reaction.

Second or subsequent step is rate determining

If the second (or a subsequent) step is rate determining, the derivation of the mechanism is more complex.

Consider the acid-catalysed reaction of propanone with iodine:

$$CH_3COCH_3 + I_2 \xrightarrow{\text{H}^+} CH_2ICOCH_3 + HI$$

The reaction is first order in propanone and acid but zero order in iodine (p. 166). This means that the iodine enters the mechanism after the rate-determining step.

Step 1: the lone pair of electrons on the oxygen forms a bond with an H^+ from the catalyst. This step is rapid and reversible (Figure 6.14).

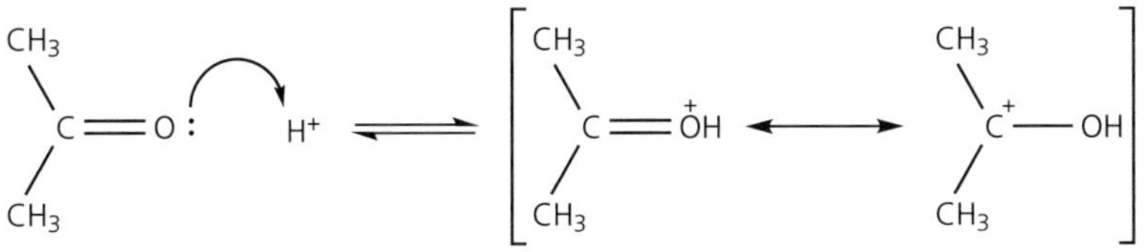

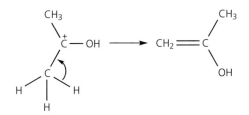

Figure 6.14

> **Tip**
>
> The two intermediates are resonance structures. The reality is that the positive charge is shared by the oxygen and the carbon atoms.

Step 2: Formation of the enol intermediate. This is slow because a C–H bond has to be broken and hence is the rate determining step (Figure 6.15).

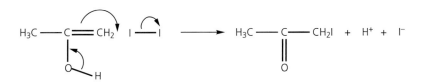

Figure 6.15

> **Tip**
>
> An enol is a species with a C=C and an OH group.

Step 3: addition of iodine and loss of H^+. This is a fast step and as the iodine appears in the mechanism *after* the rate determining step, it does not appear in the rate equation (Figure 6.16).

> **Tip**
>
> If the partial order of a reactant is zero, that reactant enters the mechanism *after* the rate-determining step.

Figure 6.16

overall rate = rate of the slowest step = $k_2[(CH_3)_2\overset{+}{C}OH]$

The relationship between the concentrations of the species in an equilibrium reaction was explained in the first year of the course.

equilibrium constant for step 1, $K_1 = \dfrac{[(CH_3)_2\overset{+}{C}OH]}{[\text{propanone}][H^+]}$

$[(CH_3)_2\overset{+}{C}OH] = K_1[\text{propanone}][H^+]$

So:

overall rate = rate of step 2 = k_2K_1[propanone][H⁺] = k[propanone][H⁺]

The evidence supporting this mechanism is

- The reaction can be shown to be 1st order with respect to propanone and to H⁺ and zero order with respect to iodine.
- Changing the halogen to bromine or to chlorine has no effect on the rate of this reaction.

Reaction profile diagrams for multi-step reactions

In a multi-step reaction, the reactants go via a transition state to an intermediate, which then reacts via a further transition state to form the products. The intermediate may be at a higher or at a lower energy level than the reactants.

In Figure 6.17a, the activation energy for the production of the intermediate is greater than the activation energy for the intermediate going to the products. This means that the first step is the rate-determining step.

In Figure 6.17b, the second activation energy is greater, so the second step is the rate-determining step.

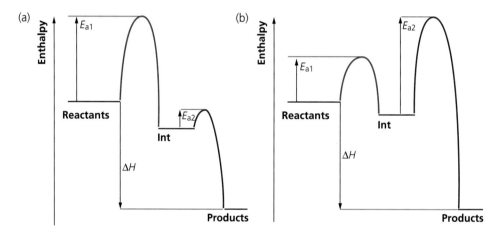

Figure 6.17 Energy profile diagrams for two different reactions

Pseudo-zero-partial-order reactions

The classic examples of pseudo-zero-partial-order reactions are the enzyme-catalysed reactions in living organisms.

The rate of reaction depends on the concentration of the enzyme and not on the concentration of the substrate.

A simplified explanation of enzyme activity is that the enzyme rapidly adsorbs the reactant and slowly converts it to a product that is then rapidly released by the enzyme (Figure 6.18). As long as there is enough reactant (the substrate) to saturate the enzyme, the reaction rate is not increased by increasing the concentration of reactant. Therefore, the reaction has an apparent zero partial order, even though the substrate enters the mechanism before the rate-determining step.

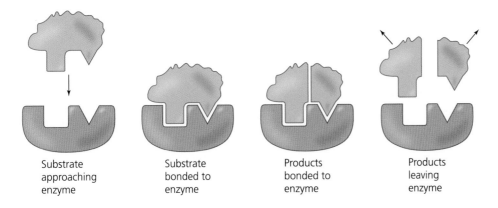

Figure 6.18

Substrate approaching enzyme

Substrate bonded to enzyme

Products bonded to enzyme

Products leaving enzyme

If the concentration of the substrate drops too far, the enzyme ceases to be saturated and the reaction becomes dependent on the concentration of the substrate.

Catalysis

Heterogeneous catalysts

These are catalysts that are in a different phase from the reactants. Many industrial processes use this type of catalyst; they have the advantage that the catalyst can be separated from the equilibrium mixture by simple physical means.

For example, the solid iron catalyst in the Haber process is in a different phase from the nitrogen and hydrogen, and stays in the reaction chamber as the product gases pass through.

A similar mechanism occurs in almost all metal-catalysed gaseous reactions. The catalyst has active sites on its surface that rapidly become saturated by reactants, which are then slowly converted into products. These then leave the metal surface, thus allowing more of the reactant to be adsorbed. This means that the rate of a reaction is not altered by an increase in pressure of the gaseous reactants. This is true of:

- the Haber process, in which the reaction between nitrogen and hydrogen is catalysed by iron
- the manufacture of hydrogen from steam and methane, which is catalysed by nickel
- the oxidation of ammonia by air, which is catalysed by platinum

These reactions are all zero order with respect to both reactant gases, unless the pressure is very low.

A typical route would be:

gaseous reactants + surface of catalyst ⇌ adsorbed reactants　　*fast*

adsorbed reactants → adsorbed products　　*slow*

adsorbed products → gaseous products + free catalyst surface　　*fast*

Homogeneous catalysts

The catalyst and the reactants are in the same phase, either the gas phase or in solution.

The rate of reaction depends on the concentrations of the catalyst and one of the reactants. An example is the oxidation of iodide ions by persulfate ions:

$$2I^-(aq) + S_2O_8^{2-}(aq) \rightarrow I_2(aq) + 2SO_4^{2-}(aq)$$

This is a slow reaction because it requires two negative ions to collide. The reaction is catalysed by iron(III) ions. The catalysed route is oxidation of iodide ions by iron(III) ions, followed by reduction of persulfate ions by iron(II) ions and the regeneration of the catalyst of iron(III) ions:

Reaction 1 $2Fe^{3+}(aq) + 2I^-(aq) \rightarrow I_2(aq) + 2Fe^{2+}(aq)$

Reaction 2 $2Fe^{2+}(aq) + S_2O_8^{2-}(aq) \rightarrow 2Fe^{3+}(aq) + 2SO_4^{2-}(aq)$

This reaction is also catalysed by iron(II) ions. These rapidly reduce the persulfate ions (reaction 2) and are oxidised to iron(III) ions, which then rapidly oxidise iodide ions (reaction 1) etc.

Altering the order by the method of excess reagent

Consider a reaction:

$$2A + B \rightarrow C + D$$

The rate equation is of the form:

rate $= k[A]^p[B]^q$

However, if the initial concentration of B is made at least ten times that of A, the change in [B] during the reaction will be negligible. This means that [B] is constant within experimental error, and so the rate equation becomes:

rate $=$ constant $\times [A]^p$

where the constant $= k \times$ the approximately constant value of $[B]^q$.

The value of p (the order with respect to substance A) can be found by the usual methods of initial rate or half-life. If the experiment is repeated with the same initial concentration of A but 20 times as much B (doubling the concentration of B from the first experiment) the way in which the initial rate alters will depend on the order with respect to B. If the rate doubles, the reaction is first order with respect to B. If the rate quadruples, the reaction is second order in B.

Effect of temperature and a catalyst on the rate constant

The value of the rate constant depends on:

- the complexity of the geometry of the molecules. This is also called the orientation factor. If only 1 in 10 collisions occurs with the correct orientation, the orientation factor equals 0.1. This factor is a constant for a particular reaction.
- the activation energy of the reaction

   The activation energy is defined as the minimum energy that the species must have in order to react on collision.

- the temperature

The second and third factors cause the rate constant to be proportional to:

$$e^{(-E_a/RT)}$$

where E_a is the activation energy, R is the gas constant and T is the temperature in kelvin.

A large E_a results in a large negative exponent and, therefore, a small value for the rate constant. A catalyst effectively lowers the activation energy (by providing a different route for the reaction). Therefore, the exponent becomes less negative and k gets larger, and so the rate of reaction increases.

A rise in temperature increases the denominator of the exponential term and makes its value less negative, increasing the value of k. This means that the rate of reaction increases. The relationship between the rate constant and temperature is described by the Arrhenius equation:

$$\ln k = \ln A - \frac{E_a}{RT}$$

where A is a constant.

If the value of the rate constant is measured at different temperatures, a graph can be plotted of $\ln k$ against $1/T$ (or a graph of $\ln(1/\text{time})$ against $1/T$). The graph will be a straight line of slope $-E_a/R$. This enables the activation energy to be determined.

Worked example 1

The second-order rate constant for the reaction of 1-bromopropane with aqueous hydroxide ions was measured as a function of temperature.

$$CH_3CH_2CH_2Br(aq) + OH^-(aq) \rightarrow CH_3CH_2CH_2OH(aq) + Br^-(aq)$$

The results are shown in the table below.

Temperature/°C	Temperature/K	$\frac{1}{T}$ / K^{-1}	k/mol^{-1}dm^{3}s^{-1}	$\ln k$
25	298	0.00336	1.4×10^{-4}	−8.9
35	308	0.00325	3.0×10^{-4}	−8.1
45	318	0.00314	6.8×10^{-4}	−7.3
55	328	0.00306	1.4×10^{-3}	−6.6

Plot a graph of $\ln k$ against $1/T$. Measure the slope (gradient) of the line and hence calculate the activation energy of the reaction.

Tip

The activation energy is always positive because it is the energy that the colliding molecules must have for a reaction to take place.

Answer

See Figure 6.19.

$$\text{slope} = \frac{-1.7}{0.00023} = -7391 \, \text{K}$$

$$= \frac{-E_a}{R}$$

$$E_a = -\text{slope} \times R$$

$$= -(-7391 \, \text{K}) \times 8.13 \, \text{J K}^{-1} \, \text{mol}^{-1}$$

$$= +60\,090 \, \text{J mol}^{-1}$$

$$= +60 \, \text{kJ mol}^{-1}$$

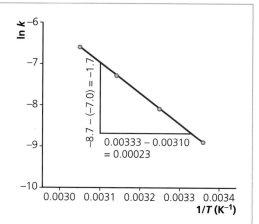

Figure 6.19

Worked example 2

The activation energy of the oxidation in acid solution of iodide ions by iodate(v) ions can be found by experiment using a clock reaction:

- Place 25 cm³ of a solution of potassium iodate(v) in a beaker and add 5 drops of starch solution.
- Place 25 cm³ of a solution of potassium iodide and 5 cm³ of a solution of sodium thiosulfate in another beaker. Mix the two solutions, start a stop clock immediately and stir with a thermometer. Read and record the temperature of the mixture.
- Record the time when the solution turns intense blue.
- Repeat the experiment with the same volumes of the solutions but at a higher temperature.
- Repeat the experiment using at least two more different temperatures.

The temperature must be in kelvin. The conversion necessary is $x°C = (x + 273) \, \text{K}$.

The equation for the reaction is:

$$\text{IO}_3^-(\text{aq}) + 5\text{I}^-(\text{aq}) + 6\text{H}^+(\text{aq}) \rightarrow 3\text{I}_2(\text{aq}) + 3\text{H}_2\text{O}(\text{l})$$

The iodine produced then reacts with the sodium thiosulfate:

$$\text{I}_2(\text{aq}) + 2\text{S}_2\text{O}_3^{2-}(\text{aq}) \rightarrow 2\text{I}^-(\text{aq}) + \text{S}_4\text{O}_6^{2-}(\text{aq})$$

When all the sodium thiosulfate has been used up, the next iodine that is produced forms an intense blue colour with the starch.

The results are shown in the table below.

Time/s	$\frac{1}{\text{time}} / \text{s}^{-1}$	$\ln\left(\frac{1}{T}\right)$	Temperature/°C	Temperature/K	$\frac{1}{T} / \text{K}^{-1}$
135	0.0074	−4.9	25	298	0.00336
46	0.0217	−3.8	40	313	0.00319
14	0.0714	−2.6	60	333	0.00300

Plot a graph of ln(1/time) on the *y*-axis against 1/*T* on the *x*-axis.

Measure the gradient of the line and evaluate the activation energy.

You may assume that the gradient of this line is the same as that of ln *k* against 1/*T* and that its value is $-E_a/R$.

Answer

See Figure 6.20.

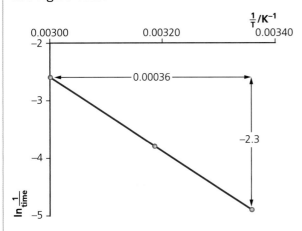

Figure 6.20

Four or five readings at different temperatures would make the result more reliable.

$$\text{gradient of line} = \frac{-2.3}{0.00036} = -6389\,\text{K}$$

As the Arrhenius equation is $\ln k = \dfrac{-E_a}{RT} + \text{a constant}$, the gradient equals $\dfrac{-E_a}{R}$:

$$E_a = -\text{gradient} \times RT = -(-6389)\,\text{K} \times 8.31\,\text{J K}^{-1}\,\text{mol}^{-1}$$

$$= +53\,090\,\text{J mol}^{-1} = +53.1\,\text{kJ mol}^{-1}$$

Note that the units of the gas constant, R, are $\text{J K}^{-1}\,\text{mol}^{-1}$ and so the activation energy will be calculated in J mol^{-1}.

Test yourself

8 The time for 10% of a reactant to react was measured at different temperatures. At 25°C it was 40 s and at 35°C it was 20 s. Calculate the activation energy.

Summary tasks

Make sure that you can:

- draw Maxwell–Boltzmann distribution curves and use them to explain the effect of a change in temperature on the rate of reaction
- define activation energy
- explain the effect of an increase in pressure on the rate of homogeneous gas reactions

Check that you can describe experimental methods for following a reaction by:

- titration
- colorimetry or infrared spectroscopy
- pH change

- volume of gas produced (or loss of mass because of gas evolved)
- time for a visible change to be observed

Check that you can:

- deduce order from initial rates
- deduce order from concentration–time graphs
- write the rate equation given the partial orders
- calculate the value of the rate constant and its units
- calculate the activation energy from rate constant and temperature data
- draw reaction profile diagrams
- draw mechanisms of nucleophilic substitution reactions of halogenoalkanes that are consistent with the deduced order of reaction
- differentiate between homogeneous and heterogeneous catalysed reactions

Questions

1 a) Draw the distribution of energies of a mixture of hydrogen and iodine at a temperature T_1 and at a lower temperature, T_2.

b) Explain, in terms of energy and frequency of collisions, why the reaction between hydrogen and iodine is slower at the lower temperature.

c) Which of energy and frequency of collisions is more important in causing the rate to decrease?

d) What effect would an increase in pressure have on the frequency and energy of collisions and hence on the rate of the reaction?

2 Potassium manganate(VII) reacts slowly with a solution of ethanedioic acid in dilute sulfuric acid at room temperature. The equation is:

$$2MnO_4^-(aq) + 6H^+(aq) + 5(COOH)_2(aq) \rightarrow 2Mn^{2+}(aq) + 8H_2O(l) + 10CO_2(g)$$

a) Describe a *chemical* method by which the progress of this reaction could be followed.

b) Describe a *physical* method by which the progress of this reaction could be followed.

c) If this reaction is carried out at a constant higher temperature, the rate at first increases and then slows down. Suggest an explanation for this and suggest an experiment to confirm your hypothesis for the initial increase in rate.

3 Consider the reaction:

$$2A + B \rightarrow \text{products}$$

It was found to be second order. Write two rate equations that fit these data.

4 The kinetics of the reaction:

$$C_2H_5I + KOH \rightarrow C_2H_5OH + KI$$

were studied at a temperature T. The following initial rate data were obtained:

Experiment	$[C_2H_5I]/$ mol dm^{-3}	$[KOH]/$ mol dm^{-3}	Initial rate/ mol dm^{-3} s^{-1}
1	0.20	0.10	2.2×10^{-5}
2	0.40	0.10	4.4×10^{-5}
3	0.20	0.20	4.4×10^{-5}

a) Deduce the partial orders of reaction with respect to iodoethane (C_2H_5I), and potassium hydroxide.

b) Write the rate equation for the reaction.

c) Calculate the value of the rate constant at this temperature and give its units.

5 The reaction between persulfate ions, $S_2O_8^{2-}$, and iodide ions was studied by an iodine clock method.

$$S_2O_8^{2-}(aq) + 2I^-(aq) \rightarrow 2SO_4^{2-}(aq) + I_2(aq)$$

a) Describe the iodine clock method.

b) The initial rates of reaction were measured at different concentrations. The results are shown below.

Experiment	$[S_2O_8^{2-}]/$ mol dm^{-3}	$[I^-]/$ mol dm^{-3}	Initial rate/ mol dm^{-3} s^{-1}
1	0.038	0.050	1.2×10^{-5}
2	0.076	0.050	2.4×10^{-5}
3	0.152	0.100	9.6×10^{-5}

Deduce the overall order of reaction.

c) Write the rate equation and calculate the value of the rate constant.

6 The reaction between 2-bromopropane and an aqueous solution of sodium hydroxide is as follows:

$$CH_3CHBrCH_3 + NaOH \rightarrow$$
$$CH_3CH(OH)CH_3 + NaBr$$

In an experiment, the initial concentration of both reagents was $0.10 \, mol \, dm^{-3}$. The concentration of hydroxide ions was measured at set time intervals, the graph of $[OH^-]$ against time was plotted and the rate of reaction found by drawing tangents to the graph at two different values of $[OH^-]$:

- $[OH^-] = 0.10 \, mol \, dm^{-3}$; slope of tangent = 1.6×10^{-3}
- $[OH^-] = 0.05 \, mol \, dm^{-3}$; slope of tangent = 0.8×10^{-3}

a) What is the order of reaction?

b) In a separate experiment, [2-bromopropane] was measured at intervals of time. The starting concentration of each reactant was $0.10 \, mol \, dm^{-3}$. What would be the relative values of the slopes of tangents drawn to a graph of [2-bromopropane] against time at the points where [2-bromopropane] were $0.10 \, mol \, dm^{-3}$ and $0.050 \, mol \, dm^{-3}$?

c) How would you modify the experiment to find out the partial orders of the two reagents?

7 The half-lives of two different reactions were measured. The results are shown in the table.

Reaction I		Reaction II	
[Reactant]/ mol dm^{-3}	Half-life/ min	[Reactant]/ mol dm^{-3}	Half-life/ min
0.8	20.0	0.8	2.2
0.4	19.7	0.4	4.3
0.2	19.9	0.2	8.5
0.1	20.4	0.1	17.0

Deduce the order of both reactions.

8 The data in the table refer to a reaction between A and B.

[A]/mol dm^{-3}	Time/s
0.20	0
0.16	10
0.13	20
0.11	30
0.07	50
0.04	80

a) Plot a graph of [A] against time.

b) Draw tangents at $[A] = 0.16 \, mol \, dm^{-3}$ and at $[A] = 0.08 \, mol \, dm^{-3}$. Measure the slope of both tangents.

c) Use your answers from (b) to estimate the order of the reaction.

9 The values of the rate constant, k, at different temperatures for the cracking of ethane into ethene and hydrogen are given in the table.

Temperature/K	660	680	720	760
Rate constant/s^{-1}	0.00037	0.0011	0.0082	0.055

The Arrhenius equation is:

$$\ln k = \ln A - \frac{E_a}{RT}$$

a) Draw a graph of $\ln k$ against $1/T$.

b) Measure the slope of the line and hence calculate the value of the activation energy of this reaction.

c) Use the graph to calculate the value of the rate constant at a temperature of $700 \, K$.

Exam practice questions

1 The reaction between small, equal-sized lumps of calcium carbonate and dilute hydrochloric acid was studied at different temperatures T. The acid was in excess and the time taken for the production of bubbles to stop was determined. $50\,cm^3$ of $0.50\,mol\,dm^{-3}$ hydrochloric acid were added to one lump of calcium carbonate of mass $0.20\,g$. The time for bubble production to stop was measured. The results are shown in the table.

Time/s	$\frac{1}{time}$/s^{-1}	$\ln\left(\frac{1}{time}\right)$	T/°C	T/K	$\frac{1}{T}$/K^{-1}
120			17		
69			25		
36			35		
14			50		

a) Complete the table. (2)

b) Calculate the percentage by moles of the acid used up in the experiment. Hence, suggest whether 1/time is a reasonable measure of the rate of reaction. (3)

c) Plot a graph of $\ln(1/time)$ against 1/kelvin temperature and measure its gradient. (3)

d) Assuming that the gradient of the line is the same as that of the graph of $\ln k$ against $1/T$, calculate the activation energy for the reaction. Give a sign and units with your answer. The Arrhenius equation is:

$$\ln k = \ln A - \frac{E_a}{RT}$$

(The gas constant $R = 8.31\,J\,K^{-1}\,mol^{-1}$) (3)

e) Assume that the reaction is first order. The units for k are:

A s   **C** $mol\,dm^{-3}\,s^{-1}$

B s^{-1} **D** $dm^3\,mol^{-1}\,s$ (1)

f) i) The value of ΔH for this reaction is $-351\,kJ\,mol^{-1}$. Calculate the heat energy released when $0.20\,g$ of calcium carbonate reacts with $50\,cm^3$ of dilute hydrochloric acid. Hence, calculate the temperature change during the reaction. The solution has a specific heat capacity of $4.2\,J\,g^{-1}\,°C^{-1}$. (3)

ii) What effect would this have on the accuracy of the value of the activation energy? (1)

(Total 16 marks)

2 The alkaline hydrolysis of 2-chlorobutane, $CH_3CHClC_2H_5$, was studied. The results are shown in the table. The equation for the hydrolysis is:

$$CH_3CHClC_2H_5 + OH^- \rightarrow$$
$$CH_3CH(OH)C_2H_5 + Cl^-$$

Experiment	[CH$_3$CHClC$_2$H$_5$]/ mol dm^{-3}	[OH$^-$]/ mol dm^{-3}	Initial rate/ mol dm^{-3} s^{-1}
1	0.10	0.10	1.4×10^{-4}
2	0.20	0.20	2.9×10^{-4}
3	0.30	0.10	4.1×10^{-4}

a) Deduce the order of reaction with respect to:

i) 2-chlorobutane

ii) hydroxide ions (4)

b) Write the rate equations for this reaction. (1)

c) Calculate the rate constant, based on the data from experiment 3. Give your answer to two significant figures and include a unit. (2)

d) Draw the mechanism for this reaction that is consistent with your answer to (b), including relevant lone pairs of electrons. (4)

e) If a single optical isomer of primary halogenoalkane had been used, what would be the effect of the product on the plane of polarisation of plane-polarised light? (1)

A It would rotate it in the same direction

B It would rotate it in the opposite direction

C It would not rotate it at all as the product would not be chiral

D It would not rotate it at all as a racemic mixture was obtained.

(Total 12 marks)

3 Persulfate ions, $S_2O_8^{2-}$, are reduced by iodide ions according to the equation:

$$S_2O_8^{2-}(aq) + 2I^-(aq) \rightarrow 2SO_4^{2-}(aq) + I_2(aq)$$

a) The structure of the persulfate ion is shown in Figure 6.22.

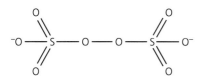

Figure 6.22

Calculate the oxidation number of oxygen in this ion and write the ionic half-equation for its reduction. (2)

b) Describe how you could follow this reaction. (4)

c) When 25 cm³ of sodium persulfate of concentration 0.10 mol dm⁻³ and 25 cm³ of potassium iodide of concentration 2.0 mol dm⁻³ were mixed with a trace of a catalyst of iron(II) sulfate, a steady reaction took place. The results of the experiment are shown below.

Time/s	[I₂]/mol dm⁻³
50	0.030
100	0.050
200	0.075
300	0.088
400	0.094
500	0.097

i) Draw a graph of [I₂] on the *y*-axis against time on the *x*-axis. (3)

ii) Use your graph to calculate the initial rate of reaction either by drawing a tangent at $t = 0\,s$ or by other means. (3)

iii) The experiment was repeated but using sodium persulfate solution of concentration 0.050 mol dm⁻³. The initial rate was found to be $2.0 \times 10^{-4}\,mol\,dm^{-3}\,s^{-1}$. What information does this give about the partial order of one of the reactants? Justify your answer. (2)

d) The experiment was first done at a temperature of 25°C and then repeated at 35°C. It was found that the rate constant, *k*, doubled at the higher temperature. Use the expression below to calculate the value of the activation energy of this reaction, giving a sign and units with your answer. (3)

$$\ln\left(\frac{k_2}{k_1}\right) = \frac{E}{R}\left(\frac{1}{T_1} - \frac{1}{T_2}\right)$$

$$R = 8.31\,J\,mol^{-1}\,K^{-1}$$

(Total 17 marks)

4 Cyclopropane can be converted into its isomer, propene by heating to 500°C:

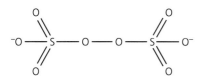

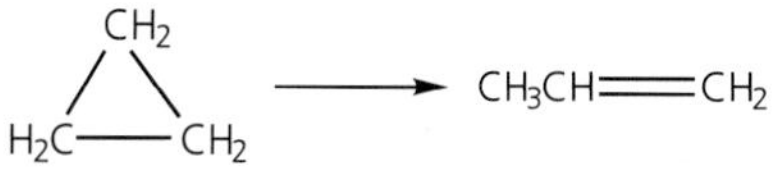

[Cyclopropane]/mol dm⁻³	Time/min
0.080	0
0.062	5
0.048	10
0.038	15
0.023	25
0.014	35
0.0065	50

a) Use the data in the table to plot a graph of concentration (*y*-axis) against time (*x*-axis). (3)

b) Measure three consecutive half-lives and hence deduce the order of the reaction. (3)

c) Calculate the value of the rate constant, stating its units. (2)

(Total 8 marks)

5 Consider a reaction that has a two-step mechanism in which both steps are exothermic. Step 2 is the rate-determining step.

Step 1: A + B → intermediate
Step 2: A + intermediate → C

a) Write the overall equation for the reaction. (1)

b) Draw the reaction profile diagram for the overall reaction. (4)

c) Predict the rate equation for the reaction. (1)

d) How would the rate equation differ if step 1 were the rate-determining step? (1)

(Total 7 marks)

7 Chirality (Topic 17)

Required year 1 knowledge

Isomers are different compounds that have the same molecular formula.

Structural isomerism

Structural isomers are compounds with the same molecular formula but different structural formulae.

Structural isomers can be divided into three categories: carbon–chain, positional and functional group.

Carbon-chain isomerism

In **carbon–chain isomerism**, the difference between the isomers is the length of the carbon chain. For example, if the compound contains four carbon atoms, they can be arranged with two different chain lengths (Figure 7.1).

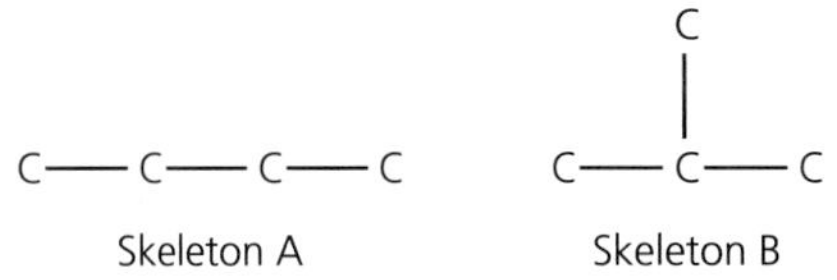

Figure 7.1 Chain lengths for a four carbon atom compound

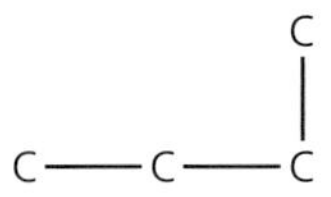

Figure 7.2

Note that the carbon skeleton in Figure 7.2 is the same as that of A in Figure 7.1, because they both contain a chain of four carbon atoms.

The bond angle around a sp^3 hybridised carbon atom is $109\frac{1}{2}°$, but is often drawn as 180° or 90° for simplicity.

Positional isomerism

Positional isomers have the same functional group in different locations on the carbon skeleton. For example, there are two isomers of molecular formula C_3H_8O. In one isomer (propan-1-ol) the −OH group is bonded to an end carbon atom; in the other (propan-2-ol) it is bonded to the middle carbon atom (Figure 7.3).

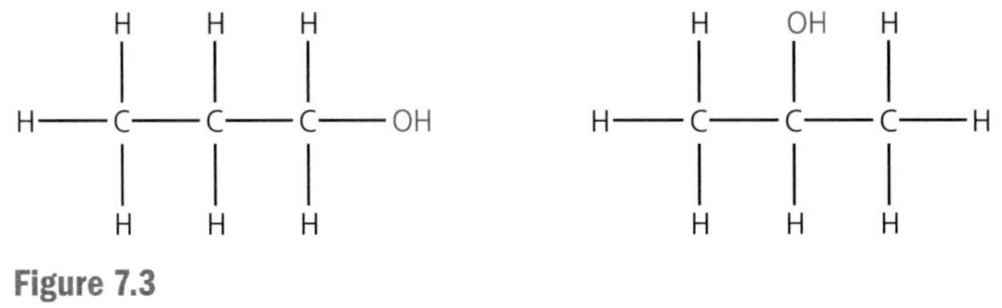

Figure 7.3

Worked example

Draw and name the structural isomers of C_4H_9Cl.

Answer

There are two ways of arranging the four carbon atoms (Figure 7.4).

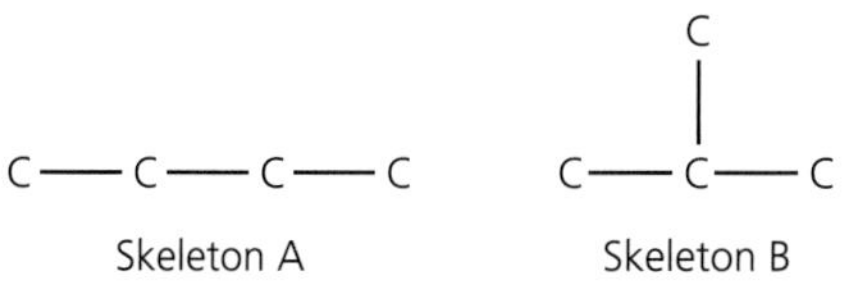

C — C — C — C   C — C — C
                                      |
                                      C

   Skeleton A   Skeleton B

Figure 7.4

There are two positions on the four-carbon skeleton for the chlorine atom (Figure 7.5).

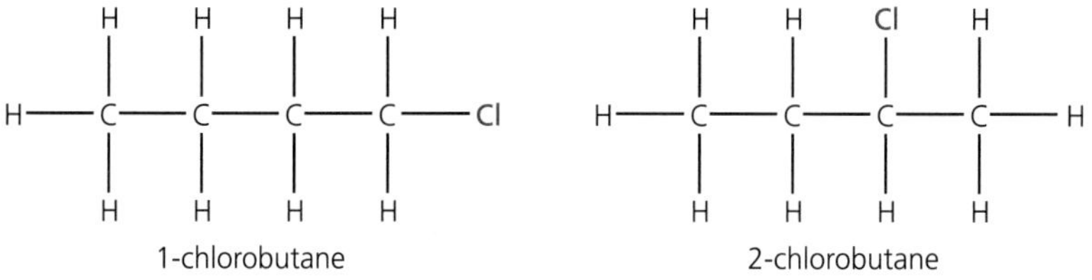

1-chlorobutane   2-chlorobutane

Figure 7.5

There are also two positions on the three-carbon skeleton for the chlorine atom (Figure 7.6).

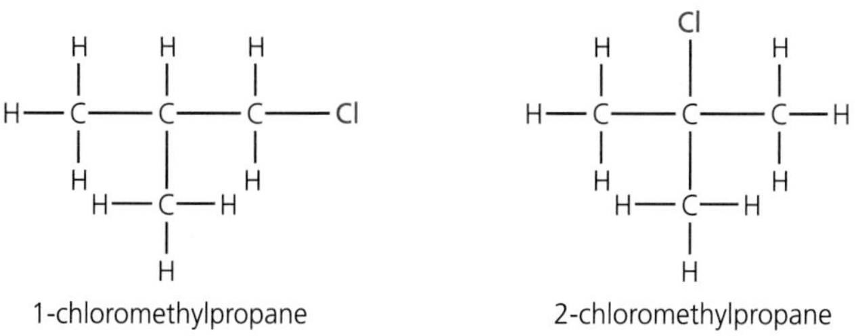

1-chloromethylpropane   2-chloromethylpropane

Figure 7.6

These structures can also be represented by skeletal formulae (Figure 7.7).

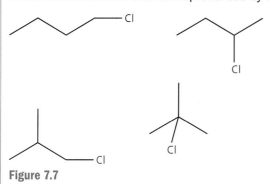

Figure 7.7

Functional-group isomerism

In **functional-group isomerism**, the isomers are members of different homologous series and, therefore, have different functional groups. For example, there are two isomers of molecular formula C_2H_6O. One isomer is the alcohol ethanol, CH_3CH_2OH; the other is the ether methoxymethane, CH_3OCH_3.

Stereoisomerism

Stereoisomers are compounds with the same structural formula but which have the atoms arranged differently in space.

There are two types of stereoisomerism — geometric and optical.

Geometric isomerism

Geometric isomerism is also called *cis–trans* or *E–Z* isomerism. In organic chemistry it is caused by the presence of a functional group that restricts rotation. For example, a C=C group consists of a σ-bond, which lies along the axis between the two carbon atoms and a π-bond, which is above and below that axis (Figure 7.8).

Figure 7.8

For rotation round the σ-bond to occur, the π-bond would have to break and then reform. The energy required to do this is far too great for this to occur at room temperature.

Alkenes exhibit geometric isomerism if there are different groups on each carbon atom of the C=C bond. The simplest example is but-2-ene, which has two geometric isomers (Figure 7.9).

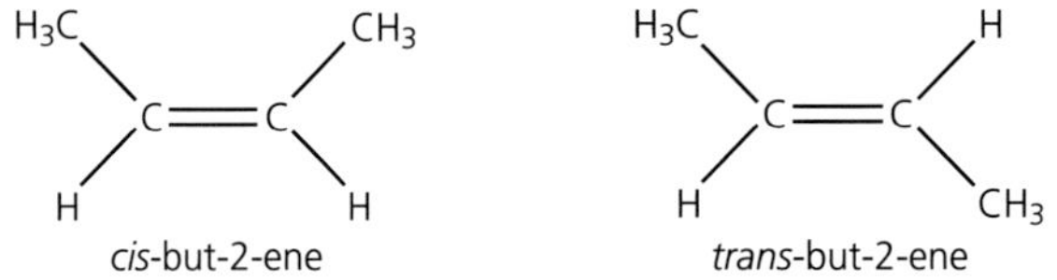

cis-but-2-ene   *trans*-but-2-ene

Figure 7.9

In *cis*-but-2-ene, the two −CH₃ groups are on the same side of the double bond; in *trans*-but-2-ene they are on opposite sides. These two compounds are isomers because the double bond restricts rotation and there are different groups (−H and −CH₃) on each of the double-bonded carbon atoms.

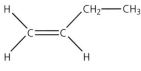

Figure 7.10

But-1-ene does not have geometric isomers, because one of the carbon atoms in the C=C group has two hydrogen atoms bonded to it (Figure 7.10).

Test yourself

1 Explain why 1-chloroprop-1-ene, $CH_3CH{=}CHCl$, exists as two geometric isomers whereas 3-chloroprop-1-ene, $CH_2{=}CHCH_2Cl$, does not.

The **E/Z system** of naming isomers must also be known. Each group attached to the C=C group is assigned a priority. The higher the atomic number of the atom attached the higher the priority. If the two highest priority atoms or groups are on different sides of the C=C group, the compound is the *E*-isomer. Thus *trans*-but-2-ene is also called *E*-but-2-ene and *cis*-but-2-ene is called *Z*-but-2-ene.

> A way of remembering this is 'Z meanz on zee zame zide'!

If two different groups are bonded through carbon atoms to the C=C group, then the one with the greater sum of atomic numbers has the higher priority. Thus a C_2H_5 group has a higher priority than a CH_3 group.

Tip

It is advisable to draw correct bond angles around the C=C bond.

Geometric isomers have the same chemical properties, and slightly different physical properties:

	Melting point/°C	Boiling point/°C
E-but-2-ene	−105	+3.0
Z-but-2-ene	−139	+3.8

Geometric isomerism can occur in cyclic compounds in which rotation is not possible. When chlorine adds to cyclohexene, one of two possible geometric isomers is formed (Figure 7.11).

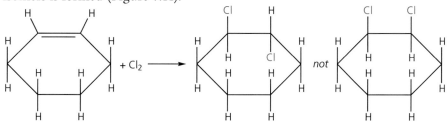

Figure 7.11

The fact that the *trans* isomer is formed is evidence that the second chlorine atom adds to alkenes on the opposite side from the first chlorine. This is called *trans* addition.

Geometric isomerism also occurs in some transition metal complexes. For example, platinum(II) forms planar complexes with four ligands. The complex $[PtCl_2(NH_3)_2]$ exists as two geometric isomers (Figure 7.12).

cis-diamminedichloroplatinum(II)   trans-diamminedichloroplatinum(II)

Figure 7.12

The *cis*–isomer (known as cisplatin) and similar *cis*-platinum complexes are used in the treatment of cancer. The complexes inhibit cell division and cancer cells are particularly susceptible. The treatment, known as chemotherapy, also causes hair loss because cisplatin stops the regrowth of hair. The *trans*-isomer has no biological activity.

Cisplatin blocks DNA replication because it is the correct shape to bond to the base guanine in DNA. The *trans* form cannot do this.

The *cis*–*trans* method of naming geometric isomers breaks down in more complex compounds. For example, there are two geometric isomers of the unsaturated acid, 2-methylpent-2-enoic acid, $C_2H_5CH=C(CH_3)COOH$ (Figure 7.13).

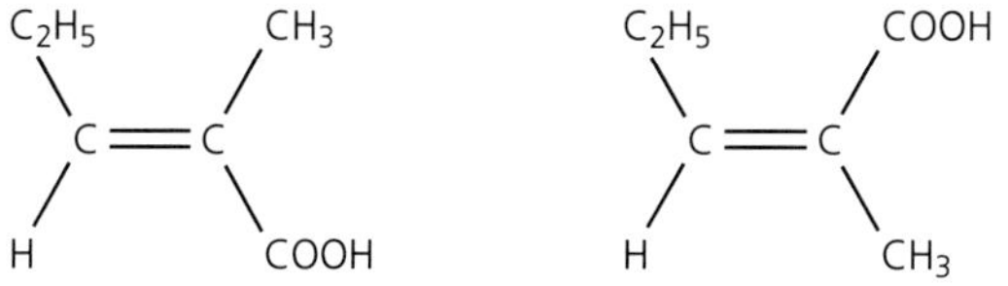

Figure 7.13 The *E-/Z*-isomers of 2-methylpent-2-enoic acid

The priority numbers for some common groups are:

- $-CH_3 = 9$
- $-C_2H_5 = 17$
- $-COOH = 23$

The prefix *Z* is given to the isomer with the two higher priority groups on the same side of the double bond; *E* is given to the isomer with the two higher priority groups on opposite sides. Thus, the left substance in Figure 7.13 is *E*-2-methylpent-2-enoic acid and the other is *Z*-2-methylbut-2-enoic acid.

Test yourself

2 Draw the *E*- isomer of $CH_2ClCH=C(CH_3)CH_2Br$.

Year 2 isomerism

Optical isomerism

Compounds that show **optical isomerism** do not have a plane (or axis or centre) of symmetry. They are said to be **chiral**. Such compounds have two isomers, which are mirror images. The isomers are called **enantiomers**.

A left hand is different from a right hand, yet looks like a right hand when reflected in a mirror.

Non-superimposable means that it is impossible to put one beside the other in such a way that their shapes are the same.

Note that the two isomers are drawn as mirror images. The wedges and dashes are meant to give an idea of the three-dimensional shapes of the molecules.

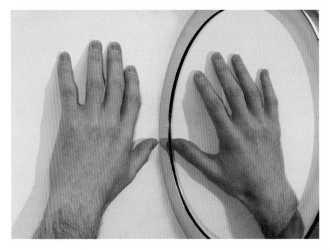

A left hand and its reflection

A chiral centre in a molecule or ion causes it to have two optical isomers, which are called enantiomers.

An enantiomer is an isomer that is non-superimposable on its mirror image.

The most common cause of chirality in organic chemistry is when a carbon atom has four different groups or atoms attached to it. For example, the compound CHFClBr is chiral (Figure 7.14).

Enantiomers of CHFClBr

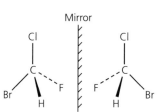

Figure 7.14 Enantiomers of CHFClBr

Lactic acid is produced when milk goes sour and in muscles as a result of anaerobic respiration. Its formula is $CH_3CH(OH)COOH$ and its systematic name is 2-hydroxypropanoic acid. It contains a chiral carbon atom that has $-H$, $-OH$, $-CH_3$ and $-COOH$ attached. The presence of these four different groups means that the substance exists as two optical isomers (Figure 7.15).

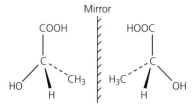

Figure 7.15

Test yourself

3 Draw the stereoisomers of:

a) $CH_3CH(OH)CN$ b) $CH_3CH=CHCN$

Enantiomers have identical chemical properties and the same boiling temperatures and solubilities. They differ in two ways:

- Uniquely among chemical compounds, they rotate the plane of polarisation of plane-polarised light.
- Optical isomers often have different biochemical reactions.

Glucose, $CHO(CHOH)_4CH_2OH$, is one of 16 optical isomers. Glucose is the only one of the 16 that can be metabolised by humans.

Plane-polarised light

Light waves have peaks and troughs in all planes. When ordinary light is passed through a piece of Polaroid, the light that comes out only has peaks and troughs in a single plane. This light is said to be polarised.

A solution of one enantiomer rotates the plane of polarisation of **plane-polarised light** in a clockwise direction (+); the other enantiomer rotates it in an anticlockwise direction (−) (Figure 7.16).

> **Tip**
>
> Always make sure that the bonds are drawn from the central carbon atom to the correct atom in the group, for example, to the oxygen atom of the $-OH$ group and to the carbon atom of the $-CH_3$ group.

This property is optical and provides the origin of the name 'optical isomerism'.

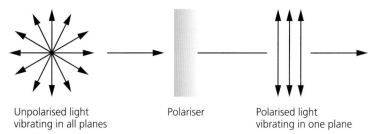

Unpolarised light vibrating in all planes

Polariser

Polarised light vibrating in one plane

Figure 7.16 Unpolarised and polarised light

Lactic acid produced in muscles is a crystalline solid that melts at 26°C and rotates the plane of polarisation clockwise. Lactic acid obtained from the action of microorganisms on milk sugar (lactose) is a crystalline solid that also melts at 26°C, but rotates the plane of polarisation of plane-polarised light in an anticlockwise direction.

A solution containing equimolar amounts of the two enantiomers is called a racemic mixture. It does not rotate the plane of polarisation of plane-polarised light.

The extent by which an enantiomer rotates the plane of polarisation can be measured using a **polarimeter** (Figure 7.17).

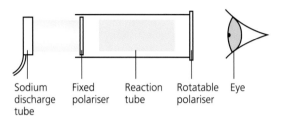

Sodium discharge tube   Fixed polariser   Reaction tube   Rotatable polariser   Eye

Figure 7.17 A polarimeter

The angle through which the plane of polarisation is rotated depends on:

- the nature of the enantiomer
- the concentration of the enantiomer in the solution
- the length of the reaction tube

The second factor is useful in determining the change in concentration during a reaction. For example, the rate of the hydrolysis of sucrose can be followed using a polarimeter:

$$C_{12}H_{22}O_{11} + H_2O \rightarrow C_6H_{12}O_6 + C_6H_{12}O_6$$
sucrose   glucose   fructose

Sucrose rotates the plane of polarisation in one direction and the mixture of glucose and fructose rotates it in the other direction.

The rate of hydrolysis of one enantiomer of a halogenoalkane can also be followed using a polarimeter:

$$CH_3CHClC_2H_5 + OH^- \rightarrow CH_3CH(OH)C_2H_5 + Cl^-$$
one enantiomer   a racemic mixture

The rotation of the plane of polarisation of plane-polarised light drops from the original value to zero as the reaction progresses. This is because the reaction is mostly via an S_N1 mechanism, which goes through a planar intermediate. This can be attacked from either side, resulting in equimolar amounts of each enantiomer.

Test yourself

4 Alanine, $NH_2CH(CH_3)COOH$, is an amino acid found in many proteins. Draw the structures of the two optical isomers of alanine.

Biological differences

Stereoisomers have the same chemical reactions. Both enantiomers of lactic acid have identical chemical properties. However, most biochemical reactions take place with only one of the two enantiomers. Ibuprofen, $(CH_3)_2CHCH_2C_6H_4CH(CH_3)COOH$, for example, is chiral and the tablets available commercially are a racemic mixture. Only the (−) form is active as a painkiller and anti-inflammatory drug.

In the 1950s, the drug thalidomide was introduced as a cure for morning sickness in pregnant women. Sadly, it had not been tested properly on a sufficient range of pregnant mammals. About 10000 children, whose mothers had been taking thalidomide, were born with severe abnormalities — for example, vestigial limbs. It was found subsequently that one enantiomer suppressed morning sickness and the other caused the birth defects.

Two chiral centres

If a molecule has two different chiral centres, there are up to four possible optical isomers. Let one chiral centre be called A. It has two mirror image structures, one of which will rotate the plane of polarisation of plane-polarised light clockwise, +A; the other will rotate it anticlockwise, −A. Let the second chiral centre be called B. The B centre also has two mirror image structures, +B and −B.

The four optical isomers are: +A with +B, −A with −B, +A with −B, and −A with +B. The first isomer rotates the plane of polarisation of plane-polarised light clockwise, the second rotates it anticlockwise by the same amount and the third and fourth each rotate it slightly, depending on the extent to which the A and B chiral centres each rotate the plane.

If the two halves have the same formula (A is the same as B), then the last two enantiomers are identical. This enantiomer is called the *meso* form.

> **Tip**
>
> If a molecule has two identical chiral centres, the isomer with a plane of symmetry will not be optically active because one chiral centre will rotate the plane of polarisation of plane-polarised light clockwise and the other chiral centre will rotate it equally anticlockwise.

Test yourself

5 a) Draw and name the four structural isomers of $C_3H_6Cl_2$.

  b) One of these exists as optical isomers. Identify which and draw the structural formulae of these two isomers, showing clearly how they differ.

Summary

- Optical activity occurs in organic compounds when four different groups are attached to the same carbon atom. This carbon atom is the chiral centre of the molecule.
- A chiral centre results in two optical isomers (enantiomers) that are non-superimposable mirror images of each other.
- Enantiomers rotate the plane of polarisation of plane-polarised light in opposite directions.
- An equimolar mixture of enantiomers is called a racemic mixture. It has no effect on plane-polarised light.

Chirality and mechanisms

Nucleophilic substitution of halogenoalkanes

Nucleophilic substitution of halogenoalkanes can proceed either through an S_N1 or an S_N2 mechanism. There are two pieces of evidence that enable the elucidation of the correct mechanism. One is from the kinetics of the reaction. An S_N1 mechanism is zero order with respect to the nucleophile and first order with respect to the halogenoalkane; an S_N2 mechanism is first order with respect to both the nucleophile and the halogenoalkane.

S_N1: rate = k[halogenoalkane]^1 × [nucleophile]^0

S_N2: rate = k[halogenoalkane]^1 × [nucleophile]^1

The other piece of evidence is the effect of the product of the reaction on plane-polarised light.

If a single optical isomer of a halogenoalkane is reacted with hydroxide ions and the reaction has an S_N2 mechanism, the result will be a single optical isomer of the product alcohol. The OH^- ion attacks from the side opposite to the halogen and thus a single optical isomer with an inverted stereostructure is obtained (Figure 7.18).

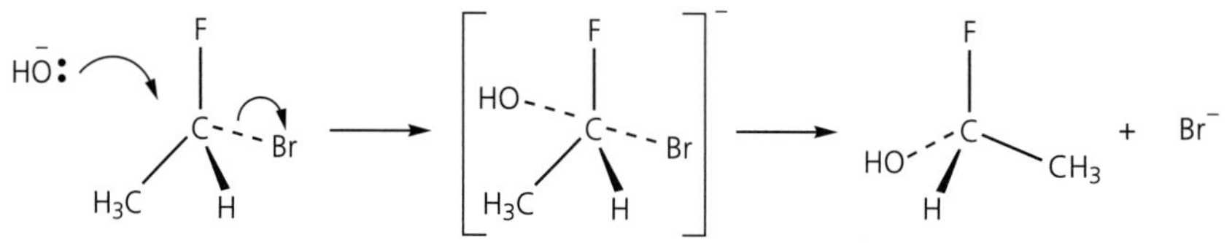

Figure 7.18

However, if the mechanism is S_N1, the result is optically inactive because the racemic mixture of the two enantiomers is produced (Figures 7.19 and 7.20).

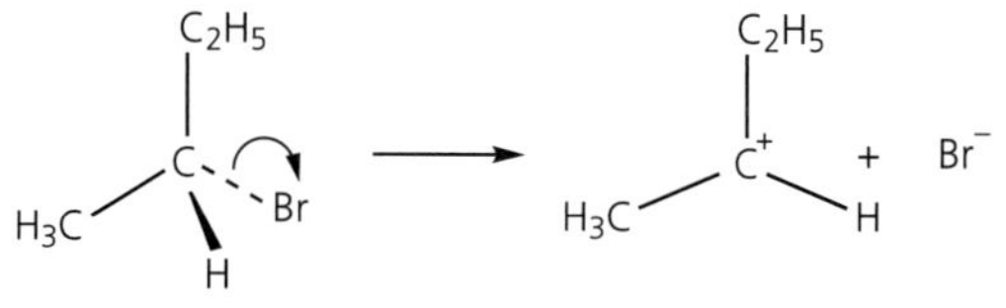

Figure 7.19

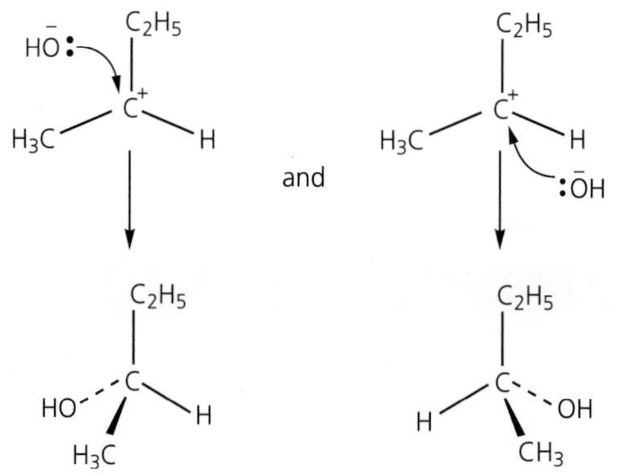

Figure 7.20

The first step is the loss of the halide ion from the halogenoalkane. The resulting carbocation has three pairs of bonding electrons and no lone pairs, so its shape is triangular planar around the positive carbon atom. The nucleophile can then attack from the top (left-hand side of the two step 2 mechanisms), producing one enantiomer, or from the bottom (right-hand side of step 2), producing the other.

As the chance of attack from the top is identical to that from the bottom, the two optical isomers (enantiomers) are produced in equal amounts. This is the definition of a racemic mixture.

Nucleophilic addition to carbonyl compounds

The production of a racemic mixture in nucleophilic addition to aldehydes is evidence for the type of mechanism. This is explained in Chapter 8.

Summary tasks

Make sure that you:

- can write formulae clearly showing the difference between different structural isomers, between *cis* and *trans* (E/Z) isomers and between optical isomers (enantiomers)
- can define chirality and know how to identify a chiral centre in a structure
- know in what way optical isomers differ and how this can be demonstrated
- understand the chirality involved in S_N1 and S_N2 substitution reactions

Questions

1 The complex ion $[Cr(NH_3)_4(Cl)_2]^+$ has four ammonia molecules and two chloride ions attached to the central chromium ion by dative covalent bonds. Its shape is octahedral and similar to that of the hydrated magnesium ion $[Mg(H_2O)_6]^{2+}$. Draw the two geometric isomers of the chromium complex ion. Mark in the bond angles on your diagram.

2 Geraniol is a perfume found in rose petals. Its formula is shown in Figure 7.21.

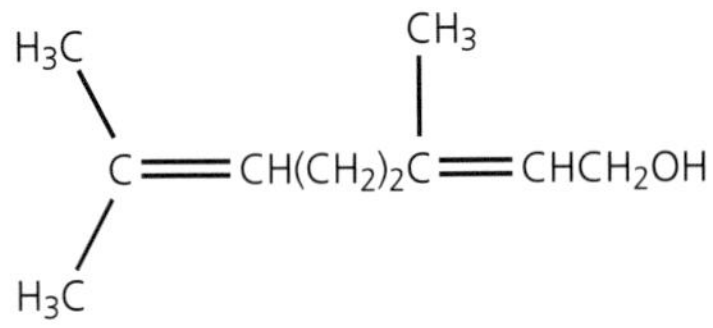

H_3C
CH_3
C===$CH(CH_2)_2C$===$CHCH_2OH$
H_3C

Figure 7.21

Explain why geraniol exists as two geometric isomers.

3 Name the compounds in Figure 7.22.

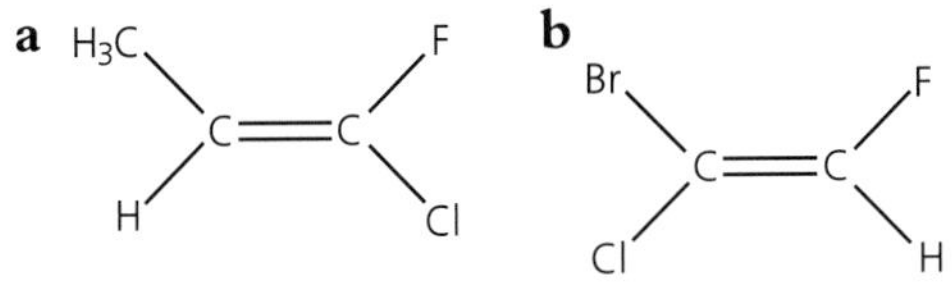

a H_3C
C===C
H F
       Cl

b Br
C===C
Cl F
       H

Figure 7.22

4 Draw the two optical isomers of $CH_3CH(OH)C_2H_5$ to show clearly the way in which they differ.

5 Limonene is a chiral molecule found in the oil of citrus fruits. Its structure is shown in Figure 7.23.

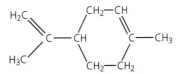

Figure 7.23

Redraw the structure, marking the chiral centre with an asterisk, ★.

6 Alanine, 2-aminopropanoic acid, is an amino acid found in many proteins. It is chiral.

a) Explain the meaning of the term 'chiral'.

b) Describe how optical activity is detected experimentally.

7 Tartaric acid, 2,3-dihydroxybutanedioic acid, has the formula HOOCCH(OH)CH(OH)COOH.

a) Draw the full structural formula of this molecule, marking each chiral centre with an asterisk, ★.

b) Explain why there are only three optical isomers of this compound.

8 How would you demonstrate the difference in properties of two optical isomers?

9 Search the web for information on cisplatin and write approximately 100 words about its discovery, uses and problems.

Exam practice questions

1   **a)** An enantiomer is
   A an equal mixture of two optical isomers
   B one particular optical isomer
   C one particular geometric isomer
   D a compound with four different groups
      attached to a carbon atom (1)

b) Bromine dissolved in an inert solvent reacts
   with propene to form 1,2-dibromopropane.
   This product contains one chiral carbon atom.
   i) What do you understand by the term
      chiral? (1)
   ii) Draw the mechanism for this
      reaction. (3)

c) Tiglic acid is the *E* isomer of 2-methylbut-2-
   enoic acid, $CH_3CH=C(CH_3)COOH$.
   i) Draw the structural formula of tiglic acid
      showing the orientation of the groups
      around the C=C group. (1)
   ii) Explain why it is an *E*- isomer. (2)
   iii) A chemist tried to prepare tiglic acid from
      2-bromo-2-methyl butan-1-ol, in two
      steps. Suggest reagents and conditions for
      each of these steps and write equations for
      each step. (6)
   Step 1: Reagents
         Conditions
         Equation
   Step 2: Reagents
         Conditions
         Equation
   iv) Explain whether tiglic acid alone
      would be produced or whether it would
      be a mixture of tiglic acid and
      its isomers. (2)
   (Total 16 marks)

2   **This question is about**

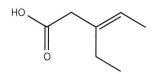

a) Its molecular formula is
   A $C_6H_{12}O_2$ **C** $C_7H_{12}O_2$
   B $C_6H_{11}O_2$ **D** $C_7H_{11}O_2$ (1)
b) Its name is
   A *E*-3-ethylpent-3-enoic acid
   B *Z*-3-ethylpent-3-enoic acid
   C *E*-3-ethylpent-2-enoic acid
   D *Z*-3-ethylpent-2-enoic acid (1)
c) It reacts with gaseous hydrogen bromide in
   A a nucleophilic addition reaction
   B an electrophilic addition reaction
   C a nucleophilic substitution reaction
   D an electrophilic substitution
      reaction (1)
d) Write the skeletal formula of the major
   product formed when it reacts with HBr
   and explain why it, and not its isomer, is
   formed. (3)
   (Total 6 marks)

8 Carbonyl compounds (Topic 17)

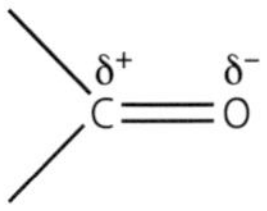

Figure 8.1

Other compounds contain the C=O group but are not carbonyl compounds. These are carboxylic acids and their derivatives and are discussed in Chapter 9.

Carbonyl compounds contain the >C=O group. The carbon atom is bonded to the oxygen by a σ-bond and a π-bond. Oxygen is more electronegative than carbon, so the bonding electrons are pulled towards the oxygen atom, making it δ− and the carbon δ+ (Figure 8.1).

The polar nature of the bond makes the carbon atom susceptible to attack by nucleophiles.

A nucleophile is a species with a lone pair of electrons that is used to form a bond with a δ+ atom.

There are two types of carbonyl compounds: aldehydes and ketones.

Aldehydes

- Aldehydes have a hydrogen atom bonded to the carbon of the C=O group.
- The formulae of aldehydes can be represented by RCHO, where R is a hydrogen atom, an alkyl group or benzene ring, for example H, $-CH_3$, $-C_2H_5$ or $-C_6H_5$.

Aliphatic aldehydes have the general formula $C_nH_{2n+1}CHO$, where n is 0, 1, 2, 3 etc.

Tip

Never write the formula of an aldehyde as RCOH.

Formula	Name	Boiling temperature/°C
HCHO	Methanal	−21
CH_3CHO	Ethanal	20
CH_3CH_2CHO	Propanal	49
$CH_3CH_2CH_2CHO$	Butanal	76
$(CH_3)_2CHCHO$	Methylpropanal	62

If you are asked for the structural formula in an exam, it is a good idea to show the bonding in the −CHO group. For example, it is helpful to write the structural formula of ethanal as shown in Figure 8.2.

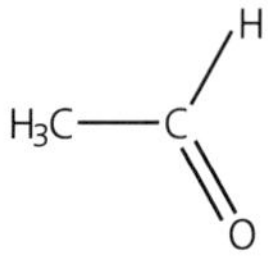

Figure 8.2

The boiling temperatures increase from methanal to butanal as the number of electrons increase, causing stronger London forces. Methylpropanal has a lower boiling temperature than its isomer, as it has a branched chain, which weakens the London forces.

Ketones

Ketones do *not* have a hydrogen atom bonded to the carbon of the group.

The formula of ketones can be represented as RCOR′, where R and R′ are alkyl or benzene ring groups such as $-CH_3$, $-C_2H_5$ or $-C_6H_5$. The simplest ketone is propanone, which contains three carbon atoms.

Tip

Propanone used to be called acetone.

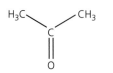

Figure 8.3

Tip

Strictly speaking the CH_3 groups should also be displayed, but this formula will not be penalised.

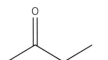

Figure 8.4

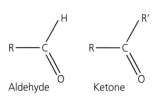

Aldehyde   Ketone

Figure 8.5

Figure 8.6

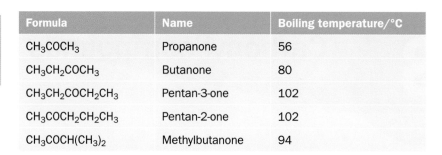

Formula	Name	Boiling temperature/°C
CH_3COCH_3	Propanone	56
$CH_3CH_2COCH_3$	Butanone	80
$CH_3CH_2COCH_2CH_3$	Pentan-3-one	102
$CH_3COCH_2CH_2CH_3$	Pentan-2-one	102
$CH_3COCH(CH_3)_2$	Methylbutanone	94

You may be asked for the displayed formula of a ketone. If so, you must show the bonding in the carbonyl group. For example, Figure 8.3 shows propanone.

Figure 8.4 shows the skeletal formula for butanone.

Test yourself

1 Write the formulae of the ketone isomers of molecular formula, $C_5H_{10}O$.

General structural formulae

The general structural formulae of aldehydes and ketones, showing double bonds, can be represented by Figure 8.5.

Geometry around the C=O group

The carbon atom has two single bonds, one double bond and no lone pairs, so the electrons in the three bonds repel each other and take up the position of maximum separation. This is a planar triangular shape with bond angles of 120° (Figure 8.6).

This planar shape makes it easy for nucleophiles to attack the carbon atom from either above or below, and so a single optical isomer is never obtained by addition to carbonyl compounds.

The polarity of the $\overset{\delta+\ \ \delta-}{>C=O}$ group is not cancelled out by the other two groups attached to the carbon atom. Therefore aldehyde and ketone molecules are polar.

Physical properties

Boiling point

Methanal is a gas. The other carbonyl compounds are liquid at room temperature.

The molecules are polar, so dipole–dipole forces as well as London (dispersion) forces exist between them. Alkanes and alkenes are not polar, so their intermolecular forces are weaker and their boiling points lower than those of aldehydes and ketones with the same number of electrons in the molecule.

Intermolecular hydrogen bonding is not possible in carbonyl compounds because neither aldehydes nor ketones have a hydrogen atom that is sufficiently δ+. Therefore, they have boiling points that are lower than those of alcohols, which do form intermolecular hydrogen bonds.

Test yourself

2 Explain why butanone has a boiling temperature between those of butan-1-ol and pentane.

Solubility

The lower members of both series are soluble in water. This solubility is due to hydrogen bonding between the lone pair of electrons in the $\delta-$ oxygen in the carbonyl compound and the $\delta+$ hydrogen in a water molecule (Figure 8.7).

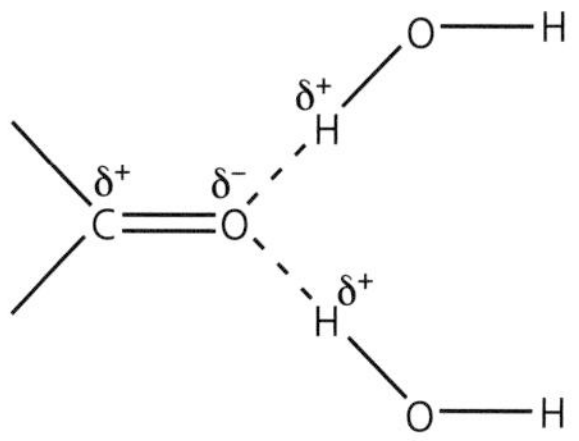

Propanone is an excellent solvent for organic substances.

Figure 8.7

Smell

- The lower members of the homologous series of aldehydes have pungent odours.
- Ketones have much sweeter smells than aldehydes.
- Complex aldehydes and ketones are often used as perfumes. Citral, an ingredient of lemon grass oil, is an aldehyde; β–ionone is a ketone that smells of violets and is used in perfume (Figure 8.8).

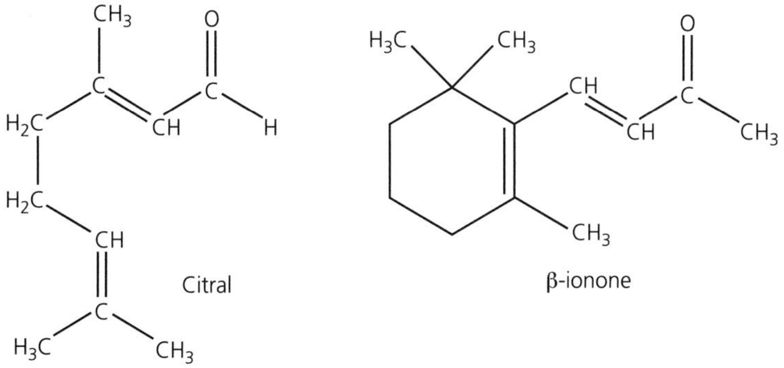

Citral

β-ionone

Figure 8.8

Laboratory preparation

Aldehydes

Aldehydes are prepared by the partial oxidation of a *primary* alcohol. The usual oxidising agent is a solution of potassium (or sodium) dichromate(VI) in dilute sulfuric acid. The temperature must be below the boiling point of the alcohol and above that of the aldehyde. In this way the aldehyde is boiled off as it is formed and, therefore, cannot be oxidised further. If the mixture were to be heated under reflux, the aldehyde would be further oxidised to a carboxylic acid.

Ethanal can be prepared as follows:

- Heat ethanol in a flask to about 60°C, using an electric heater.
- Add a solution of potassium dichromate(VI) in dilute sulfuric acid slowly from a tap funnel.
- As it distils off, collect the ethanal in a flask surrounded by iced water.

The iced water keeps the collecting flask cool and so prevents evaporation of the ethanal.

The reaction is exothermic and so heat is generated. This maintains the temperature above the boiling point of ethanal, so it boils off before it can be oxidised further.

The preparation of ethanal (Figure 8.9) is represented by the equation:

$$CH_3CH_2OH + [O] \rightarrow CH_3CHO + H_2O$$

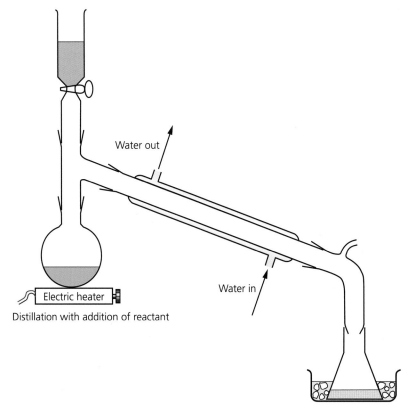

Figure 8.9 Laboratory preparation of ethanal

Reagents: excess ethanol and potassium dichromate(vi) dissolved in dilute sulfuric acid

Conditions: a temperature of 60°C; collect the ethanal as it distils off.

Observation: the orange colour of potassium dichromate(vi) changes to green because chromium(iii) ions are formed

Ethanal can be purified by re-distilling it, using a water bath as a source of heat and collecting the fraction that boils in the range 20–23°C

Ketones

Ketones are prepared by the oxidation of *secondary* alcohols. If acidified potassium dichromate(vi) is used as the oxidising agent, the ketone is not further oxidised.

Propanone can be prepared as follows:

- Place propan-2-ol and a solution of potassium dichromate(vi) in dilute sulfuric acid in a round-bottomed flask.
- Fit a reflux condenser.

- Heat, using an electric heater, so that the mixture boils for about 15 minutes.
- Remove the reflux condenser and set up the apparatus for distillation. Distil off the propanone (boiling point 56°C) from any unreacted propan-2-ol (boiling point 82°C).

The preparation of propanone (Figure 8.10) is represented by the equation:

$$CH_3CH(OH)CH_3 + [O] \rightarrow CH_3COCH_3 + H_2O$$

Reagents: propan-2-ol and excess potassium dichromate(VI) dissolved in dilute sulfuric acid

Conditions: heat under reflux for about 15 minutes, and then distil off the propanone

Observation: the orange colour of potassium dichromate(VI) changes to green because chromium(III) ions are formed

Aromatic ketones

Ketones that have a benzene ring attached to the carbonyl group, such as phenylethanone, $C_6H_5COCH_3$, can be prepared using the **Friedel–Crafts reaction** (p. 239).

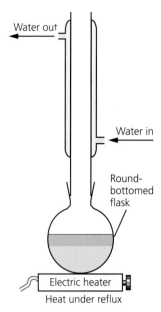

Figure 8.10 Laboratory preparation of propanone

Reactions of aldehydes and ketones

- Both aldehydes and ketones undergo **nucleophilic addition** reactions because of the polar nature of the C=O bond.
- Aldehydes and ketones both undergo **addition/elimination** reactions.
- Aldehydes can be oxidised to carboxylic acids. Therefore, aldehydes are reducing agents.
- Ethanal and methyl ketones react with iodine in alkali to form a precipitate of iodoform, CHI_3. This is called the **iodoform reaction**.

> **Tip**
>
> Remember that ethanol and secondary 2-ols also do the iodoform reaction.

Nucleophilic addition reactions

Alkenes and carbonyl compounds contain π-bonds. However, C=C is non-polar whereas C=O is polar. The electron cloud above and below the σ-bond in the C=C group is an area of negative charge that is attacked by electrophiles.

The electron cloud in the C=O group is distorted, with the carbon atom being δ+. This δ+ carbon can be attacked by nucleophiles.

The −CH₃ group is electron releasing, so the carbon in ethanal, CH_3CHO, is less δ+ than the carbon of the C=O group in methanal (which has no −CH₃ group). The carbonyl carbon in propanone is even less δ+ than that in ethanal. The reactivity in nucleophilic addition is: $HCHO > CH_3CHO > CH_3COCH_3$.

Reduction

Aldehydes and ketones can be reduced by lithium tetrahydridoaluminate(III), $LiAlH_4$.

This compound contains AlH_4^- ions, which act as a source of H^-. The reaction takes place in two distinct steps:

- The first step is the addition of H^- to the δ+ carbon atom. In this step the reagents must be kept dry. It is carried out in ether solution.
- The second step is the addition of an aqueous solution of an acid, which protonates the O^- formed in the first step.

The result is that the carbonyl compound is *reduced* to an alcohol. For example, ethanal is reduced to ethanol:

$$CH_3CHO + 2[H] \rightarrow CH_3CH_2OH$$
$$\text{ethanal} \qquad\qquad \text{ethanol}$$

When aldehydes are reduced, *primary* alcohols are formed.

Reduction of ketones takes place by a similar two-step reaction. The equation for the reduction of propanone is:

$$CH_3COCH_3 + 2[H] \rightarrow CH_3CH(OH)CH_3$$
$$\text{propanone} \qquad\qquad \text{propan-2-ol}$$

When ketones are reduced, *secondary* alcohols are formed.

$LiAlH_4$ is a reducing agent that reacts specifically with polar π-bonds. Thus, it reduces C=O group in aldehydes, ketones, acids and acid derivatives, and C≡N in nitriles, but does *not* reduce the π-bond in C=C groups, which are non-polar.

Both C=C and C=O groups can be reduced by hydrogen and a platinum catalyst.

To summarise:

- Aldehydes and ketones are reduced to alcohols by:
  - $LiAlH_4$ in dry ether
  - H_2/Pt
- Alkenes are only reduced by H_2/Pt.

Sodium tetrahydridoborate(III), NaBH4, in aqueous solution also reduces polar C=O bonds.

Test yourself

3 Write the formula of the organic product of the reaction of $CH_2=CHCH_2CHO$ with:

a) lithium tetrahydridoaluminate(III) in dry ether followed by the addition of dilute acid

b) hydrogen gas with a platinum catalyst

Reaction with hydrogen cyanide

The reaction between ethanal and hydrogen cyanide takes place at about pH 6 to 8. This pH provides enough of the catalyst, which is the cyanide ion, CN^-.

$$CH_3CHO + HCN \rightarrow CH_3CH(OH)CN$$

The product is 2-hydroxypropanenitrile.

Hydrogen cyanide, HCN, is a very weak acid and produces few CN^- ions in solution. The necessary conditions are such that there must be a significant amount of both CN^- ions and HCN molecules.

Reagent: excess potassium cyanide + some dilute sulfuric acid:

$$K^+CN^- + H^+ \rightleftharpoons HCN + K^+$$

or hydrogen cyanide + some sodium hydroxide:

$$HCN + OH^- \rightleftharpoons {:}CN^- + H_2O$$

Hydrogen cyanide is a very weak acid and produces few CN^- ions.

or hydrogen cyanide (HCN) + some potassium cyanide (K^+CN^-)

Worked example

Calculate the ratio of CN^- ions to HCN molecules in a HCN/CN^- buffer solution of pH = 8, given that K_a of hydrogen cyanide = $5 \times 10^{-10}\,mol\,dm^{-3}$.

Answer

$$HCN \rightleftharpoons H^+ + CN^-$$

$$K_a = [H^+][CN^-]/[HCN]$$

$$[CN^-]/[HCN] = K_a/[H^+] = 5 \times 10^{-10}/1.0 \times 10^{-8} = 5 \times 10^{-2}\text{ or } 1:20$$

The mechanism of this reaction is shown in Figure 8.11.

The lone pair of electrons on the carbon atom of the CN^- ion forms a bond with the $\delta+$ carbon atom — as shown by the red curly arrow. At the same time, the π-electrons in the C=O group move to the oxygen atom — as shown by the blue curly arrow.

The anion formed in the first step removes a proton from a HCN molecule to form the organic product and another CN^- ion (Figure 8.12).

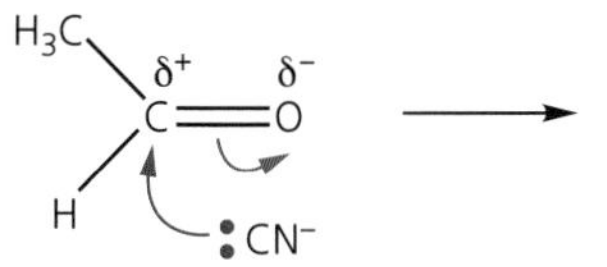

Figure 8.11 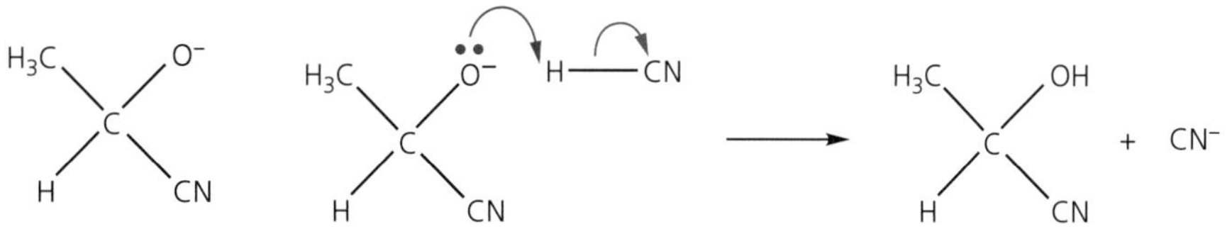   **Figure 8.12**

The O^- group in the intermediate donates a lone pair of electrons to the hydrogen in an HCN molecule (red arrow) as the σ-bond between the H and the CN breaks (blue arrow). This regenerates CN^- ions, which catalyse the reaction.

The conditions for this reaction are very important. If the pH is too low, there are not enough CN^- ions for the first step to take place; if the pH is too high there are not enough HCN molecules for the second step.

The same type of reaction with the same mechanism occurs with ketones, but at a slower rate — for example, with propanone (Figure 8.13).

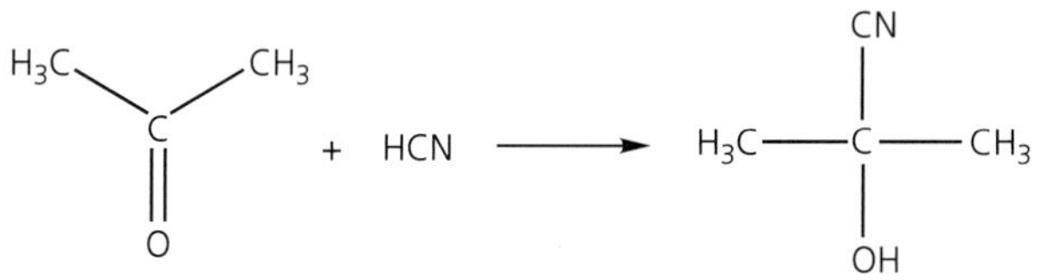

Figure 8.13

The product is 2-hydroxy-2-methylpropanenitrile.

Stereochemistry of addition

When hydrogen cyanide adds on to an aldehyde or to an asymmetric ketone, the product is a racemic mixture. This is because the carbonyl compound is planar around the >C=O group and, therefore, the cyanide ion can attack from the left or from the

The mechanism of the reaction of aldehydes and ketones with lithium aluminium hydride is almost the same as that for the addition of HCN. Step 1 requires curly arrows from the H^- ion of the AlH_4^- to the carbon of the C=O group and from the π-bond to the oxygen atom. Step 2 requires a curly arrow from the O^- group to the H^+ of the acid.

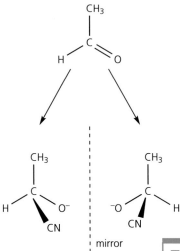

Figure 8.14 Stereochemistry of addition to carbonyl compounds

right of the planar centre. Thus, the addition of hydrogen cyanide to ethanal gives the racemic mixture of both enantiomers of 2-hydroxypropanenitrile (Figure 8.14).

There is often confusion when explaining the stereochemical outcomes of nucleophilic addition to asymmetric carbonyl compounds and S_N1 substitution to halogenoalkanes. With carbonyl addition, a common error in the explanation of a racemic mixture is to say that the intermediate is planar and can be attacked from either side. This is not true, as the intermediate is tetrahedral. It is the starting aldehyde or ketone that is planar at the reaction site and so can be attacked (by the cyanide ion) from above or below the plane. With S_N1 substitution it is the intermediate carbocation that is planar and so can be attacked from the top or bottom.

> **Test yourself**
>
> 4 Explain why the product of the addition of hydrogen cyanide to propanone gives a product that has no effect on the plane of polarisation of plane-polarised monochromatic light.

Uses of nitriles in synthesis

Hydroxynitriles produced in this way can be hydrolysed to hydroxycarboxylic acids, for example:

$$CH_3CH(OH)CN + 2H_2O + H^+ \rightarrow CH_3CH(OH)COOH + NH_4^+$$

The reaction mixture is heated under reflux. The product is the racemic mixture of the two enantiomers of 2-hydroxypropanoic acid, which is also called lactic acid. Hydroxynitriles can also be reduced to hydroxyamines, for example:

$$CH_3CH(OH)CN + 4[H] \rightarrow CH_3CH(OH)CH_2NH_2$$

Suitable reducing agents for this reaction are:

- lithium tetrahydridoaluminate(III) (lithium aluminium hydride), $LiAlH_4$, in dry ether solution
- sodium tetrahydridoborate(III), $NaBH_4$, in aqueous solution
- hydrogen gas with a platinum catalyst
- sodium in ethanol

Addition–elimination reactions

Both aldehydes and ketones react with compounds containing an H_2N- group. The lone pair of electrons on the nitrogen atom acts as a nucleophile and forms a bond with the $\delta+$ carbon atom in the C=O group. However, instead of an H^+ ion adding on to the O^- formed, the substance loses a water molecule and a C=N bond is formed. The general equation is:

$$>C=O + H_2N-X \rightarrow >C=N-X + H_2O$$

Since the nitrogen atom has a lone pair of electrons, the bond angles around the nitrogen in the product are 120°. This means that in this type of reaction aldehydes (other than methanal) and asymmetric ketones produce a mixture of two geometric isomers (Figure 8.15).

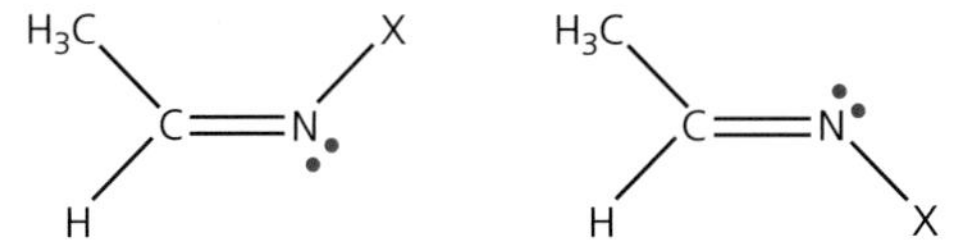

Figure 8.15

One compound that reacts in this way is 2,4-dinitrophenylhydrazine (Figure 8.16).

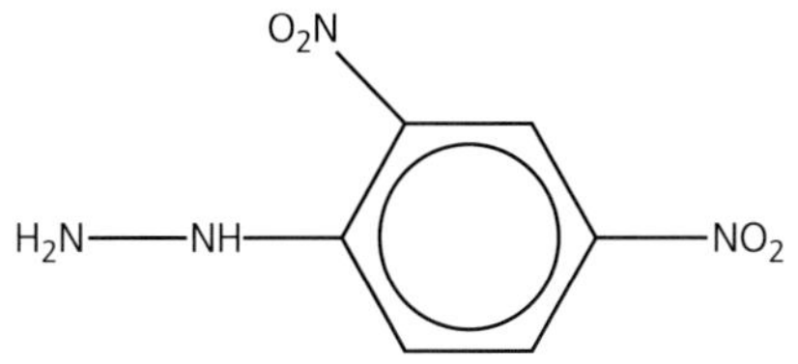

Figure 8.16

The equation for the reaction between propanone and 2,4-dinitrophenylhydrazine is shown in Figure 8.17.

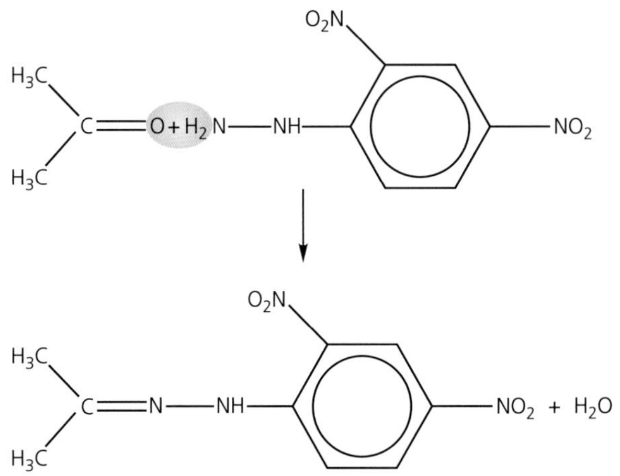

Figure 8.17

The importance of the reaction of carbonyl compounds with 2,4-dinitrophenylhydrazine is that the product is insoluble. Therefore, this reaction can be used as a test for the presence of a carbonyl group.

A solution of 2,4-dinitrophenyl-hydrazine is called Brady's reagent.

Test for a carbonyl group

Add a solution of 2,4-dinitrophenylhydrazine (**Brady's reagent**) to the suspected carbonyl compound:

- Simple aliphatic aldehydes and ketones give yellow precipitates.
- Aromatic aldehydes (e.g. benzaldehyde, C_6H_5CHO) and ketones (e.g. phenylethanone, $C_6H_5COCH_3$) give orange precipitates.

The identity of the carbonyl compound can be found by the following method:

- React the carbonyl compound with a solution of 2,4-dinitrophenylhydrazine.
- Filter off the precipitate.
- Recrystallise (p. 284) the precipitate using the minimum amount of hot ethanol.

- Dry the purified product and measure its melting temperature.
- Refer to a data book and compare this melting temperature with those of 2,4-dinitrophenylhydrazine derivatives of aldehydes and ketones. This enables the identity of the carbonyl compound to be established.

Oxidation of aldehydes

Aldehydes (but *not* ketones) are readily oxidised. If the reaction is carried out in acid solution the product is a carboxylic acid:

$$RCHO + [O] \rightarrow RCOOH$$

If the reaction is carried out in alkaline solution (Fehling's solution or Tollens' reagent), the product is the carboxylate anion:

$$RCHO + [O] + OH^- \rightarrow RCOO^- + H_2O$$

There are a number of suitable oxidising agents:

- Fehling's solution (a mixture of copper(II) sulfate and sodium potassium tartrate in alkali) is reduced from a deep-blue solution to a red precipitate of copper(I) oxide, Cu_2O, when warmed with an aldehyde. (Benedict's solution is a similar mixture and also produces a red precipitate of copper(I) oxide when warmed with an aldehyde.)
- Tollens' reagent (a solution made by adding a few drops of sodium hydroxide to silver nitrate solution and then dissolving the precipitate in dilute ammonia) is reduced to give a silver mirror on warming with an aldehyde.
- Orange potassium dichromate(VI) in acidic solution is reduced to green Cr(III) on heating with an aldehyde.
- Potassium manganate(VII) oxidises aldehydes in acidic, neutral or alkaline solution. In acidic solution, the purple manganate(VII) is reduced to give colourless Mn^{2+}. In neutral or alkaline solution, it is reduced to a brown precipitate of MnO_2.

> The reaction with Fehling's solution does not work with aldehydes of large molecular mass because they are too insoluble in water.

> Aldehydes will not reduce copper(II) or silver ions, unless the ions are complexed.

Test yourself

5 Give the formula of the organic products of the reaction between propanal and:

  a) 2,4-dinitrophenylhydrazine solution

  b) potassium dichromate(VI) in dilute sulfuric acid

Test to distinguish an aldehyde from a ketone

An aldehyde can be distinguished from a ketone by the production of:

- a red precipitate (of Cu_2O) on warming with Fehling's or Benedict's solution
- a silver mirror on warming with Tollens' reagent

In both reactions, the aldehyde is oxidised to the salt of a carboxylic acid — for example, with ethanal:

$$CH_3CHO + [O] + OH^- \rightarrow CH_3COO^- + H_2O$$
  ethanal   ethanoate ion

Ketones do not undergo these reactions. Therefore, if these tests are carried out on a ketone, Fehling's or Benedict's solution remains blue and Tollens' reagent remains colourless.

Iodoform reaction

Ethanal and methyl ketones undergo the iodoform reaction with iodine in alkali, a complicated process in which the hydrogen atoms of the $CH_3C=O$ group are replaced by iodine atoms. The alkali present in the reaction mixture then causes the C−C bond to break and a pale yellow precipitate of **iodoform** (triiodomethane), CHI_3, is formed. Iodoform also has a noticeable disinfectant smell. In large doses it is toxic.

Adolf Hitler's mother died of iodoform poisoning from her treatment for breast cancer.

The overall equation is:

$$CH_3COR + 3I_2 + 4NaOH \rightarrow CHI_3 + RCOONa + 3NaI + 3H_2O$$

where R is a hydrogen atom (ethanal) or an organic group such as $-CH_3$, $-C_2H_5$ or $-C_6H_5$ in ketones.

The sequence of reactions is as follows:

- Sodium hydroxide solution is added to iodine solution to form iodate(I) ions (IO^-):

$$I_2 + 2OH^- \rightarrow IO^- + I^- + H_2O$$

- These substitute into the $-CH_3$ group next to the $C=O$ group, forming a $CI_3C=O$ group. The electron-withdrawing effect of the three halogen atoms and the oxygen atom weaken the σ-bond between the two carbon atoms and this breaks, forming iodoform:

$$CH_3COR \xrightarrow{IO^-(aq)} CI_3COR \xrightarrow{OH^-(aq)} CHI_3 + RCOO^-$$

This reaction also takes placed with ethanol and secondary methyl alcohols. They are first oxidised by the iodate(I) ions to ethanal and methyl ketones respectively under the conditions of the reaction. For example, with propan-2-ol:

$$CH_3CH(OH)CH_3 + [O] \rightarrow CH_3COCH_3 + H_2O$$

Then as above.

To carry out the iodoform reaction, the organic substance is gently warmed with either a mixture of iodine and sodium hydroxide solution or with a solution of potassium iodide in sodium chlorate(I).

> **Tip**
>
> The iodoform reaction is a test for carbonyl compounds containing the $CH_3C=O$ group and for alcohols containing the $CH_3CH(OH)$ group.

Test yourself

6 State the type of reaction between ethanal and Fehling's solution.

Summary

Test for a carbonyl group: add a few drops of the organic compound to a solution of 2,4-dinitrophenylhydrazine. A yellow or orange precipitate indicates the presence of a carbonyl group.

Reactions of aldehydes: Figure 8.18 summarises the reactions of aldehydes.

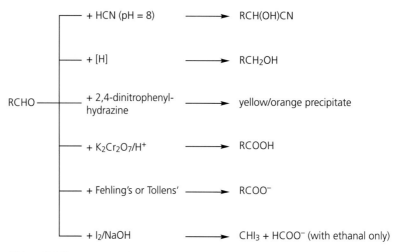

Figure 8.18

Reactions of ketones: Figure 8.19 summarises the reactions of ketones.

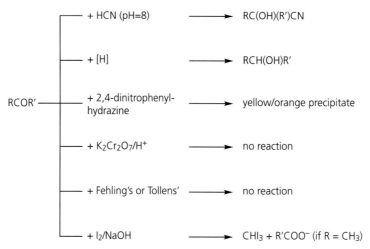

Figure 8.19

Tests to distinguish between an aldehyde and a ketone: warm the substance with:

- Fehling's or Benedict's solution — aldehydes give a red precipitate; ketones do not alter the blue colour of the Fehling's solution
- Tollens' reagent — aldehydes give a silver mirror; ketones do not

Iodoform test: if a pale yellow precipitate is obtained when a substance is gently warmed with a solution of iodine and sodium hydroxide, the substance contains either a $CH_3CH(OH)$ or CH_3CO group.

- If the substance is an aldehyde, it can only be ethanal.
- If the substance is a primary alcohol it can only be ethanol.

Summary tasks

Make sure that you understand:

- the difference in structure between aldehydes and ketones
- that both have a $\delta-$ O atom and hence are water-soluble due to hydrogen bonding
- that they are planar around the C=O group

Check that you can describe and write equations for:

- the preparation of aldehydes from primary alcohols and ketones from secondary alcohols (and are able to draw the relevant diagram)
- the reactions of aldehydes and ketones with hydrogen cyanide and 2,4-dinitrophenylhydrazine and with reducing agents ($LiAlH_4$ or H_2/Pt)
- the mechanism of nucleophilic addition with HCN and its stereochemical implications
- the reactions of aldehydes with Fehling's, Tollens' and oxidising agents (H^+/$Cr_2O_7^{2-}$ and MnO_4^-)
- the tests for carbonyl compounds and those to distinguish between aldehydes and ketones
- the iodoform reaction with ethanal and asymmetric methyl ketones, and with alcohols containing the $CH_3CH(OH)$ group

Questions

1 What is the difference in structure between an aldehyde and a ketone?

2 When propanal is prepared from propan-1-ol, the mixture is kept at a temperature between the boiling temperatures of propanal and propan-1-ol. Explain why this is necessary.

3 Explain why ethanal is soluble in water but pentanal is almost insoluble.

4 a) Write the equation for the reaction between hydrogen cyanide and propanone.

   b) Explain why this reaction does not take place unless a trace of alkali is added.

5 Write the mechanism for the reaction of propanone with lithium aluminium hydride in dry ether, followed by addition of acid.

6 Explain why the product of the addition of hydrogen cyanide to butanone gives a product that has no effect on the plane of polarisation of plane-polarised monochromatic light.

7 Give the formula of the organic products of the reaction, if any, between propanal and each of the following:

a) Fehling's solution

b) Tollens' reagent

c) a mixture of iodine and aqueous sodium hydroxide

In each case, state the observations that would be made.

8 Give details of how you would prepare a sample of butanone (Figure 8.20, boiling temperature 80°C) from butan-2-ol ($CH_3CH(OH)CH_2CH_3$, boiling temperature 100°C). Include in your answer a diagram of the apparatus that you would use.

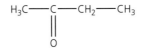

Figure 8.20 Butanone

9 a) Define the terms 'nucleophile' and 'oxidation'.

   b) State the type of reaction between ethanal and each of the following:

   i) hydrogen cyanide

   ii) Fehling's solution

   iii) 2,4-dinitrophenylhydrazine

10 Describe how you would identify the compound that gave an orange precipitate with 2,4-dinitrophenylhydrazine and no silver mirror with Tollens' reagent.

Exam practice questions

1 a) 4.80 g of a compound X was burnt in excess oxygen and produced 11.4 g of carbon dioxide and 5.84 g of water. Show that this is consistent with compound X having a molecular formula $C_4H_{10}O$. (3)

b) When some compound X was heated with a solution of potassium dichromate in sulfuric acid it formed a product, Y, which was distilled off as it formed.

The compound Y gave a yellow precipitate with 2,4-dinitrophenylhydrazine. When Y was warmed with Fehling's solution, the Fehling's solution remained blue.

  i) Give the structural formulae of X and Y. Justify your answers. (4)

  ii) There are two isomers that could be X. Draw them both, showing clearly how they differ. (1)

c) A different compound, Z, also has the molecular formula $C_4H_{10}O$. When oxidised in the same way as X, it produced a product that also gave yellow precipitate with 2,4-dinitrophenylhydrazine, but which reacted with warm Fehling's solution, producing a red precipitate.

Deduce, showing your reasoning, two possible structural formulae for Z and name them. (5)

d) Which of the compounds shown in Figure 8.21 will give a pale yellow precipitate when gently warmed with iodine in alkali? (1)

Compound 1 : [structure with OH]

Compound 2 : [structure with OH]

Compound 3 : [structure with O]

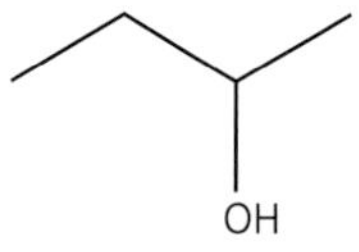

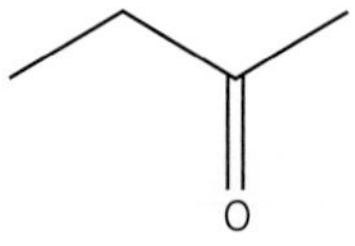

Compound 4 : [structure with O]

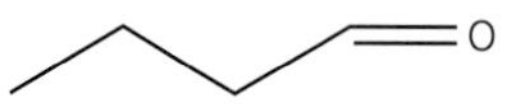

Figure 8.21

  A Compounds 1 and 2 only
  B Compounds 1 and 4 only
  C Compounds 2 and 3 only
  D Compounds 3 and 4 only

(Total 14 marks)

2 Propanal reacts with hydrogen cyanide in a nucleophilic addition reaction.
  a) Which of the following is *not* a nucleophile? (1)
    A NH_3 **C** H_3O^+
    B H_2O **D** Cl^-
  b) Draw the mechanism for this reaction. (3)
  c) State the conditions necessary and explain, in terms of the mechanism, why these conditions are necessary. (3)
  d) What kind of isomerism does the product of this reaction show? (1)
  (Total 8 marks)

3 a) Substance Q has a molecular formula of $C_5H_{10}O$. It reacts with 2,4-dinitrophenylhydrazine to give a yellow precipitate, but does not react with Fehling's solution or with iodine in alkali. What does each of these tests tell us about the structure of Q? Hence write its structural formula. (3)

  b) Q has an isomer, R, that forms a yellow precipitate with 2,4-dinitrophenylhydrazine. R also reacts with iodine in alkali to give a pale yellow precipitate.

    i) Draw the *two* structural formulae that could be substance R. (2)

    ii) Write the equation for the reaction of 2,4-dinitrophenylhydrazine with either one of the two isomers of R that you have drawn in (i). (2)

    iii) Suggest why the product you have drawn in (ii) is a mixture of two isomers. (2)

  c) Q has another isomer, S, which also reacts with 2,4-dinitrophenylhydrazine and forms a red-brown precipitate when warmed with Fehling's solution.

    i) Write the formula of the red-brown precipitate. (1)

    ii) Give the structural formulae of three isomers that could be compound S. (3)
    (Total 13 marks)

8 Carbonyl compounds (Topic 17)

9 Carboxylic acids (Topic 17)

Carboxylic acids and their derivatives contain the group shown in Figure 9.1.

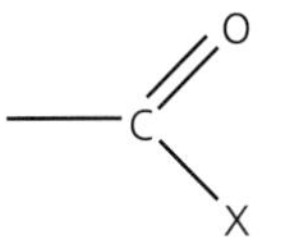

Figure 9.1

The nature of X varies as shown in Table 9.1.

Table 9.1 Carboxylic acids and their derivatives

Type of compound	Structure of X	Example	
		Name	Formula
Carboxylic acid	O–H	Ethanoic acid	CH_3COOH
Ester	O–R*	Ethyl ethanoate	$CH_3COOC_2H_5$
Acyl chloride	Cl	Ethanoyl chloride	CH_3COCl
Amide	NH_2	Ethanamide	CH_3CONH_2

* R stands for an alkyl group (e.g. CH_3, C_2H_5) or a benzene ring

The reactivity of the C=O group is considerably modified by the presence of the X group, so much so that, unlike aldehydes and ketones, carboxylic acids and their derivatives do not react with 2,4-dinitrophenylhydrazine.

The C=O group is polarised with the less electronegative carbon atom $\delta+$ and the more electronegative oxygen atom $\delta-$.

The mechanism for many of the reactions is for a nucleophile to attack the $\delta+$ carbon atom. This is then followed by the loss of the X group as an X^- ion (Figure 9.2).

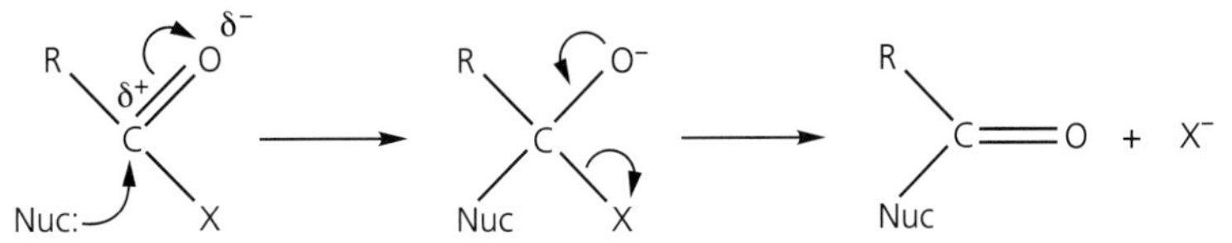

Figure 9.2

This type of reaction is called an **addition–elimination** reaction. The ease of reaction depends on:

- the strength of the C–X bond. The weakest of these bonds is the C–Cl bond, so acid chlorides are the most susceptible to nucleophilic attack.
- the stability of the leaving group, X^-. The NH_2^- ion is too strong a base to be produced in aqueous solutions. This means that amides do not undergo addition–elimination reactions.

Carboxylic acids and their derivatives in nature

Carboxylic acids are found in a number of fruits and vegetables:

- Citric acid, $HOOCCH_2C(OH)(COOH)CH_2COOH$, is a tribasic acid. Figure 9.3 shows its skeletal formula.

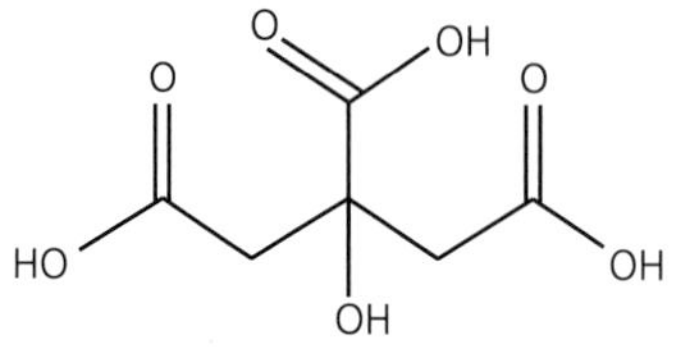

Figure 9.3

It is present in citrus fruits, particularly lemons and limes. It is an antioxidant and is used in the food industry as an additive to give flavour and, mixed with citrate, as a buffer. Its E number is E330. In the form of citrate, it is an intermediate in the Krebs cycle in cells and is, therefore, involved in the metabolism of fats, proteins and carbohydrates.

- Malic acid, $HOOCCH_2CH(OH)COOH$, is present in apples (Latin *malum*) and grapes and gives them their sharp taste. Its systematic name is 2-hydroxybutane-dioic acid.
- Ethanedioic acid (old name oxalic acid), $HOOCCOOH$, is found in rhubarb leaves.

Esters are also common in nature. Fats and vegetable oils are esters of propane-1,2,3-triol (glycerol), $CH_2OHCH(OH)CH_2OH$, and a variety of organic acids:

- Cows' milk contains an ester of the acids 2-hydroxypropanoic (lactic) acid, $CH_3CH(OH)COOH$, and butanoic acid, $CH_3CH_2CH_2COOH$; goats' milk contains an ester of octanoic (caproic) acid, $CH_3(CH_2)_5COOH$. The word 'caproic' comes from the Latin *caper* for goat, as does the Zodiac sign Capricorn. Solid animal fats are esters of acids, for example stearic acid, $C_{17}H_{35}COOH$, which is saturated.
- Vegetable and fish oils are esters containing unsaturated carboxylic acids such as $C_{17}H_{29}COOH$, $CH_3CH_2CH=CHCH_2CH=CHCH_2CH=CH(CH_2)_7COOH$, which is an omega-3 acid. It is called omega-3 because the first double bond starts at the third carbon from the end furthest from the $-COOH$ group, omega being the last letter in the Greek alphabet.

Carboxylic acids

Carboxylic acids contain the group shown in Figure 9.4.

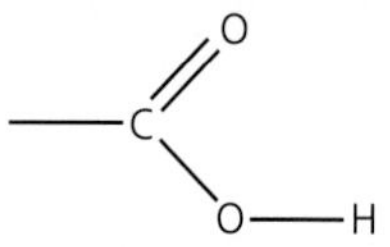

Figure 9.4

This is called the **carboxyl** group and consists of the **carb**onyl group, C=O, and the hydro**xyl** group, OH.

The names of some of the members of this homologous series, together with their melting and boiling temperatures, are given in Table 9.2.

Table 9.2 Carboxylic acids

Formula	Name	Melting temperature/°C	Boiling temperature/°C	$K_a/$ $mol\,dm^{-3}$
HCOOH	Methanoic acid	8	101	1.78×10^{-4}
CH_3COOH	Ethanoic acid	17	118	1.75×10^{-5}
CH_3CH_2COOH	Propanoic acid	−21	141	1.39×10^{-5}
$CH_3CH_2CH_2COOH$	Butanoic acid	−7	164	1.51×10^{-5}
$CH_3CH(CH_3)COOH$	Methylpropanoic acid	−47	154	1.41×10^{-5}

Methanoic acid is also called formic acid, because it is present in ant stings (Latin *formix* ant). Ethanoic acid is also called acetic acid, as it is the acid in vinegar (Latin *acetum* vinegar).

The boiling temperatures of carboxylic acids are higher than equivalent carbonyl compounds because there is considerable hydrogen bonding between molecules. With methanoic and ethanoic acids pairs of acid molecules (dimers) are formed (Figure 9.5).

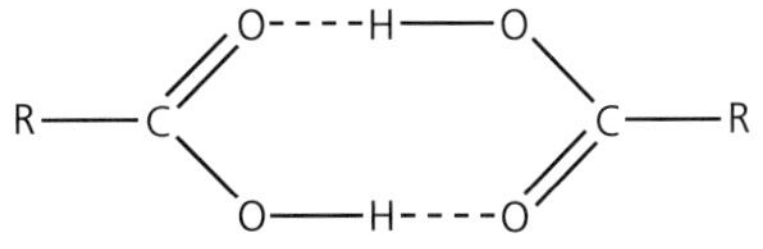

Figure 9.5

This occurs to a lesser extent with acids that have more carbon atoms, as the hydrogen bonding is inhibited by the zigzag chains of carbon atoms.

When the acid is boiled, hydrogen bonds and London forces are broken and so the boiling temperatures of the acids have the pattern that is expected from the increasing number of electrons: methanoic, 24 electrons; ethanoic, 32 electrons; propanoic, 40 electrons and so on.

Methylpropanoic acid has fewer points of contact between adjacent molecules than does the straight-chain butanoic acid, so the London (temporary induced dipole–induced dipole) forces are weaker. This means that its melting and boiling temperatures are lower than those of butanoic acid. This is as expected with a branched-chain compound and its straight-chain isomer.

Names of carboxylic acids

The names of carboxylic acids are derived from the number of carbon atoms in the chain, *including* the carbon atom of the −COOH group. This carbon atom is regarded as the first carbon atom. Therefore, $ClCH_2CH_2COOH$ is called 3-chloropropanoic acid and $CH_3CH(OH)COOH$ is called 2-hydroxypropanoic acid.

Tip

Never write the formula of butanoic acid as C_3H_7COOH because this could also represent its isomer, methylpropanoic acid.

The old name for 2-hydroxypropanoic acid is lactic acid, which is still used in biochemistry.

Worked example

Name the compound that has the formula $CH_3CHClCH(CH_3)CH{=}CHCOOH$.

Answer

The carbon chain is six carbon atoms long (hex-). There is:

- a double bond on carbon number 2
- a $-CH_3$ group on carbon number 4
- a chlorine atom on carbon number 5

Its name is 5-chloro-4-methylhex-2-enoic acid.

Some organic acids have two $-COOH$ groups. Examples are:

- HOOCCOOH (sometimes written $H_2C_2O_4$), which is ethanedioic acid
- HOOCCH=CHCOOH, which exists as two geometric isomers — *cis*-butenedioic acid and *trans*-butenedioic acid

Test yourself

1 Name the following compounds:

a) $(CH_3)_2C(OH)COOH$ b) $CH_3CHClCOCl$ c) $C_2H_5COOCH(CH_3)_2$

Aromatic acids contain a benzene ring. The formula of benzenecarboxylic acid (benzoic acid) is shown in Figure 9.6.

Figure 9.7 shows the formula of benzene-1,4-dicarboxylic acid (terephthalic acid).

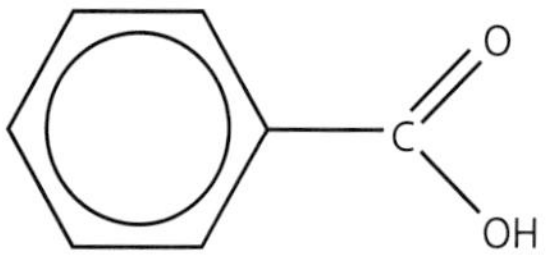

Figure 9.6

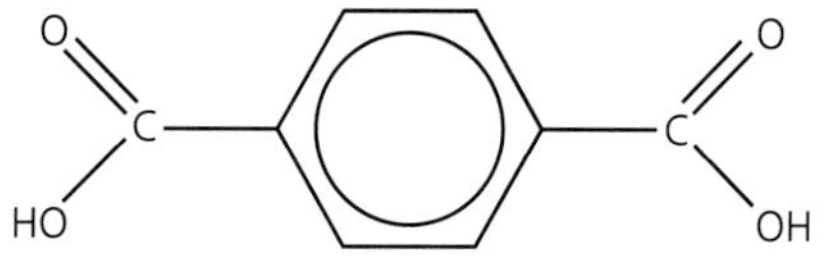

Figure 9.7

Physical properties

The acids in the homologous series $C_nH_{2n+1}COOH$ are liquids up to $n = 9$.

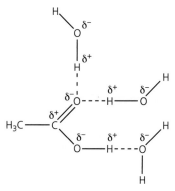

Figure 9.8

- All carboxylic acids have strong smells. Vinegar is a dilute solution of ethanoic acid. The smell of rancid butter comes from butanoic acid formed by the action of bacteria on butter fat.
- Hydrogen bonding with water molecules enables those carboxylic acids with only a few carbon atoms to dissolve in water (Figure 9.8). Methanoic acid and ethanoic acid mix with water in all proportions. The solubility in water decreases as the hydrocarbon chain lengthens. This is because the chain is hydrophobic. Conversely, solubility in lipids increases as the chain lengthens.
- Benzoic acid, C_6H_5COOH, is a solid that melts at 122°C. It is sparingly soluble in cold water and soluble in hot water. This makes water a suitable solvent for purifying benzoic acid by recrystallisation (p. 284).

Preparation

Carboxylic acids can be prepared by:

- the oxidation of a primary alcohol. When heated under reflux with acidified potassium dichromate(VI), the primary alcohol is oxidised to a carboxylic acid. For example, propan-1-ol is oxidised to propanoic acid:

$$CH_3CH_2CH_2OH + 2[O] \rightarrow CH_3CH_2COOH + H_2O$$

- the oxidation of an aldehyde. Aldehydes are oxidised to carboxylic acids by the same reagent and under the same conditions as primary alcohols, for example:

$$CH_3CHO + [O] \rightarrow CH_3COOH$$

- the hydrolysis of an ester (p. 222)
- the hydrolysis of a nitrile. Nitriles are compounds that contain the $C \equiv N$ group. When heated under reflux with dilute acid, a nitrile is hydrolysed to a carboxylic acid and an ammonium salt, for example:

$$CH_3CN + H^+ + 2H_2O \rightarrow CH_3COOH + NH_4^+$$

If heated under reflux with aqueous alkali, the salt of the carboxylic acid is formed. Subsequent addition of a strong acid, such as dilute sulfuric acid, protonates the carboxylate ion and the carboxylic acid is formed:

$$CH_3CN + OH^- + H_2O \rightarrow CH_3COO^- + NH_3$$

then:

$$CH_3COO^- + H^+ \rightarrow CH_3COOH$$

Hydroxynitriles (p. 202) are hydrolysed to hydroxyacids in a similar way, for example:

$$CH_3CH(OH)CN + H^+ + 2H_2O \rightarrow CH_3CH(OH)COOH + NH_4^+$$

2-hydroxypropanenitrile $\rightarrow$ 2-hydroxypropanoic acid (lactic acid)

- the iodoform reaction of a methyl ketone or a secondary alcohol (p. 207). On addition of a solution of iodine in aqueous sodium hydroxide to a methyl ketone (such as butanone, $CH_3CH_2COCH_3$), the salt of the acid with one *fewer* carbon atoms (propanoic acid, CH_3CH_2COOH) is produced. The free carboxylic acid is formed by adding excess strong acid to the mixture.

$$CH_3CH_2COCH_3 + 3I_2 + 4OH^- \rightarrow CH_3CH_2COO^- + CHI_3 + 3I^- + 3H_2O$$

then

$$CH_3CH_2COO^- + H^+ \rightarrow CH_3CH_2COOH$$

Butan-2-ol, $CH_3CH_2CH(OH)CH_3$, would also produce propanoic acid in this reaction.

Chemical reactions

The reactions of carboxylic acids are illustrated using ethanoic acid as the example.

As an acid
Carboxylic acids are weak acids (p. 29).

> **Tip**
>
> Vinegar is a 3% solution of ethanoic acid. It is produced from ethanol, which is made by the fermentation of grains and sugars. Ethanol is then oxidised by the oxygen in the air in a reaction catalysed by enzymes in specific bacteria.

The carboxylic acid has to be distilled off from the reaction mixture.

Reaction with water

Carboxylic acids react reversibly with water:

$$CH_3COOH + H_2O \rightleftharpoons CH_3COO^- + H_3O^+$$

Aqueous solutions of ethanoic acid have pH $\approx$ 3.

The $-OH$ group in carboxylic acids is more acidic than the $-OH$ group in alcohols. There are two reasons for this. First, the $C=O$ group pulls electrons away from the $-OH$ group, making the hydrogen atom more $\delta+$ and therefore easier to remove as an H^+ ion.

Second, the carboxylate anion has the negative charge shared between two oxygen atoms. The p_z-orbital of the carbon atom (containing one electron), the p_z-orbital of the oxygen double-bonded to it (containing one electron), and the p_z-orbital of the other oxygen (containing its one electron and the one gained by the formation of the $O-$ ion) all overlap (Figure 9.9).

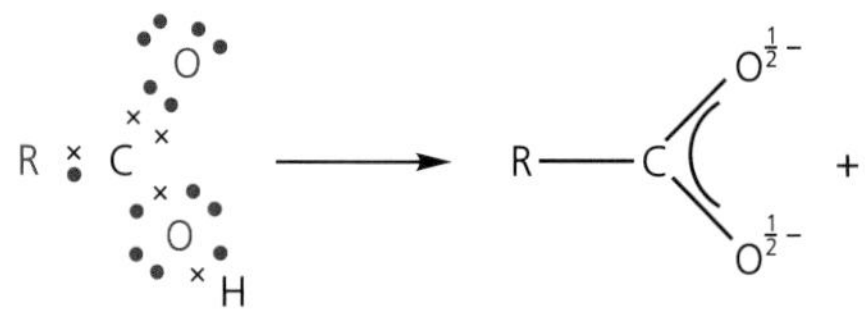

Figure 9.9

This delocalisation of charge stabilises the conjugate base, RCO_2^-, with respect to the acid.

Reaction with bases

Carboxylic acids form salts with bases such as sodium hydroxide:

$$CH_3COOH + NaOH \rightarrow CH_3COONa + H_2O$$

All carboxylic acids are weak acids (see Table 9.2 on p. 213 for their acid dissociation constants). The concentration of a carboxylic acid can be found by titrating it with a strong base, such as sodium hydroxide, using phenolphthalein as the indicator. The amount (moles) of citric acid in lemon juice can be estimated in this way.

Reaction with carbonates and hydrogencarbonates

Carboxylic acids produce carbon dioxide with effervescence when added to a carbonate:

$$2CH_3COOH(aq) + Na_2CO_3 \rightarrow 2CH_3COONa(aq) + CO_2(g) + H_2O(l)$$

Similarly, with hydrogencarbonate:

$$CH_3COOH(aq) + NaHCO_3(s) \rightarrow CH_3COONa(aq) + CO_2(g) + H_2O(l)$$

Reduction

Carboxylic acids are reduced by lithium tetrahydridoaluminate(III), $LiAlH_4$, dissolved in dry ether (ethoxyethane). The H^- ion in the AlH_4^- is a powerful nucleophile. It adds on to the $\delta+$ carbon atom in the $-COOH$ group. A series of reactions takes place and the final product has to be hydrolysed by dilute acid. The carboxylic acid is reduced to a primary alcohol. The overall equation is:

$$CH_3COOH + 4[H] \rightarrow CH_3CH_2OH + H_2O$$

Tip

The symbol [H] is used in organic reactions involving a reducing agent such as $LiAlH_4$, because the full equation is too complex. However, the equation must still balance, which is why 4[H] is written in this equation.

Carboxylic acids are *not* reduced by hydrogen gas in the presence of a catalyst of nickel or platinum, unlike alkenes, which are reduced to alkanes.

$$CH_2{=}CHCOOH \xrightarrow{\text{LiAlH}_4} CH_2{=}CHCH_2OH$$

$$CH_2{=}CHCOOH \xrightarrow{\text{H}_2/\text{Pt}} CH_3CH_2COOH$$

The H⁻ ion in LiAlH₄ attacks δ+ sites. Therefore, LiAlH₄ will not reduce a C=C group as it has a high electron density.

Test yourself

2 Identify the organic product obtained on reducing CHOCH=CHCH(OH)COOH with:

a) lithium tetrahydridoaluminate(III) in dry ether followed by dilute hydrochloric acid

b) hydrogen gas and a platinum catalyst

With phosphorus(v) chloride: formation of acyl chloride

Ethanoic acid can be converted to ethanoyl chloride by adding solid phosphorus pentachloride to the dry acid:

$$CH_3COOH + PCl_5 \rightarrow CH_3COCl + POCl_3 + HCl$$

This is a similar reaction to that between PCl_5 and an alcohol. In both reactions, the −OH group is replaced by a chlorine atom and clouds of misty fumes of hydrogen chloride are given off. The conversion can also be performed using thionyl chloride, $SOCl_2$:

$$RCOOH + SOCl_2 \rightarrow RCOCl + SO_2 + HCl$$

The advantage of this reagent is that the inorganic products are gases, so only the acyl chloride is left in the reaction flask.

Reaction with alcohols: esterification

Carboxylic acids do not react readily with nucleophiles. However, they do react with alcohols in the presence of concentrated sulfuric acid (as a catalyst) in a reversible reaction to form esters:

acid + alcohol ⇌ ester + water

For example:

$$\underset{\text{ethanoic acid}}{CH_3COOH} + \underset{\text{ethanol}}{C_2H_5OH} \overset{\text{H}_2\text{SO}_4(\text{l})}{\rightleftharpoons} \underset{\text{ethyl ethanoate}}{CH_3COOC_2H_5} + H_2O$$

The catalyst acts by protonating the C=O group of the ethanoic acid, which then loses a water molecule:

$$CH_3COOH + H_2SO_4 \rightarrow HSO_4^- + CH_3C^+(OH)_2$$

This is then attacked by the lone pair of electrons on the alcohol's oxygen atom. Finally water and H^+ ions are lost and the ester formed.

Methyl butanoate is prepared by the reaction of butanoic acid with methanol in the presence of a few drops of concentrated sulfuric acid:

$$CH_3CH_2CH_2COOH + CH_3OH \rightleftharpoons CH_3CH_2CH_2COOCH_3 + H_2O$$

Methyl butanoate, an ester, smells of pineapples and is used to flavour sweets. This can be shown experimentally:

- Add a few drops of concentrated sulfuric acid to a mixture of butanoic acid and methanol.
- Warm for several minutes in a water bath.
- Pour the contents into a beaker of dilute sodium hydrogencarbonate solution.
- The smell of pineapples can be noticed readily.

Test yourself

3 Write equations for the reactions of propanoic acid with:

  a) aqueous sodium hydroxide   b) methanol

Free radical substitution: formation of a halogenoacid

If chlorine is bubbled into a boiling carboxylic acid in the presence of sunlight or ultraviolet (UV) light, a chlorine atom replaces one of the hydrogen atoms in the alkyl chain:

$$CH_3COOH + Cl_2 \rightarrow CH_2ClCOOH + HCl$$

This is an example of free-radical substitution. It is similar to the reaction of methane with chlorine in the presence of UV light.

If propanoic acid is used in place of ethanoic acid, the product is 2-chloropropanoic acid, not 3-chloropropanoic acid:

$$CH_3CH_2COOH + Cl_2 \rightarrow CH_3CHClCOOH + HCl$$

Summary

The chemical reactions of carboxylic acids are summarised in Figure 9.10.

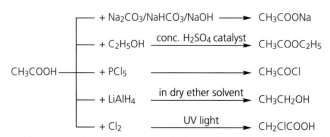

Figure 9.10

Acyl chlorides

These are also known as acid chlorides and have the functional group shown in Figure 9.11.

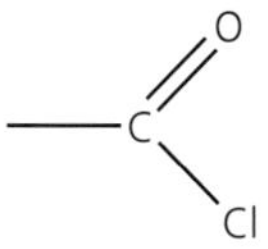

Figure 9.11

Physical properties

- Most acyl chlorides are volatile liquids at room temperature.
- They are soluble in several organic solvents, but react with water.

The names, formulae and boiling temperatures of some acyl chlorides are given in Table 9.3. Methanoyl chloride has never been isolated as it decomposes at room temperature into carbon monoxide and hydrogen chloride.

Table 9.3 Some acyl chlorides

Name	Formula	Boiling temperature/°C
Ethanoyl chloride	CH_3COCl	51
Propanoyl chloride	CH_3CH_2COCl	80
Butanoyl chloride	$CH_3CH_2CH_2COCl$	102
Benzoyl chloride	C_6H_5COCl	197

Preparation

Acyl chlorides are prepared from carboxylic acids. The $-OH$ group is replaced by a chlorine atom. The reagents that can be used are phosphorus(v) chloride (phosphorus pentachloride), phosphorus(III) chloride or thionyl chloride. Starting from ethanoic acid, the equations are:

$$CH_3COOH + PCl_5 \rightarrow CH_3COCl + POCl_3 + HCl$$

$$3CH_3COOH + PCl_3 \rightarrow 3CH_3COCl + H_3PO_3$$

$$CH_3COOH + SOCl_2 \rightarrow CH_3COCl + SO_2 + HCl$$

The organic product is ethanoyl chloride.

Chemical reactions

In acid chlorides, the carbon atom of the C=O group is very $\delta+$ as the carbon atom is joined to two highly electronegative atoms; the $C-Cl$ bond is not very strong and Cl^- is a good leaving group. Taken together, this makes the molecule very susceptible to nucleophilic attack in addition–elimination reactions. The end result is a **substitution** in which the nucleophile replaces the chlorine atom.

Acid chlorides react much more quickly than carboxylic acids. The carbon in carboxylic acids is less $\delta+$ than the carbon in acid chlorides, the $C-OH$ bond is stronger than the $C-Cl$ bond and OH^- is a less good leaving group than Cl^-.

Reaction with water

Ethanoyl chloride reacts vigorously with water, forming ethanoic acid and clouds of hydrogen chloride gas:

$$CH_3COCl + H_2O \rightarrow CH_3COOH + HCl$$

The first step is the addition of water. The oxygen atom in water has a lone pair of electrons. This makes it a nucleophile. The lone pair forms a bond with the $\delta+$ carbon atom in the C=O group. Simultaneously, the π-bond breaks and the C=O oxygen becomes O^- (Figure 9.12).

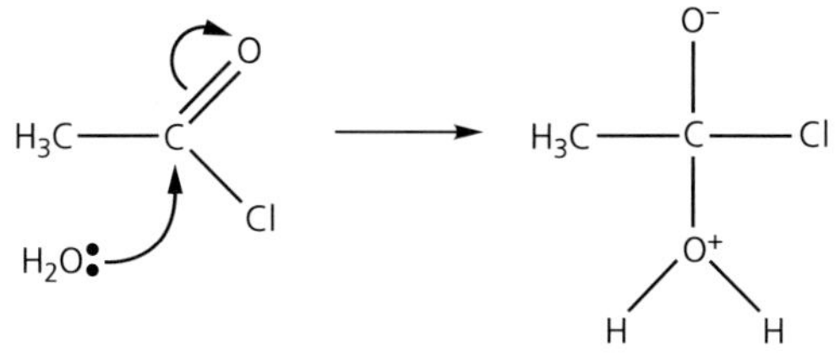

Figure 9.12

This is followed by the loss of H^+ and Cl^- as gaseous HCl in the form of steamy fumes (Figure 9.13).

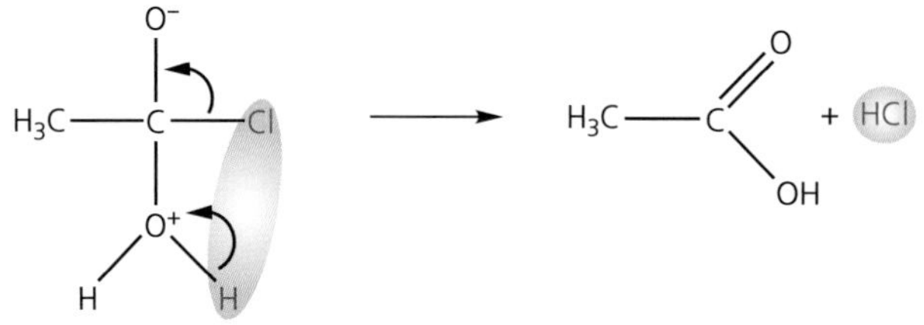

Figure 9.13

This rapid reaction with water means that when using ethanoyl chloride as a reactant, all reagents and glassware must be dry.

Benzoyl chloride is less reactive than ethanoyl chloride and reacts only slowly with water. Therefore, it can be used with reagents in aqueous solution.

Reaction with alcohols

Ethanoyl chloride reacts rapidly in a non-reversible reaction with alcohols. The products are an ester and misty fumes of hydrogen chloride vapour:

$$\underset{\text{ethanoyl chloride}}{CH_3COCl} + \underset{\text{methanol}}{CH_3OH} \rightarrow \underset{\text{methyl ethanoate}}{CH_3COOCH_3} + HCl$$

The mechanism of this reaction is analogous to that of the reaction with water.

> The alcohol must be dry, or the acyl chloride will be hydrolysed by the water.

As this is a non-reversible reaction with a good yield, it is a more efficient method of making an ester than reacting the alcohol with a carboxylic acid. The latter reaction is reversible with a maximum possible yield of under 70%.

Reaction with concentrated ammonia

The nitrogen atom in ammonia has a lone pair of electrons, which is used in a nucleophilic attack on the C=O group. The product is an amide (p. 257), for example:

$$\underset{\text{ethanoyl chloride}}{CH_3COCl} + NH_3 \rightarrow \underset{\text{ethanamide}}{CH_3CONH_2} + HCl$$

With excess ammonia, the hydrogen chloride forms a white smoke of ammonium chloride:

$$HCl + NH_3 \rightarrow NH_4Cl$$

Reaction with amines

Amines also have a lone pair of electrons on the nitrogen atom. They react with acyl chlorides in the same way as ammonia. The product is a substituted amide, for example:

$$CH_3COCl \quad + CH_3NH_2 \rightarrow \quad CH_3CONHCH_3 \quad + HCl$$

ethanoyl chloride $\qquad\qquad$ N–methylethanamide

> The prefix *N*- indicates that the methyl group is attached to a nitrogen atom.

Reaction with lithium tetrahydridoaluminate(III)

Acyl chlorides, like carboxylic acids and esters, are reduced by lithium tetrahydridoaluminate(III) in dry ether solution to form a primary alcohol. For example:

$$CH_3COCl + 4[H] \rightarrow CH_3CH_2OH + HCl$$

Reaction with aromatic compounds

Ethanoyl chloride reacts with benzene and with phenol (pp. 240 and 245).

Test yourself

4 Write equations for the reaction of propanoyl chloride with:

   a) ammonia   b) water   c) 2-aminoethanol, $NH_2CH_2CH_2OH$

Summary

Figure 9.14 summarises the chemical reactions of acid chlorides.

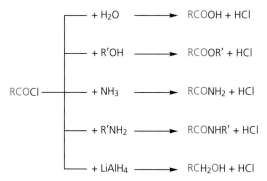

Figure 9.14

Esters

Esters have the structural formula shown in Figure 9.15.

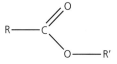

Figure 9.15

The group R can be a hydrogen atom or an organic residue, such as $-CH_3$. The group R′ must be a residue of an alcohol with a carbon atom attached to the oxygen of the ester linkage.

Esters are named after the alcohol residue, R′, followed by the name of the carboxylate group, RCOO:

- $HCOOCH_3$ is methyl methanoate.
- $CH_3COOCH_2CH_2CH_3$ is called 1-propyl ethanoate.

The prefix '1-' indicates the position of the ester linkage in the propyl chain.

> **Tip**
>
> Do not write the formula of an ester as ROCOR′ as this is ambiguous. Is the parent acid RCOOH or R′COOH?

Physical properties

Most esters are liquids at room temperature. The names and boiling points of the first four members of the series of esters derived from ethanoic acid are shown in Table 9.4.

Table 9.4 Esters derived from ethanoic acid

Name	Formula	Boiling temperature/°C
Methyl ethanoate	CH_3COOCH_3	57
Ethyl ethanoate	$CH_3COOC_2H_5$	77
1-propyl ethanoate	$CH_3COOCH_2CH_2CH_3$	102
2-propyl ethanoate	$CH_3COOCH(CH_3)_2$	93

Confusingly, an ester is written with the acid residue first then the alcohol residue but named with the alcohol residue first.

Solubility

Despite being polar molecules, all esters are insoluble in water. The reason for this is that they cannot form hydrogen bonds with water molecules because they do not have any $\delta+$ hydrogen atoms and the $\delta-$ oxygen atoms are sterically hindered, preventing close approach by water molecules.

Preparation

Esters can be prepared by warming an alcohol and a carboxylic acid under reflux with a few drops of concentrated sulfuric acid:

$$C_2H_5OH + CH_3COOH \rightleftharpoons CH_3COOC_2H_5 + H_2O$$

A higher yield is obtained if the alcohol is reacted with an acyl chloride at room temperature, because the reaction is not reversible and has a lower activation energy and so is faster:

$$C_2H_5OH + CH_3COCl \rightarrow CH_3COOC_2H_5 + HCl$$

Chemical reactions

Hydrolysis

Esters are hydrolysed when heated under reflux with either aqueous acid or aqueous alkali:

$$CH_3COOC_2H_5 + H_2O \overset{H^+(aq)}{\rightleftharpoons} CH_3COOH + C_2H_5OH$$

$$CH_3COOC_2H_5 + NaOH \rightarrow CH_3COONa + C_2H_5OH$$

Note the difference between these two reactions. In the first, the acid is a catalyst and the reaction is reversible. Therefore, the yield of acid and alcohol is low.

The hydrolysis with aqueous alkali is not reversible, so there is a good yield of the salt of the carboxylic acid and the alcohol. If the organic acid is required, the solution is cooled and excess dilute strong acid, such as hydrochloric or sulfuric, is added:

$$CH_3COONa + HCl \rightarrow CH_3COOH + NaCl$$

Soaps are produced by the hydrolysis of natural esters such as vegetable oils and animal fats. This is achieved by heating the fats/oils with aqueous sodium hydroxide.

$$\begin{array}{ll} CH_2COOR & CH_2OH \\ | & | \\ CHCOOR' + 3OH^- \rightarrow & CHOH + RCOO^- + R'COO^- + R''COO^- \\ | & | \\ CH_2COOR'' & CH_2OH \end{array}$$

This reaction is also called saponification.

The fatty acids in the ester are usually different, but many kinds of triglyceride are known. The chain lengths of the fatty acids in naturally occurring triglycerides vary, but most contain 16, 18, or 20 carbon atoms. Natural fatty acids found in plants and animals are typically composed of only even numbers of carbon atoms, reflecting the pathway for their biosynthesis from the two–carbon building–block acetyl CoA.

Transesterification

There are two types of transesterification reaction.

This reaction is also called **interesterification**.

Reaction with another organic acid

The acid part of the ester is replaced by the acid reactant. The simplest example is the reaction between ethyl ethanoate and methanoic acid in the presence of an acid catalyst. The products are ethyl methanoate and ethanoic acid:

$$CH_3COOC_2H_5 + HCOOH \rightleftharpoons HCOOC_2H_5 + CH_3COOH$$

This type of reaction is used in the manufacture of low-fat margarine (p. 224) where the incoming acid is saturated and the product acid is unsaturated.

Reaction with another alcohol

The alcohol part of the ester is replaced by the alcohol reactant. A simple example is the reaction between ethyl ethanoate and methanol in the presence of an acid catalyst. The products are methyl ethanoate and ethanol:

$$CH_3COOC_2H_5 + CH_3OH \rightleftharpoons CH_3COOCH_3 + C_2H_5OH$$

This type of reaction is used in the manufacture of biodiesel (p. 225) where the reactant alcohol is methanol or ethanol and the product alcohol is propane-1,2,3-triol.

Natural esters

Animal fats and vegetable oils are examples of triglycerides. These are esters formed from acids with long hydrocarbon chains (fatty acids) and the alcohol propane-1,2,3-triol (glycerol).

In both animal fats and vegetable oils, the three fatty acids that form the ester links with propane-1,2,3-triol are usually different — some being fully saturated, some monounsaturated and some polyunsaturated. One thing they have in common is that they contain an even number of carbon atoms. Stearic acid, $C_{17}H_{35}COOH$, is a saturated fatty acid present in animal fats; it is never found on the middle carbon of the triglyceride.

The percentages of the three different kinds of fatty acid in a variety of fats and oils are given in Table 9.5.

Table 9.5 Percentages of the different types of fatty acid present in some fats and oils

Source	% polyunsaturated	% monounsaturated	% saturated
Soya oil	62	23	15
Rapeseed oil	32	58	10
Sunflower oil	66	23	11
Olive oil	10	76	14
Butter	7	36	57
Spreading margarine	20–40	40–60	15–20

Vegetable oils contain between 80% and 90% unsaturated fat, whereas butter contains approximately 45% unsaturated fat. Saturated fats are harmful to health, as they tend to cause high levels of 'bad' cholesterol in the bloodstream, which may result in blockages to the arteries (atherosclerosis).

Spreading margarine

Vegetable oils can be converted into a semi-liquid form, which is put into tubs and sold as spreading or low-fat margarine. This can be carried out by two methods.

Transesterification

A catalyst (either inorganic or an enzyme) is added with some stearic acid to the vegatable oil. This takes the place of one of the unsaturated fatty acids. By a process of controlled crystallisation, the harder (less unsaturated) triglycerides crystallise first and are separated off. Stearic acid is used because it does not affect the low-density lipoprotein ('bad cholesterol') levels in the blood.

- Advantage: no *trans* fatty acids are produced.
- Disadvantage: some of the stearic acid goes onto the middle carbon position of the triol. This is thought to be slightly harmful to health.

Partial hydrogenation

A controlled amount of hydrogen is added to the oil in the presence of a catalyst (normally nickel). Some of the double bonds are saturated and a harder fat is produced.

- Advantage: there is no interference with the order of the fatty acids on the triol.
- Disadvantage: the C=C is weakened as it bonds to the active sites on the catalyst. On desorption, some of the molecules rotate around the remaining weakened double bonds and some *trans* isomers are formed. These are believed to increase cholesterol levels in the blood.

The altered oils, made by either method, are then mixed with untreated vegetable oils and with lipid-soluble additives such as vitamins, colouring agents and emulsifiers. This mixture is then blended with water-soluble additives such as milk whey, milk proteins and salt. The result is a spreadable margarine.

Omega-3 and omega-6

Omega-3 oils have a carbon–carbon double bond between the third and fourth carbon atoms, counting from the methyl end. If it is polyunsaturated, the other double bonds are between the sixth and seventh, and ninth and tenth, carbon atoms (confusingly counting from the other end from the IUPAC system).

One such example is α-linolenic acid, 9-Z,12-Z,15-Z-octadeca-9,12,15-trienoic acid, $C_{17}H_{29}COOH$ or $HOOC(CH_2)_7CH{=}CHCH_2CH{=}CHCH_2CH{=}CHCH_2CH_3$.

Omega-3 acids are found in fish oils and, to a lesser extent, in some vegetable and nut oils. Omega-6 acids have the first double bond between the sixth and seventh carbon atoms from the methyl end, e.g. linoleic acid, 9-Z,12-Z-octadeca-9,12-dienoic acid. Both are believed to be good for health and can be found in many dietary supplements (Figure 9.16).

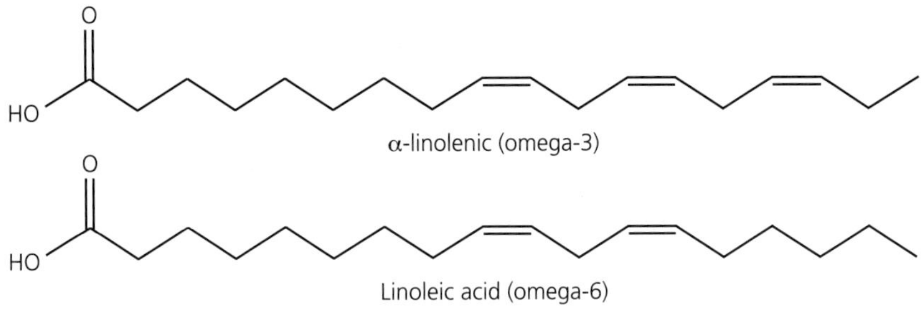

α-linolenic (omega-3)

Linoleic acid (omega-6)

Figure 9.16

Biodiesel

Biodiesel is made from natural vegetable oils. One such is rapeseed oil, 1000 kg of which is obtained per hectare of crop. Another source of biodiesel is the seeds from the *Jatropha* tree. This grows on poor soil and so will not use land that could be used for food production. Research is taking place to develop the production of natural oils from algae. The potential yield is thought to be as high as $40\,000\,\text{kg}\,\text{ha}^{-1}$ and waste domestic water could be used as a growing medium.

Rudolf Diesel first demonstrated his diesel engine using peanut oil, but vegetable oils are not good fuels for these engines, as they tend to clog the fuel injection nozzles. A more volatile liquid is needed. This is obtained by transesterification (Figure 9.17). Unlike the process used in making margarine, the natural oil ester is mixed with methanol and a catalyst. Transesterification takes place, forming the methyl esters of the fatty acids present in the vegetable oils.

The methanol can be made from hydrogen and carbon monoxide.

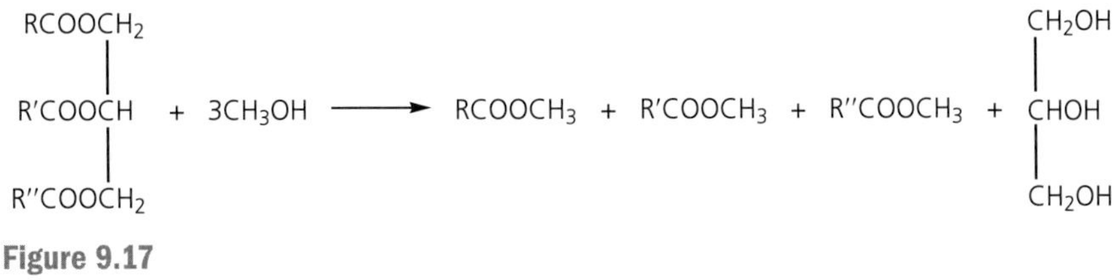

Figure 9.17

Polyesters

Polyesters are condensation polymers.

> **A condensation polymer is formed when monomers join together, with the elimination of a simple molecule, such as water or hydrogen chloride.**

The monomers that condense must have two groups, one at each end of the molecule. For example, a dicarboxylic acid has two −COOH groups, a diacyl chloride has two −COCl groups and a diol has two −OH groups in the molecule.

A polyester is formed if a dicarboxylic acid, such as benzene-1,4-dicarboxylic acid (terephthalic acid), reacts with a diol, such as ethane-1,2-diol, CH_2OHCH_2OH. One of the −COOH groups in the dicarboxylic acid reacts with one of the −OH groups in the diol. The remaining −OH group in the diol then reacts with one of the −COOH groups in a second diacid molecule. The remaining −COOH group then reacts with the −OH in a second diol molecule and so on, thousands of times.

The reaction also takes place with the dimethyl ester or a diacyl chloride. An example is the formation of the polymer Terylene® or PET (**P**oly **E**thylene **T**erephthalate) (Figure 9.18).

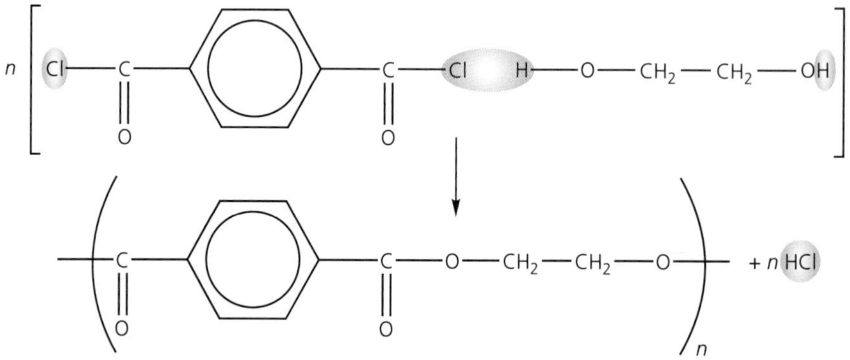

Figure 9.18

Uses of polyesters

Polyesters, such as Terylene, are used in the manufacture of synthetic fibres. Some shirts, sheets, socks and trousers are made from a mix of polyester and a natural fibre such as cotton or wool. The polyester gives the material strength and crease resistance; the natural fibre gives a softer feel and allows the material to absorb some perspiration from the wearer.

Polyesters are also excellent thermal insulators and can be used as fillings for duvets.

PET can be extruded into different shapes and is used to make bottles for fizzy drinks and water. The bottle does not allow the dissolved carbon dioxide to escape as gas and the material is shatterproof, so will not break if dropped.

Disposal of polyesters

Polyesters are not biodegradable because enzymes have not evolved that hydrolyse the ester linkages in the artificial fibres. This means that they do not rot in a landfill site. If burnt, toxic fumes are produced if the temperature and amount of air are not closely controlled.

Homopolymeric esters

A **homopolymer** is a polymer made from a single type of monomer. This monomer must have a group at one end that can react with the group at the other end of the molecule. Hydroxyacids are examples.

A copolymer is a polymer made from two different monomers.

Polylactic acid (PLA)

Lactic acid (2-hydropropanoic acid) can be made by the bacterial fermentation of cornstarch. It is dimerised and finally polymerised (Figure 9.19).

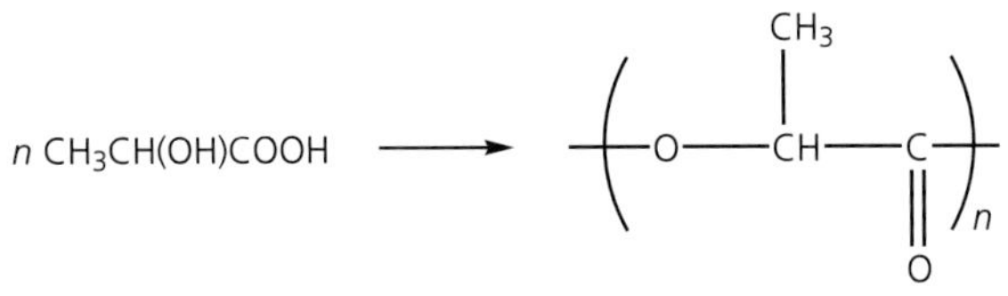

$$n \ CH_3CH(OH)COOH \longrightarrow \left(O - \underset{\underset{CH_3}{|}}{CH} - \underset{\underset{O}{\parallel}}{C} \right)_n$$

Figure 9.19

The polymer is fully biodegradable. Because it degrades into innocuous lactic acid, PLA is used as medical implants in the form of anchors, screws, plates and pins. Depending on the exact type used, it breaks down inside the body within 6 months to 2 years. This gradual degradation is desirable for a support structure, because it gradually transfers the load to the body (e.g. the bone) as that area heals.

Biopol

3-hydroxybutanoate, $CH_3CH(OH)CH_2COOH$, is produced as an energy store by the microorganism *Alcaligenes*. After extraction, it is polymerised catalytically (Figure 9.20).

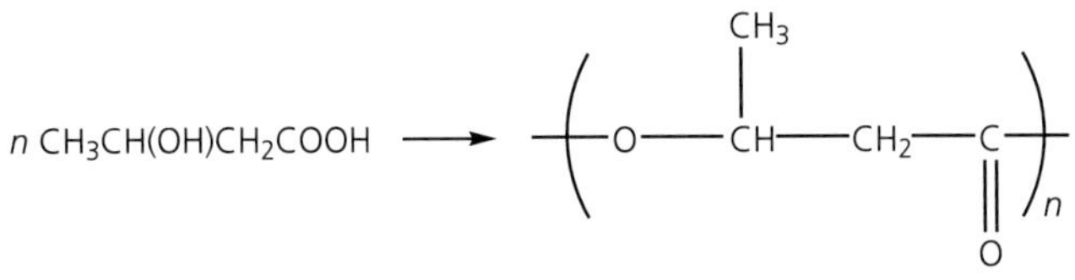

$$n \ CH_3CH(OH)CH_2COOH \longrightarrow \left(O - \underset{\underset{CH_3}{|}}{CH} - CH_2 - \underset{\underset{O}{\parallel}}{C} \right)_n$$

Figure 9.20

This polymer is known as Biopol and is fully biodegradable. Greenpeace uses Biopol to make its credit cards. Some bottles containing hair lotions are made of Biopol, as is some disposable plastic cutlery. Its cost and lack of tensile strength makes it, as yet, unsuitable for major use.

Summary tasks

Test yourself

5 A polyester has the repeat unit shown in Figure 9.21.

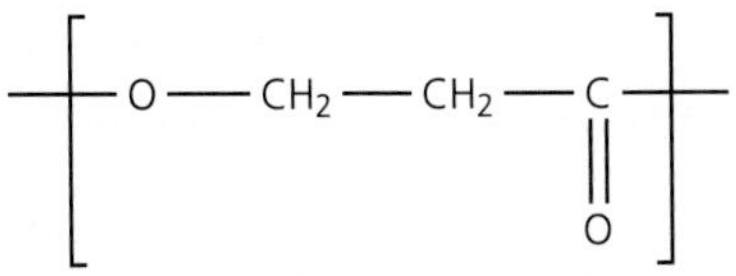

$$\left[O - CH_2 - CH_2 - \underset{\underset{O}{\parallel}}{C} \right]$$

Figure 9.21

Draw the structural formula of its monomer.

Make sure that you can:

- draw the structural formulae for, and name, carboxylic acids, esters, acyl chlorides and amides
- explain why carboxylic acids have a higher boiling point and are more soluble in water than esters

Carboxylic acids:

- Check that you know their preparation from primary alcohols, aldehydes and from esters.

- Make sure that you can describe their reactions with water (including calculating the pH of the solution), bases, carbonates and hydrogencarbonates, alcohols, lithium aluminium hydride and phosphorus pentachloride.

Esters:

- Can you explain why their preparation from acyl chlorides is better than from carboxylic acids?
- Check that you know their reactions with acids and alkalis, and with organic acids or alcohols (transesterification).
- Check that you know the difference between fats and oils.
- Make sure that you can write the repeat units of polyesters and can work out the monomers given the repeat unit.

Acyl chlorides:

- Make sure that you know their structure and their preparation.
- Check that you can write equations for their reactions with water, alcohols, ammonia, amines and lithium aluminium hydride.

Questions

1 Explain why propanoic acid is soluble in water whereas propane is insoluble.

2 If the molar mass of ethanoic acid is measured when dissolved in an organic solvent such as benzene, it is found to be $120 \, \text{g mol}^{-1}$. Explain this.

3 Aspirin can be prepared by the reaction of ethanoyl chloride with the substance in Figure 9.22.

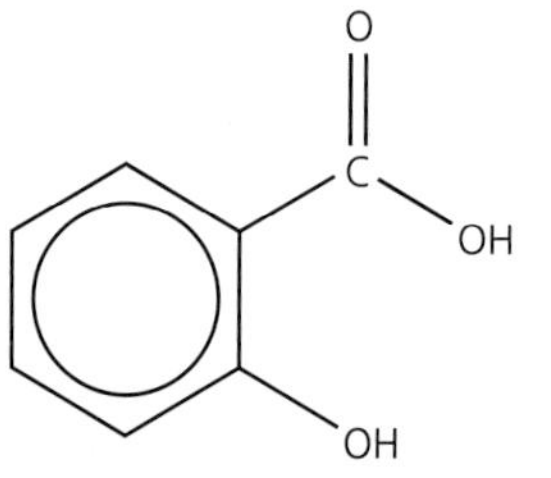

Figure 9.22

Write the structural formula of aspirin.

4 Describe how you would prepare a pure, high-yield sample of benzoic acid, C_6H_5COOH, from ethyl benzoate, $C_6H_5COOC_2H_5$.

5 Describe how you would prepare a sample of propanoyl chloride from propanoic acid.

6 Explain the meaning of the term **transesterification**.

7 In terms of their chemical composition, explain the difference between animal fats and vegetable oils.

8 Explain why it is preferable to use an acid chloride, rather than a carboxylic acid, when making large quantities of an ester.

9 2-hydroxypropanoic acid can be polymerised. Draw the structure of *two* repeat units of this polymer.

10 Explain why, when making a low-fat spreading margarine, transesterification is preferable to hydrogenation.

11 Describe the chemistry of converting a vegetable oil into biodiesel.

12 Give one advantage of growing *Jatropha* trees, rather than soyabeans, for the manufacture of biodiesel.

13 Write the necessary reagents and conditions for each step in the reaction sequence shown below.

$$\text{CH}_3\text{COOH} \xrightarrow{\text{Step 1}} \text{CH}_3\text{CH}_2\text{OH} \xrightarrow{\text{Step 2}} \text{CH}_3\text{CHO}$$

14 Write the repeat unit of the polyester from $\text{HOOCCH}_2\text{COOH}$ and $\text{HOCH}_2\text{CH}_2\text{OH}$.

Exam practice questions

1 a) The name of the ester $CH_3COOCH(CH_3)_2$ is:
  A propyl ethanoate **C** methyl propanoate
  B 2-propyl ethanoate **D** methyl 2-propanoate **(1)**

b) i) Define the term transesterification. **(1)**
  ii) Describe how biodiesel could be made from a vegetable oil, such as palm oil, using this process. **(3)**
  iii) Explain why the physical properties of the biodiesel and the palm oil differ and why this makes the biodiesel a better fuel for a car or lorry. **(3)**
  (Total 8 marks)

2 Draw a reaction sequence for the high yield preparation of ethyl ethanoate from ethanal using *no* other organic reagent. State the reagents and conditions for each step. **(8)**
  (Total 8 marks)

3 This question is about compounds that have a C=O in their structures.
  a) Consider the compounds S, P, Q and R:

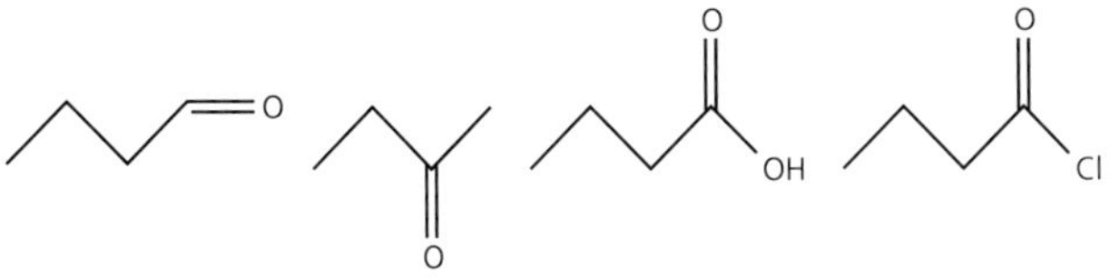

  S   **P**   **Q**   **R**

  i) Which will react with 2,4-dinitrophenylhydrazine? **(1)**
    A S only   **C** S and P only
    B P only   **D** all four
  ii) Which will react with Fehling's solution? **(1)**
    A S only   **C** S and P only
    B P only   **D** all four
  iii) Which will react with aqueous sodium carbonate? **(1)**
    A Q only   **C** Q and R only
    B R only   **D** all four
  iv) Which will react with $LiAlH_4$ in dry ether? **(1)**
    A S and P only
    B Q and R only
    C S, P and Q only
    D all four

b) Rapeseed oil is a triglyceride which can be converted into a solid fat such as margarine or into biodiesel.
  i) The production of margarine can require catalytic hydrogenation. Name a suitable catalyst and state one disadvantage of this method. **(2)**
  ii) The production of biodiesel involves transesterification. Explain this term with reference to its production from rapeseed oil. **(2)**
  (Total 8 marks)

4 a) i) Compound X contained 58.8% carbon, 9.8 % hydrogen and 31.4% oxygen. Show that these data are consistent with X having an empirical formula of $C_5H_{10}O_2$. **(2)**
  ii) The mass spectrum of X had a peak at $m/z = 102$. Write down its molecular formula. **(1)**

b) Compound X was heated under reflux with aqueous sodium hydroxide and then compound Y was distilled out. The remaining solution was acidified with dilute sulfuric acid and compound Z was distilled out. Compound Y gave a pale yellow precipitate when warmed with iodine in alkali. The ^{13}C NMR spectrum of compound Z showed C atoms in two environments.
  i) Use the information above to deduce the structural formulae of Z and Y and hence that of X. Justify your answers.**(5)**
  ii) Why was it necessary to add acid before distilling out compound Z? **(2)**
  iii) Write the equation for the reaction of compound X with aqueous sodium hydroxide. **(1)**

c) W is an isomer of X. It was treated in the same way and gave a product similar to Z which has only one carbon atom. W has two optical isomers. Draw the structural formula of W and circle the chiral centre. **(2)**
  (Total 13 marks)

Arenes (Topic 18)

Organic chemistry can be divided into three categories:

- **Aliphatic chemistry:** this is the study of simple compounds that have straight or branched carbon chains or rings of singly bonded carbon atoms. Alkenes, ethanol, propanone, ethylamine, cyclohexane and cyclohexene are examples of aliphatic compounds (Figure 10.1).

Cyclohexane   Cyclohexene

Figure 10.1

- **Arenes:** these are also called **aromatic compounds**. They all contain a benzene ring. This is a ring of six carbon atoms in which each forms two σ-bonds with its neighbouring carbon atoms and has one *p*-electron in a π-bond. The fourth valence electron is in a σ-bond with an atom that is joined to the ring.
- **Natural products:** these compounds are complex organic substances found in nature. They include colouring matter, poisons, flavourings, proteins, hormones and compounds with specific odours that may be used to attract animals, for example pheromones.

The benzene ring

Benzene has the formula C_6H_6. There was doubt about its structure until the German chemist Kekulé suggested that the carbon atoms were arranged in a ring with alternate single and double bonds.

There are three major problems with the Kekulé structure:

Problem 1 In aliphatic compounds a C=C bond is shorter than a C−C bond, but all the bonds between the carbon atoms in benzene are the same length.

X-ray diffraction shows the position of the centre of atoms. Analysis of the diffraction pattern of benzene shows clearly that all the bond lengths between the carbon atoms are the same (Table 10.1).

August Kekulé 1829-96

Table 10.1 Bond lengths

Bond	Bond length/nm
Carbon–carbon single bond in cyclohexene	0.15
Carbon–carbon double bond in cyclohexene	0.13
Carbon–carbon bond in benzene	0.14

This is also shown by the electron density map of benzene. The map also shows that there is a significant electron density in rings above and below the plane of the six carbon atoms (Figure 10.2).

Problem 2 The enthalpies of hydrogenation are not as would be expected if benzene had three separate double bonds.

When benzene vapour and hydrogen are passed over a heated nickel catalyst, 3 mol of hydrogen per mole of benzene add on and cyclohexane is formed. Hydrogen is adsorbed as atoms at the active sites on the surface of the catalyst. These hydrogen radicals add on, one at a time, breaking the π-bonds until saturated cycloalkane is formed (Figure 10.3).

Figure 10.2 Electron density map of benzene

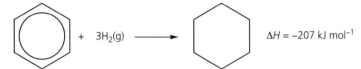

Figure 10.3

The reaction is similar to the addition of hydrogen to cyclohexene, which has one localised π-bond (Figure 10.4).

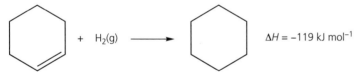

Figure 10.4

If benzene had three *localised* π-bonds, the enthalpy change for the addition of 3 mol of hydrogen would be $3 \times -119 = -357\,kJ\,mol^{-1}$. The difference between this value and the actual enthalpy change for the addition of 3 mol of hydrogen to benzene is $150\,kJ\,mol^{-1}$. This is the value by which the benzene molecule is stabilised because of the delocalisation of the π-electrons (resonance stabilisation energy).

The theoretical molecule with three localised double bonds is called 'cyclohexatriene'. The energy levels of this molecule and the actual molecules of benzene and cyclohexane are shown in Figure 10.5.

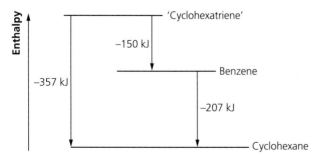

Figure 10.5 Energy level diagram showing delocalisation energy of 150 kJ

Benzene is at an energy level $150\,\text{kJ}\,\text{mol}^{-1}$ lower than that of 'cyclohexatriene'. Therefore, the resonance stabilisation energy is $150\,\text{kJ}\,\text{mol}^{-1}$.

Problem 3 Benzene does not show the typical electrophilic addition reactions of unsaturated compounds such as ethene and cyclohexene. For example, it reacts with bromine by substitution rather than by addition.

One solution to these problems was to apply the concept of a **resonance structure**. This was first used to account for the identical bond lengths in ozone, $O=O{\rightarrow}O$. In theory, the double bond should be shorter than the dative bond. However, both bonds are the same length. The reason is that the molecule of ozone is a unique structure that appears to resonate between $O=O{\rightarrow}O$ and $O{\leftarrow}O=O$.

The idea of resonance is that the actual molecule is a definite structure that is a hybrid of two theoretical structures. An ozone molecule is neither $O{\leftarrow}O=O$ nor $O=O{\rightarrow}O$ and it does not oscillate between the two. Resonance can be shown as a double-headed arrow between the two theoretical structures, both of which must obey the normal rules of bonding.

Ozone can be written as:

$$O=O{\rightarrow}O \leftrightarrow O{\leftarrow}O=O$$

This can also be used to describe the bonding in a carboxylate ion (Figure 10.6).

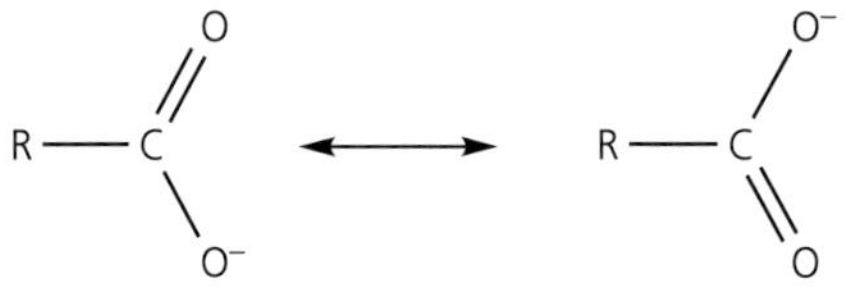

Figure 10.6 Resonance structures of the carboxylate ion

Benzene can be written as in Figure 10.7.

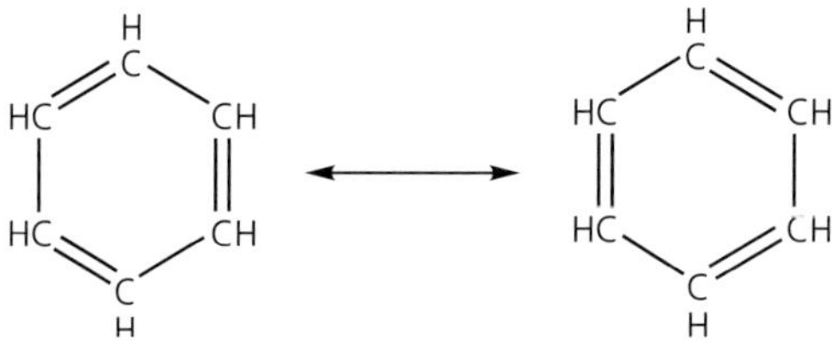

Figure 10.7

It is usual to write the formula of benzene without showing either the carbon atoms or the hydrogen atoms. Thus, a hexagon with alternate double and single bonds can be used to represent benzene, as in Figure 10.8.

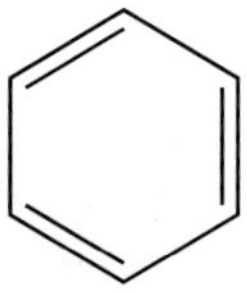

A double bond is a σ-bond, resulting from an overlap of atomic orbitals between two atoms, and a π-bond, resulting from an overlap, above and below the σ-bond, of the p-orbitals of the two atoms.

Figure 10.8 The Kekulé formula of benzene

The best representation of a benzene molecule is six carbon atoms in a hexagonal plane bonded to each other and each bonded to a hydrogen atom by σ-bonds. The fourth valence electron on each carbon atom is in a p_z-orbital at right angles to the plane of the six carbon atoms. The p_z-orbital of one carbon atom overlaps equally with the p_z-orbitals of both adjacent carbon atoms, forming a continuous π-bond above and below the ring of carbon atoms (Figure 10.9). These six p_z-electrons are

delocalised over the ring. This gives the molecule greater stability compared with a theoretical molecule in which the π-electrons are localised between individual atoms.

This gain in stability is called the **resonance stabilisation energy**. In benzene, its value is $150\,\text{kJ}\,\text{mol}^{-1}$.

The way in which a delocalised π-system is written in a formula is to draw a continuous curve round the atoms that are part of that system — for benzene, a circle is drawn within the hexagon representing the six carbon atoms (Figure 10.10a). However, Kekulé formulae are acceptable at A level and at university. The formula of cyclohexane, which has no π-electrons, is drawn as in Figure 10.10b.

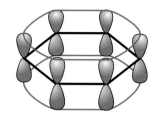

Figure 10.9 Overlap of p_z-orbitals in benzene

Figure 10.10 The skeletal formula for (a) benzene and (b) cyclohexane

---

Tip

Remember that there is a hydrogen atom attached to each carbon atom in benzene. When benzene reacts by substitution, a hydrogen atom is replaced by another group. Therefore, one of the products is a simple molecule such as HBr, HCl or H_2O.

Test yourself

1 Draw the resonance structures of the ethanoate, CH_3COO^-, ion.

Nomenclature of arenes

An arene is a compound with a benzene ring.

Single substituents

If a single atom or group replaces one hydrogen atom in a benzene ring, the name of the compound has the stem -benzene with a prefix of the group or atom entering, thus:

- C_6H_5Cl is called chlorobenzene.
- $C_6H_5CH_3$ is called methylbenzene.
- $C_6H_5NO_2$ is called nitrobenzene.
- $C_6H_5NH_2$ can be called aminobenzene.

An additional naming system is based on the **phenyl group**, $-C_6H_5$ group, thus:

- C_6H_5OH is called phenol.
- $C_6H_5NH_2$ is called either phenylamine or aminobenzene.
- $CH_3CH(C_6H_5)CH_3$ is called 2-phenylpropane.
- $C_6H_5COCH_3$ has a phenyl group substituted into a carbon chain of two atoms (ethan-) and is a ketone (-one), so it is called phenylethanone.

Methylbenzene was originally called toluene because it was first isolated from the resin of the South American tree *Tolu balsam*.

Aminobenzene was called aniline.

Two or more substituents

If there are two or more groups in a benzene ring, positional isomerism occurs. For example, there are three isomers of $C_6H_4Cl_2$. The relative positions of the two chlorine atoms are defined by numbers. One substituent is always named as being in the 1-position and the second substituent by the lower of the possible numbers. In Figure 10.11:

- Structure A is 1,2-dichlorobenzene (not 1,6-dichlorobenzene).
- Structure B is 1,3-dichlorobenzene (not 1,5-dichlorobenzene).
- Structure C is 1,4-dichlorobenzene.

The old name for A was *ortho*-dichlorobenzene, the prefix *ortho-* indicating that the two substituents are on adjacent carbon atoms; B was *meta*-dichlorobenzene (the substituents being one carbon apart); C was *para*-dichlorobenzene (the substituents being opposite each other).

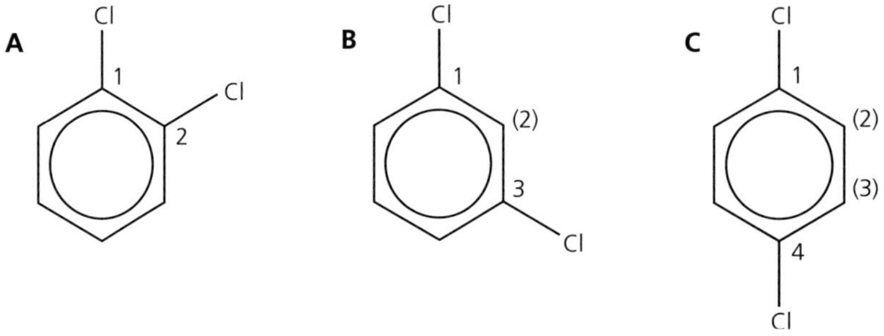

Figure 10.11

Figure 10.12

Test yourself

2 Draw and name all the aromatic isomers of $C_6H_4ClNO_2$.

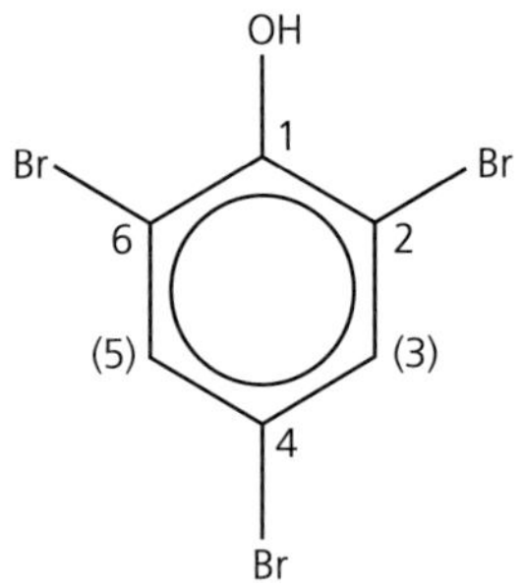

Figure 10.12 shows the formula for the compound 2,4,6-tribromophenol.

TNT is 2,4,6-trinitrotoluene and has the formula shown in Figure 10.13.

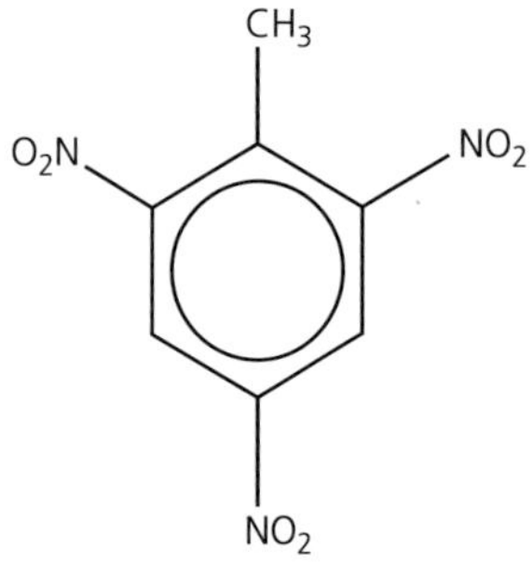

Figure 10.13

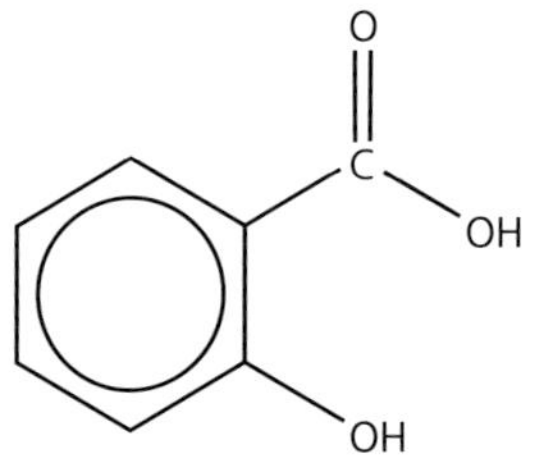

Figure 10.14

An exception to the rules for naming aromatic compounds is C_6H_5COOH, which is called benzoic acid, rather than the cumbersome phenylmethanoic acid.

Many aromatic substances are still known by their old names, which were derived from the source of the chemical. For example, the compound with the formula in Figure 10.14 is commonly referred to as salicylic acid, rather than 2-hydroxybenzoic acid.

Salicylic acid is derived from *Salix,* the Latin name for a willow tree.

Benzene, C_6H_6

Physical properties

Benzene and many compounds that contain a substituted benzene ring have a characteristic smell — hence the name aromatic. The modern name for compounds that contain a benzene ring is **arene**.

Benzene is a non-polar liquid at room temperature. The main forces between molecules are London (instantaneous induced dipole) forces, and as the molecule has 42 electrons, these forces are strong enough for benzene to be a liquid. It cannot form hydrogen bonds with water and so it is immiscible.

The physical properties of benzene are:

- melting temperature, 5.5°C
- boiling temperature, 80.1°C
- density, $0.878\,\mathrm{g\,cm^{-3}}$

Arene is derived from aromatic and -ene, representing a carbon–carbon double bond.

Benzene and some other compounds that contain a benzene ring are carcinogenic.

Chemical reactions

Benzene, like all organic compounds, burns in air. It also undergoes addition and substitution reactions.

Combustion

In excess air, benzene burns to form carbon dioxide and water:

$$C_6H_6(l) + 7\frac{1}{2}O_2(g) \rightarrow 6CO_2(g) + 3H_2O(l) \quad \Delta H_c^\ominus = -3273\,\mathrm{kJ\,mol^{-1}}$$

It has an octane rating of 101 and is used, in small quantities, as a petrol additive. Its main problem is that it is carcinogenic.

In a limited amount of air it burns with a smoky flame since carbon is formed, rather than carbon dioxide:

$$C_6H_6(l) + 1\frac{1}{2}O_2(g) \rightarrow 6C(s) + 3H_2O(g)$$

The smoky flame can be used as a test to suggest the presence of a benzene ring in an organic compound.

Free-radical addition

Reaction with bromine

When bromine is heated under reflux with benzene in the presence of ultraviolet light, addition slowly takes place and 1,2,3,4,5,6-hexabromocyclohexane is produced:

$$C_6H_6 + 3Br_2 \rightarrow C_6H_6Br_6$$

The mechanism involves ultraviolet light splitting bromine molecules into two radicals:

$$Br_2 + \text{light energy} \rightarrow 2Br\bullet$$

A mixture of the geometric isomers is obtained with different *cis* and *trans* arrangements on adjacent carbon atoms.

The bromine radicals add on, one at a time, to the benzene ring until all the π-bonds have been broken.

Chlorine reacts in a similar way.

Reaction with hydrogen

When heated with a nickel catalyst, hydrogen adds on and cyclohexane is formed (Figure 10.15).

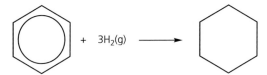

Figure 10.15

Electrophilic substitution reactions

Electrophiles attack the high-electron density in the delocalised π-ring of the benzene molecule.

- The first step is the addition of the electrophile to form an intermediate that is positively charged and in which the full delocalisation has been partially broken.
- The second step is the elimination of an H^+ ion. The fully delocalised ring and stabilisation energy are thus regained.

The reaction is:

addition then elimination = substitution

The delocalised π-system is stable compared with the localised π-bond in alkenes, so the activation energy required to break it is fairly high. Therefore, the electrophilic substitution reactions of benzene always require a catalyst.

The mechanism is that an electrophile, E^+, adds on to a carbon atom in the benzene ring (Figure 10.16).

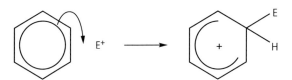

Figure 10.16

This step is similar to the addition of an electrophile to an alkene. However, a fully delocalised ring of π-electrons stabilises the benzene ring. Therefore, rather than the second step being the subsequent addition of an anion (as with alkenes), it is loss of an H^+ (Figure 10.17).

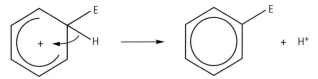

Figure 10.17

Nitration: the reaction with nitric acid

When concentrated nitric acid, benzene and a catalyst of concentrated sulfuric acid are warmed together at a temperature of 50°C in a flask fitted with a reflux condenser, nitrobenzene and water are formed (Figure 10.18).

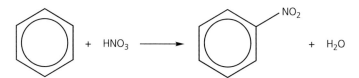

Figure 10.18

Below 50°C the reaction is too slow; above 60°C a second NO₂ group is substituted into the ring.

Reagent: concentrated nitric acid

Catalyst: concentrated sulfuric acid

Conditions: 50°C

Formation of the electrophile: concentrated sulfuric acid protonates a nitric acid molecule, forming $H_2NO_3^+$. This loses water, forming NO_2^+, which is a powerful electrophile.

$$H_2SO_4 + HNO_3 \rightarrow H_2NO_3^+ + HSO_4^-$$

$$H_2NO_3^+ \rightarrow NO_2^+ + H_2O$$

The reaction then proceeds in two steps.

> The H₂0 is then protonated by another H₂SO₄ molecule.

Step 1: the electrophilic NO_2^+ ion draws a pair of electrons from the π-system and forms a covalent bond (Figure 10.19).

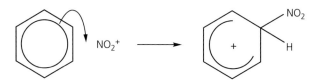

Figure 10.19

Step 2: the intermediate loses an H⁺ ion to a HSO_4^- ion. The stability of the benzene ring is regained and the H_2SO_4 catalyst is regenerated (Figure 10.20).

> **Tip**
>
> Do not forget to put the positive charge in the ring in the formula of the intermediate. Also, make sure that the delocalised circle goes round five carbon atoms but not the one to which the NO₂ group is attached.

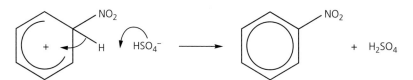

Figure 10.20

If the temperature is too high, a second NO₂ group is substituted in the 3-position (Figure 10.21).

> Nitrobenzene can be reduced to phenylamine (p. 256).

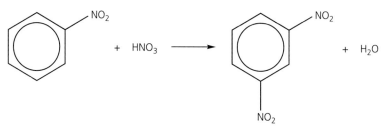

Figure 10.21

The products are 1,3-dinitrobenzene and water.

Reaction with halogens

Under certain conditions, chlorine and bromine react rapidly with benzene. A catalyst of anhydrous iron(III) halide (or aluminium halide) must be used and all the reagents must be dry. For the bromination of benzene, the catalyst is made *in situ* by adding iron filings to a mixture of benzene and liquid bromine. Clouds of hydrogen bromide fumes are given off in this exothermic reaction (Figure 10.22).

In situ means in the same apparatus.

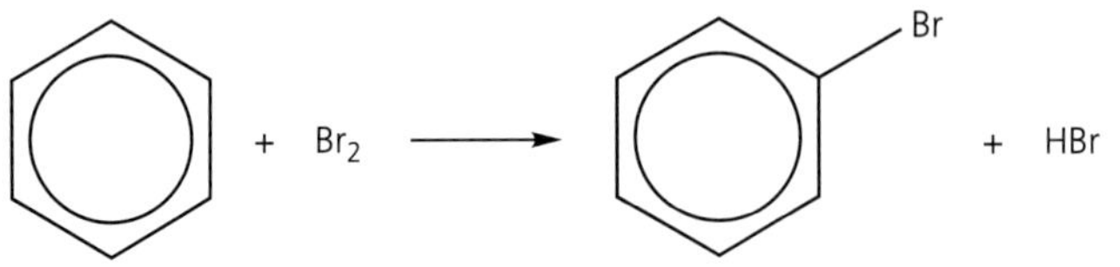

Figure 10.22

Reagent: liquid bromine

Catalyst: iron(III) bromide

Conditions: anhydrous

Test yourself

3 State the conditions for the conversion of nitrobenzene, $C_6H_5NO_2$, to:

  a) $C_6H_5Br_6NO_2$

  b) $C_6H_4BrNO_2$

Formation of the electrophile: if iron filings are added (rather than iron(III) bromide), they react to form the catalyst:

$$2Fe + 3Br_2 \rightarrow 2FeBr_3$$

This then reacts with more bromine to form the electrophile, Br^+:

$$FeBr_3 + Br_2 \rightarrow Br^+ + FeBr_4^-$$

The reaction then proceeds in two steps.

Step 1: the Br^+ electrophile attacks the benzene ring (Figure 10.23).

> **Tip**
>
> Alkenes, such as ethene, react with bromine water. There is no reaction between bromine water and benzene.

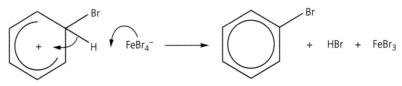

Figure 10.23

Step 2: The $FeBr_4^-$ removes H^+ from the intermediate. HBr is formed and the catalyst, $FeBr_3$, is regenerated (Figure 10.24).

Bromine reacts with benzene in a *substitution* reaction. A catalyst is needed and the reaction is rapid. Bromine also reacts with benzene in an *addition* reaction. UV light is needed and the reaction is slow.

Figure 10.24

Friedel–Crafts reactions

The French chemist Charles Friedel and the American James Crafts discovered the reaction of benzene with organic halogen compounds.

- The reaction can be represented by the equation:

  $C_6H_6 + RCl \rightarrow C_6H_5R + HCl$

- The catalyst has to be a covalent anhydrous metal chloride, for example aluminium chloride, $AlCl_3$, or iron(III) chloride, $FeCl_3$. All water must be excluded from the reaction.
- The reaction can be:
  - alkylation, with a halogenoalkane
  - acylation, with an acid chloride

Alkylation

Benzene reacts with a halogenoalkane in the presence of a catalyst of anhydrous aluminium chloride, under dry conditions, to form a hydrocarbon and gaseous hydrogen halide. For example, benzene and chloroethane react to form ethylbenzene and hydrogen chloride (Figure 10.25).

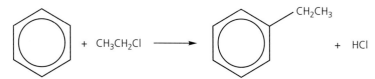

Figure 10.25

It is difficult to stop the reaction at this stage, as further alkylation to 1,2- and 1,4-diethylbenzene takes place.

Formation of the electrophile: the catalyst reacts with the halogenoalkane to form $CH_3CH_2^+$, which is the electrophile:

$CH_3CH_2Cl + AlCl_3 \rightarrow CH_3CH_2^+ + AlCl_4^-$

Step 1: the electrophile accepts a pair of π-electrons from the ring, forming a covalent bond (Figure 10.26).

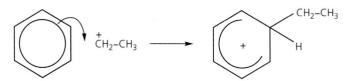

Figure 10.26

Step 2: There is a loss of H^+ from the intermediate, thus regaining the stability of the benzene ring (Figure 10.27).

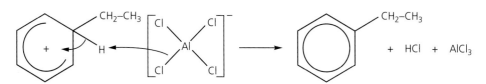

Figure 10.27

> **Tip**
>
> When drawing this mechanism, make sure that the ethyl group is bonded to the benzene ring by the CH_2 carbon and not by the carbon of the CH_3.

The intermediate is at a higher energy level than the reactants due to the loss of stability of the delocalised π-system.

The reaction profile for the two-step substitution reactions of benzene is shown in Figure 10.28.

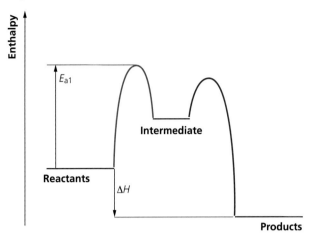

Figure 10.28 Reaction profile for the substitution reactions of benzene

Step 1 has the higher activation energy and so is rate-determining.

Reagent: a halogenoalkane

Catalyst: anhydrous aluminium chloride

Conditions: dry

Test yourself

4 Write equations for the production of the electrophiles in the following reactions of aromatic compounds:

a) nitration b) bromination c) alkylation

Acylation

Friedel–Crafts acylation reactions are carried out using an acyl chloride such as ethanoyl chloride, CH_3COCl. The catalyst is anhydrous aluminium chloride, which produces the electrophile $CH_3-C^+=O$ (Figure 10.29).

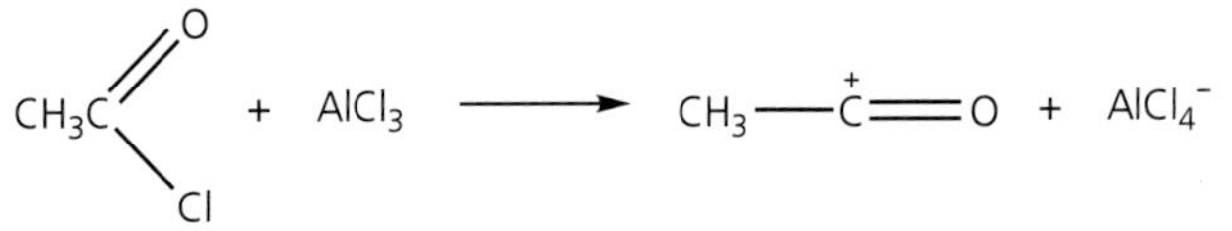

$$CH_3C\overset{O}{\underset{Cl}{\big<}} + AlCl_3 \longrightarrow CH_3-\overset{+}{C}=O + AlCl_4^-$$

Figure 10.29

The remainder of the mechanism is similar to that of Friedel–Crafts alkylation reactions.

Figure 10.30 shows the overall reaction.

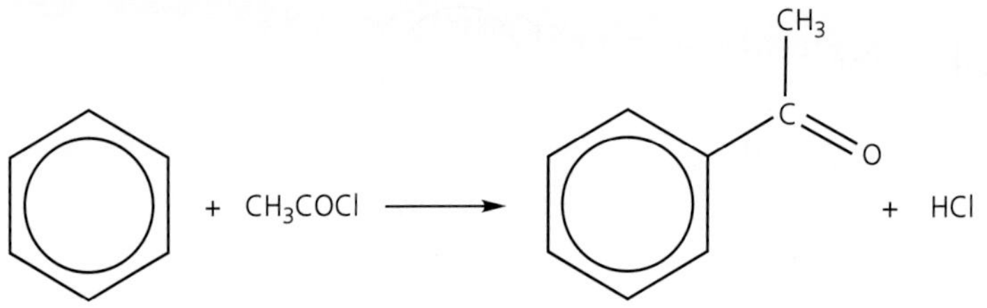

$$\text{benzene} + CH_3COCl \longrightarrow \text{acetophenone} + HCl$$

Figure 10.30

The products are the ketone (phenylethanone) and hydrogen chloride.

Further substitution does not take place, because the $COCH_3$ group deactivates the benzene ring.

Reagent: an acyl chloride

Catalyst: anhydrous aluminium chloride

Conditions: dry

Aromatic compounds with a carbon side chain

If a group is attached via a carbon atom to the benzene ring, the compound has all the properties of an aliphatic compound with that group, as well as the reactions due to the benzene ring.

Alkane side chain

Methylbenzene, $C_6H_5CH_3$, reacts similarly to both alkanes and benzene.

Reaction with chlorine

When chlorine gas is bubbled into methylbenzene in the presence of UV light, the hydrogen atoms of the $-CH_3$ group are replaced one at a time:

$C_6H_5CH_3 + Cl_2 \rightarrow C_6H_5CH_2Cl + HCl$

$C_6H_5CH_2Cl + Cl_2 \rightarrow C_6H_5CHCl_2 + HCl$ etc.

Under anhydrous conditions and with a catalyst of anhydrous aluminium chloride, a mixture of 2-chloromethylbenzene and 4-chloromethylbenzene is formed (Figure 10.31).

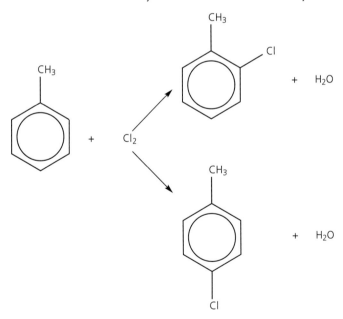

Figure 10.31

Reaction with concentrated nitric acid

If methylbenzene and concentrated nitric acid are warmed to 50°C in the presence of concentrated sulfuric acid, a mixture of 2- and 4-nitromethylbenzene and water is produced (Figure 10.32).

If the nitration or other reactions of arenes are to be carried out in the laboratory, methylbenzene or methoxybenzene, $C_6H_5OCH_3$, should be used, rather than the carcinogenic benzene.

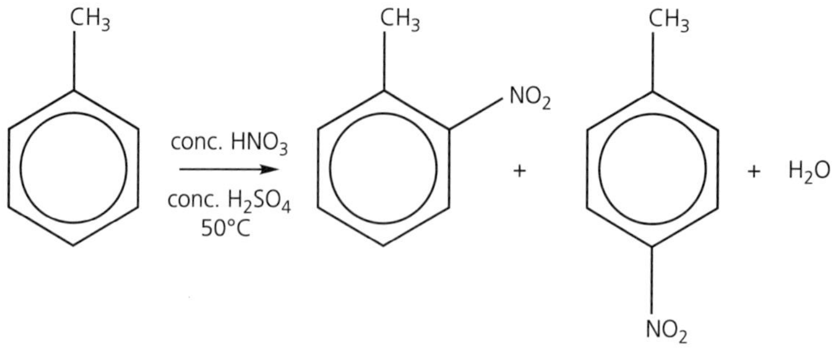

Figure 10.32

If the temperature rises above 50°C, 2,4-dinitromethylbenzene will be formed and if methylbenzene is heated under reflux with the nitrating mixture, 2,4,6-trinitrotoluene (TNT) is produced.

Ketone side chain

Phenylethanone, $C_6H_5COCH_3$, and other aromatic ketones have similar reactions to propanone such as reaction with Brady's reagent (2,4-dintrophenylhydrazine), with hydrogen cyanide and with lithium tetrahydridoaluminate(III). Phenylethanone is the only aromatic ketone that reacts in the iodoform reaction.

$$C_6H_5COCH_3 + 3I_2 + 4NaOH \rightarrow CHI_3 + 3NaI + C_6H_5COONa + 3H_2O$$

Test yourself

5 Write equations and state the conditions for the reactions of methylbenzene with:

a) ethanoyl chloride b) bromine c) nitric acid

Phenol, C_6H_5OH

Figure 10.33

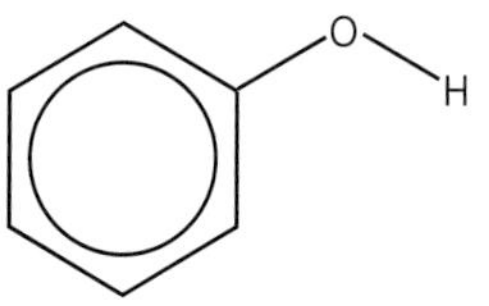

Phenol is an aromatic alcohol. It contains an –OH group bonded directly to a carbon atom in a benzene ring (Figure 10.33).

The lone pair of electrons in the p_z-orbital on the oxygen atom interacts with the delocalised π-electrons in the ring (Figure 10.34). This increases the electron density inside the ring, making it easier for phenol to be attacked by an electrophile. This explains the relative ease with which phenol reacts in electrophilic substitution reactions compared with benzene. It also decreases the δ– charge on the oxygen atom, making it less reactive as an alcohol.

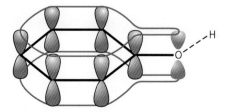

Figure 10.34 Interaction of the oxygen electrons with the aromatic ring

Pulling the p_z electrons from the oxygen atom into the ring causes the hydrogen atom to be more $\delta+$ than it is in aliphatic alcohols. This means that it is much more easily lost from phenol than it is from aliphatic alcohols, so phenol has stronger acid properties than ethanol.

Test yourself

6 Calculate the pH of a $0.20\,\mathrm{mol\,dm^{-3}}$ solution of phenol; $K_a = 1.3 \times 10^{-10}\,\mathrm{mol\,dm^{-3}}$.

Physical properties

Phenol is a white solid that absorbs water from damp air.

Melting temperature

Phenol is a polar molecule with a $\delta-$ oxygen atom and a $\delta+$ hydrogen atom. It can, therefore, form hydrogen bonds with other phenol molecules (intermolecular hydrogen bonding) (Figure 10.35).

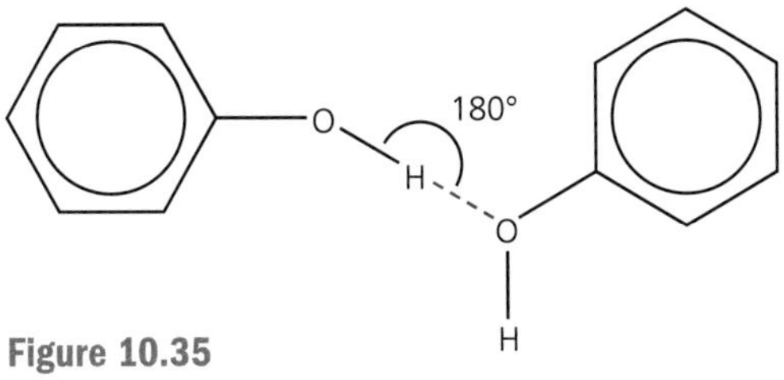

Figure 10.35

This is why phenol melts at a higher temperature than either benzene or methylbenzene, which have only weaker London forces between their molecules. Pure phenol melts at 41°C and boils at 182°C.

Solubility

When phenol is added to water at room temperature, two liquid layers are formed. One is a solution of phenol in water and the other is a solution of water in phenol. If the temperature is raised to above 66°C, a single layer is formed because phenol and water are totally miscible above this temperature.

Phenol dissolves in water because hydrogen bonds are formed between phenol molecules and water molecules (Figure 10.36).

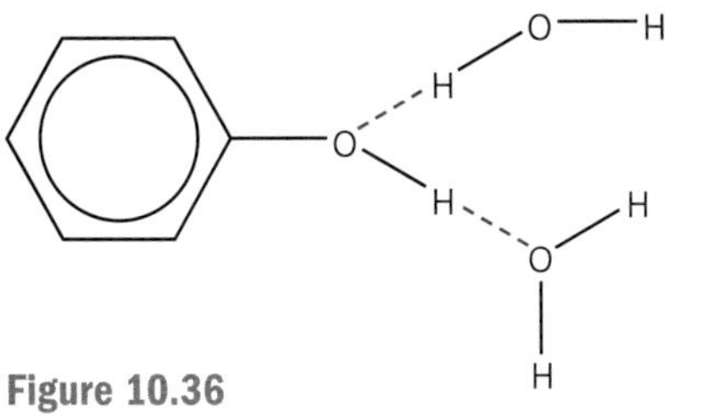

Figure 10.36

It is not very soluble in water (unlike ethanol, which is totally miscible) because of the large hydrophobic benzene ring.

Phenol is soluble in a variety of organic solvents because of the existence of London forces between its molecules and those of the solvent.

Chemical reactions

Phenol undergoes some of the reactions of aromatic compounds and some of the reactions of alcohols.

Electrophilic aromatic substitution reactions

The electron density of the delocalised π-system is greater in phenol than in benzene. This makes phenol more reactive towards electrophiles. The substituents go into the 2- and/or 4- and 6- positions. This is best explained by looking at the Kekulé resonance structures of phenol (Figure 10.37).

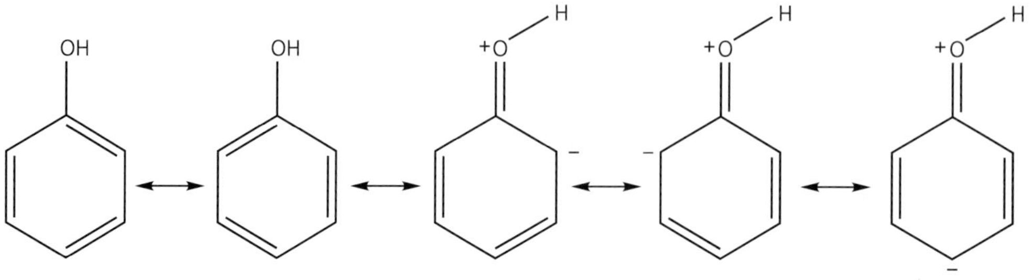

Figure 10.37

Not only are there the two benzene-type resonance structures, there are three others that have a negative charge on the 2-, 4- or 6-positions. Although the contribution of these structures is less than that of the two benzene-type structures, it is enough to make the incoming electrophile more likely to attack these electron-rich positions instead of the 3- and 5-positions.

Reaction with bromine

The conditions for the substitution of bromine into benzene are liquid bromine and a catalyst of iron(III) bromide (usually made *in situ* by adding iron filings to the bromine and benzene mixture).

The conditions for the bromination of phenol are quite different. When bromine *water* is added to a mixture of phenol and water, the red-brown bromine colour disappears and a white antiseptic-smelling precipitate of 2,4,6-tribromophenol in a solution of hydrogen bromide is immediately formed. The molecular equation for this reaction is:

$$C_6H_5OH(aq) + 3Br_2(aq) \rightarrow C_6H_2Br_3(OH)(s) + 3HBr(aq)$$

The equation, using skeletal formulae, is shown in Figure 10.38.

> **Tip**
>
> Do not forget that these are substitution reactions, so there must be two products on the right-hand side of the equation. The second product is a simple molecule, such as HBr or H_2O.

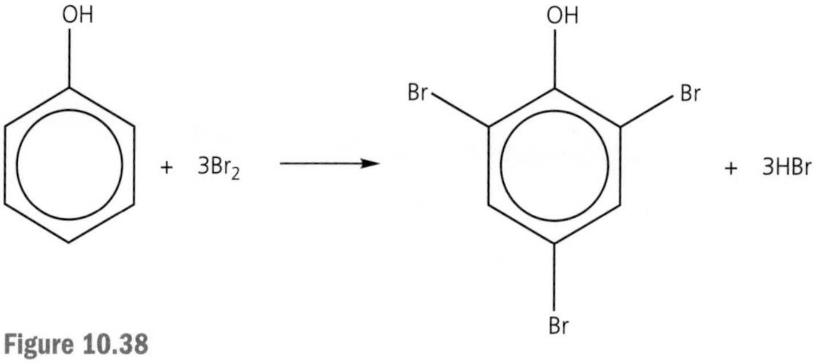

Figure 10.38

The electrophile is the $\delta+$ bromine atom in an HOBr molecule, made by the reaction of bromine and water:

$$Br_2 + H_2O \rightleftharpoons HOBr + HBr$$

2,4,6-tribromophenol, like many halogenated phenols, is an antiseptic. Dettol is 2,4-dichloro-3,5-dimethylphenol and TCP is 2,4,6-trichlorophenol. Phenol itself is also an antiseptic and was used in the nineteenth century by the surgeon Lister to reduce deaths from infection after surgery.

Nitration
Phenol reacts with dilute nitric acid to form a mixture of 2-nitrophenol and 4-nitrophenol plus water (Figure 10.39).

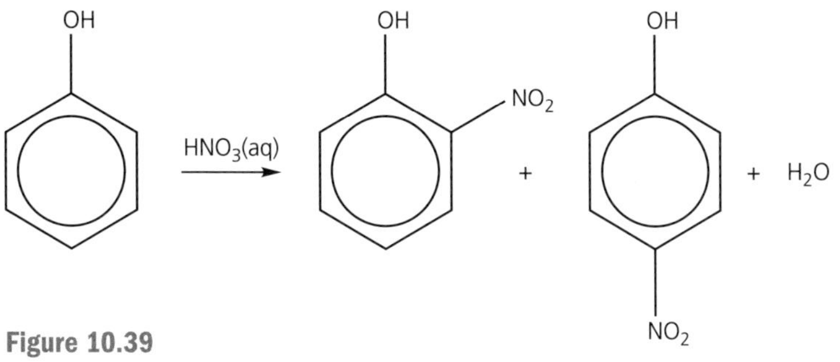

Figure 10.39

> **Tip**
> Remember that nitration of benzene requires concentrated nitric acid with a catalyst of concentrated sulfuric acid.

Reaction with acyl chlorides
Phenol reacts with acyl chlorides, but *not* in a Friedel–Crafts reaction. Instead the oxygen atom in phenol acts as a nucleophile and attacks the $\delta+$ carbon atom in the acid chloride, forming an ester (p. 220).

Phenol as an acid
The p_z-lone pair on the oxygen atom is partially drawn into the ring and this makes the hydrogen atom much more $\delta+$ than in alcohols. Thus, phenol reacts with water to form an acidic solution and with alkalis to form a salt. However, phenol is much weaker than a carboxylic acid and so does not give carbon dioxide when mixed with sodium carbonate or sodium hydrogencarbonate.

> **Tip**
> In all reactions involving the −OH group, the simplest way to write the formula of phenol is C_6H_5OH. The benzene ring needs to be drawn in full only for aromatic (electrophilic substitution) reactions.

Reaction with water

$$C_6H_5OH + H_2O \rightleftharpoons H_3O^+ + C_6H_5O^- \qquad K_a = 1.3 \times 10^{-10}\,mol\,dm^{-3}$$

The pH of a $0.10\,mol\,dm^{-3}$ solution of phenol is 5.44.

Reaction with sodium hydroxide
Aqueous hydroxide ions are a strong enough base to deprotonate phenol to form the salt sodium phenate and water:

$$C_6H_5OH + NaOH \rightarrow C_6H_5ONa + H_2O$$

The ionic equation is:

$$C_6H_5OH(s) + OH^-(aq) \rightarrow C_6H_5O^-(aq) + H_2O(l)$$

Solid phenol 'dissolves' in aqueous sodium hydroxide.

The word 'dissolves' is often used in this context. A more correct description would be that solid phenol reacts to form a solution.

Table 10.2 Acidity of alcohols, phenol and carboxylic acids

	Add blue litmus	Add sodium hydroxide	Add sodium carbonate
Alcohols	Stays blue	No reaction	No reaction
Phenol	Goes red	Salt formed	No reaction
Carboxylic acids	Goes red	Salt formed	CO_2 evolved

Phenol as an alcohol

Phenol does not react as an alcohol as readily as aliphatic alcohols, such as ethanol or propan-2-ol. For example it does not react with carboxylic acids to form esters. This is because the lone pair of electrons on the oxygen atom is drawn into the ring, making the oxygen less susceptible to electrophilic attack.

Reaction with acyl chlorides

Phenol reacts slowly with aliphatic acyl chlorides, for example ethanoyl chloride, to form an ester and fumes of hydrogen chloride:

$$C_6H_5OH + CH_3COCl \rightarrow CH_3COOC_6H_5 + HCl$$

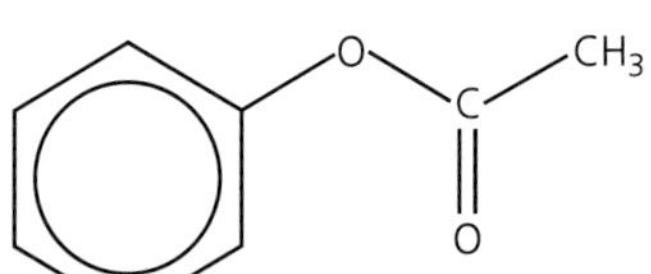

Figure 10.40 shows the structural formula of the ester phenylethanoate.

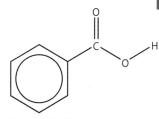

Figure 10.40

The oxygen atom in phenol acts as a nucleophile and attacks the $\delta+$ carbon atom in the acyl chloride.

Aromatic acyl chlorides, such as benzoyl chloride, C_6H_5COCl, are less reactive. Sodium hydroxide has to be added to create $C_6H_5O^-$ ions, which are a stronger nucleophile than phenol molecules. The ester, phenyl benzoate, is formed along with chloride ions:

$$C_6H_5O^- + C_6H_5COCl \rightarrow C_6H_5COOC_6H_5 + Cl^-$$

Tip

Remember that aliphatic alcohols, such as ethanol, react rapidly with both aliphatic and aromatic acyl chlorides.

Benzoic acid, C_6H_5COOH

Figure 10.41 shows the structural formula of benzoic acid.

Figure 10.41

- It is a solid with a melting temperature of 122°C.
- It is almost insoluble in cold water.
- The dissolving of benzoic acid is endothermic, so the position of the equilibrium:

$$C_6H_5COOH(s) + aq \rightleftharpoons C_6H_5COOH(aq)$$

  is driven to the right by an increase in temperature. Benzoic acid is soluble in hot water and so can be purified by recrystallisation using hot water (p. 284).
- Benzoic acid has the typical reactions of a carboxylic acid. It is a slightly stronger acid than ethanoic acid:
  - K_a of benzoic acid = $6.31 \times 10^{-5}\,mol\,dm^{-3}$; pH of $0.10\,mol\,dm^{-3}$ solution = 2.60
  - K_a of ethanoic acid = $1.74 \times 10^{-5}\,mol\,dm^{-3}$; pH of $0.10\,mol\,dm^{-3}$ solution = 2.88

2-methylnitrobenzene, $CH_3C_6H_4NO_2$

2-methylnitrobenzene, $CH_3C_6H_4NO_2$, is an oily liquid that smells of almonds. It boils at 220°C.

Preparation and purification

2-methylnitrobenzene can be prepared from methylbenzene and nitric acid (Figure 10.42).

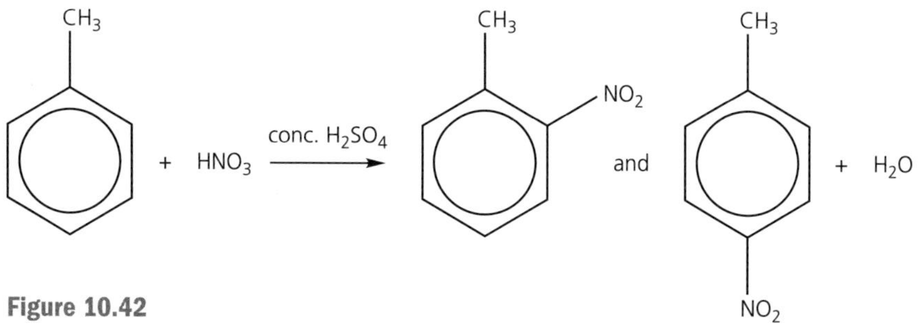

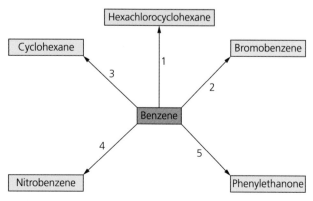

Figure 10.42

The procedure is as follows:

- The nitrating mixture, which consists of equal amounts of concentrated nitric and sulfuric acids, is mixed with benzene and the mixture is heated in a water bath maintained at 50°C. The temperature must not rise above this or a significant amount of 2,4-dinitromethylbenzene will be formed. If the temperature is allowed to fall below 50°C, the reaction becomes very slow.
- After refluxing, the mixture is cooled and water is added to dilute the acids. The mixture is then poured into a separating funnel and the bottom layer, which contains the methylnitrobenzenes, is run off. The top layer is discarded.
- The impure mixture of methylnitrobenzenes is washed with sodium carbonate solution, to remove residual acid, and then with water, to remove residual sodium carbonate. This is also carried out in the separating funnel.
- The oily liquid is dried by adding lumps of anhydrous calcium chloride and leaving for several hours.
- It is then decanted into a flask and distilled. The fraction that boils between 218°C and 222°C is collected. This is pure 2-methylnitrobenzene. The final distillation separates 2-nitromethylbenzene (boiling temperature 220°C) from 4-nitromethylbenzene (boiling temperature 238°C).

Summary tasks

Check that you can:

- recall evidence for the structure of benzene
- calculate the resonance stabilisation energy of benzene given the enthalpy of hydrogenation of it and of cyclohexane

Complete the spider diagram in Figure 10.43 by writing down the reagents, catalysts and conditions for the five reactions of benzene.

| Hexachlorocyclohexane |
| Cyclohexane |
| 1 |
| 3 |
| Bromobenzene |
| 2 |
| Benzene |
| 4 |
| 5 |
| Nitrobenzene |
| Phenylethanone |

Figure 10.43

Can you explain why:

- phenol reacts more readily than benzene in electrophilic substitution reactions?
- phenol is a stronger acid than ethanol but is less reactive as an alcohol?

Questions

1 Some enthalpy data are given below.

ΔH_a of carbon = $+715\,kJ\,mol^{-1}$

ΔH_a of hydrogen = $+218\,kJ\,mol^{-1}$

ΔH_f of benzene(g) = $+83\,kJ\,mol^{-1}$

Average bond enthalpy	ΔH/$kJ\,mol^{-1}$
C–C	+348
C=C	+612
C–H	+412

Use the data to calculate:

a) the enthalpy of formation of the theoretical gaseous molecule, 'cyclohexatriene'

b) the resonance stabilisation energy of benzene

c) Hence, draw a labelled energy-level diagram showing both the formation of 'cyclohexatriene' and benzene from solid carbon and hydrogen gas and the resonance stabilisation energy.

2 Draw and name all the aromatic isomers of $C_6H_3Br_2OH$.

3 Write the mechanism, including the production of the electrophile, of the reaction of benzene with ethanoyl chloride.

4 Explain why phenol:

a) reacts with bromine water whereas benzene requires liquid bromine and a catalyst

b) is a stronger acid than ethanol but is less reactive as an alcohol

c) has a higher boiling temperature than ethanol

d) is less soluble in water than ethanol

5 Write the structural formulae of the organic products, if any, of mixing phenol with:

a) aqueous potassium hydroxide

b) chlorine water

c) benzoyl chloride, C_6H_5COCl, in alkaline solution

6 Calculate:

a) the mass of bromine that would react with 1.23 g of phenol

b) the percentage yield, if 4.25 g of 2,4,6-tribromophenol were produced

7 Give an example of phenol reacting as a nucleophile.

8 Draw a diagram to show how two molecules of benzoic acid are hydrogen bonded. Mark in the bond angles around the hydrogen bond.

9 Explain the importance of the conditions in the nitration of benzene.

10 Write the mechanism, including the formation of the electrophile, of the nitration of methylbenzene.

11 An organic compound X burns with a smoky flame. It gives an orange precipitate with Brady's reagent but does not form a silver mirror with Tollens' reagent. It gives a yellow precipitate when warmed gently with a solution of iodine and sodium hydroxide. Draw the structural formula of a compound that could be X.

12 Fuming sulfuric acid contains dissolved SO_3 which contains a $\delta+$ sulfur atom. Suggest the mechanism for the sulfonation of benzene.

Exam practice questions

1 a) Ethene reacts rapidly with bromine, but benzene requires a catalyst of anhydrous iron(III) bromide. Write the mechanisms for the reaction of bromine with:
  i) ethene (3)
  ii) benzene (4)

b) Use your answers to (a) to explain why benzene reacts by substitution whereas ethene reacts by addition. (3)

c) Write equations for the reactions of:
  i) benzene with a mixture of concentrated nitric and sulfuric acids (1)
  ii) benzene with ethanoyl chloride in the presence of a catalyst of anhydrous aluminium chloride (1)

d) i) Write the equation for the reaction of phenol with bromine water. (1)
  ii) Compare the reactivity of the benzene ring in phenol with that in benzene itself. (3)

(Total 16 marks)

2 Benzaldehyde, C_6H_5CHO, can be prepared from benzene.
The benzene reacts with a mixture of carbon monoxide and hydrogen chloride gases in the presence of solid anhydrous aluminium chloride catalyst. The two gases react to form the unstable methanoyl chloride, $HCOCl$, which then reacts with the benzene in an electrophilic substitution reaction.

a) Suggest the mechanism for this reaction showing how the electrophile is formed and how it reacts to produce benzaldehyde. (4)

b) The benzene ring is activated towards electrophilic substitution in phenol. This is because:
  A the electrons in the C−O bond overlap with the π-electrons in the benzene ring
  B a lone pair of electrons on the oxygen overlaps with the π-electrons in the benzene ring
  C oxygen is more electronegative than carbon, so it draws electrons from the ring
  D oxygen is more electronegative than carbon, so it pushes electrons into the ring (1)

c) State the reagents and conditions necessary for converting benzaldehyde into:
  i) benzoic acid, C_6H_5COOH
  ii) phenylmethanol, $C_6H_5CH_2OH$ (4)

d) Write the equation for the reaction of benzaldehyde with 2,4-dinitrophenylhydrazine and state what you would observe. (2)

e) Benzene and phenol react with nitric acid in electrophilic substitution reactions, but under different conditions. State what these conditions are and explain why different conditions are needed. (4)

(Total 15 marks)

11 Organic nitrogen compounds (Topic 18)

Amines

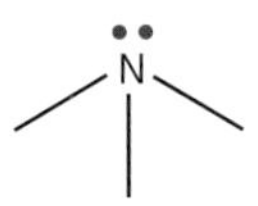

Figure 11.1

Amines contain the group shown in Figure 11.1.

There are three types of amine:

- A **primary amine** has only one carbon atom bonded to the nitrogen atom and, therefore, has an $-NH_2$ group. Methylamine, CH_3NH_2, is the simplest example.
- A **secondary amine** has two carbon atoms directly joined to the nitrogen atom. Dimethylamine, $(CH_3)_2NH$, is an example. All secondary amines have an >NH group.
- A **tertiary amine** has three carbon atoms and no hydrogen atoms attached directly to the nitrogen atom. Trimethylamine, $(CH_3)_3N$, is an example.

The nitrogen atom in all amines has three σ-bonds and a lone pair of electrons. The four pairs of electrons are arranged in a tetrahedron around the nitrogen. Therefore, the three bonding pairs are arranged pyramidally, with the H−N−H bond angle in primary amines less than the tetrahedral angle of $109\frac{1}{2}$. This is because the lone pair/bond pair repulsion is greater than the bond pair/bond pair repulsion.

Amines can be named either by:

- adding amine to the stem of the alkyl group. Thus, $C_2H_5NH_2$ is ethylamine and $CH_3CH_2CH_2CH_2NH_2$ is 1-butylamine

or

- adding the prefix amino- to the alkane from which the amine is derived. $C_2H_5NH_2$ is called aminoethane and $CH_3CH_2CH_2CH_2NH_2$ is 1-aminobutane.

> **Test yourself**
>
> 1 $C_4H_{11}N$ has several structural isomers. Write the structural formula of the isomer of $C_4H_{11}N$ that is:
>
> a) a primary amine with a branched chain
>
> b) a secondary amine with a branched chain
>
> c) a tertiary amine

Physical properties

Methylamine is a gas at room temperature and pressure. Ethylamine boils around room temperature and the next members of the homologous series of primary amines are liquids (Table 11.1). Amines have a characteristic fish-like smell.

Table 11.1 Boiling temperatures of amines

Name	Formula	Boiling temperature/°C
Methylamine (aminomethane)	CH_3NH_2	−6
Ethylamine (aminoethane)	$CH_3CH_2NH_2$	+17
1-propylamine (1-aminopropane)	$CH_3CH_2CH_2NH_2$	+49
1-butylamine	$CH_3CH_2CH_2CH_2NH_2$	+78
Dimethylamine	$(CH_3)_2NH$	+7
Trimethylamine	$(CH_3)_3N$	+4
Phenylamine (aminobenzene, aniline)	$C_6H_5NH_2$	+184

Tip

Note that the boiling temperatures of the unbranched amines increase as the number of electrons in the molecule increases. This causes the London forces to become stronger.

Hydrogen bonding occurs between amine molecules (Figure 11.2).

This explains why the boiling temperatures of amines are higher than those of the parent alkane. Methylamine (18 electrons) boils at −6°C whereas the non-hydrogen bonded ethane (also 18 electrons) boils at −89°C.

Amines are water-soluble because they form hydrogen bonds with water molecules. The nitrogen atom is δ− and the hydrogen atom attached to it is δ+ (Figure 11.3).

Tip

Remember that the strength of the intermolecular London forces depends mainly on the total number of electrons in the molecules.

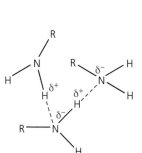

Figure 11.2　　　　　**Figure 11.3**

Tip

Note that the angle around a hydrogen-bonded hydrogen atom is 180°.

Test yourself

2 State the H–N–H bond angle in methylamine.

Preparation

Reaction of ammonia with a halogenoalkane

If a halogenoalkane is mixed with excess concentrated ammonia in aqueous ethanolic solution and left for a long time, a primary amine is obtained, for example:

$$C_2H_5Cl + 2NH_3 \rightarrow C_2H_5NH_2 + NH_4Cl$$

An excess of the halogenoalkane will yield the secondary amine.

Another condition for this reaction, often quoted in textbooks and accepted by examiners, is heating the mixture in a sealed tube.

Tip

When the base ammonia is a reactant, do not write an equation that has an acid such as HCl as a product. With excess ammonia, ammonium chloride is produced. If the ammonia is not in excess, the amine salt is formed (see the reaction of amines with acids on p. 253).

Reagents: excess ammonia

Conditions: leave for a long time or heat in a sealed tube

Type of reaction: nucleophilic substitution

Reduction of a nitrile or amide

Lithium tetrahydrido-aluminate(III) is also called lithium aluminium hydride.

A nitrile (e.g. ethanenitrile) or an amide (e.g. ethanamide) can be reduced by warming with a solution of lithium tetrahydridoaluminate(III) in dry ether (ethoxyethane), followed by hydrolysis of the adduct with dilute acid:

$$CH_3CN + 4[H] \rightarrow CH_3CH_2NH_2$$

ethanenitrile   ethylamine

$$CH_3CONH_2 + 4[H] \rightarrow CH_3CH_2NH_2 + H_2O$$

ethanamide   ethylamine

This is an example of the reduction of a polar π-bond by the nucleophilic H^- ion in lithium tetrahydridoaluminate(III). This reagent does not reduce the non-polar $C=C$ in alkenes.

Test yourself

3 Name the reagents and conditions for the two-step preparation of ethylamine from ethene.

Reduction of aromatic nitro compounds

Nitrobenzene, $C_6H_5NO_2$, can be reduced by heating with tin and concentrated hydrochloric acid.

$$C_6H_5NO_2 + 6[H] + H^+ \rightarrow C_6H_5NH_3^+ + 2H_2O$$

When sodium hydroxide is added, phenylamine is set free and can be removed from the reaction mixture by steam distillation (p. 284).

$$C_6H_5NH_3^+ + OH^- \rightarrow C_6H_5NH_2 + H_2O$$

Chemical reactions

1-butylamine, $CH_3CH_2CH_2CH_2NH_2$, is used as an example of a primary amine. The nitrogen atom has a lone pair of electrons and this causes it to be a base and a nucleophile.

As a base

Tip

A base is a substance that can accept an H^+ ion.

The base reactions of amines are similar to those of ammonia. Ammonia and amine molecules have a lone pair of electrons on the nitrogen atom that can be used to form a dative covalent bond with an H^+ ion.

Reaction with water

Amines react reversibly with water. For example:

The formula for 1-butylamine can be written as $CH_3(CH_2)_3NH_2$.

$$CH_3CH_2CH_2CH_2NH_2 + H_2O \rightleftharpoons CH_3CH_2CH_2CH_2NH_3^+ + OH^-$$

$$K_b = \frac{[CH_3CH_2CH_2CH_2NH_3^+][OH^-]}{[CH_3CH_2CH_2CH_2NH_2]} = 4.1 \times 10^{-4}\,mol\,dm^{-3}$$

As OH^- ions are produced, the solution is alkaline, with a pH of slightly less than 12. This reaction is similar to:

$$NH_3 + H_2O \rightleftharpoons NH_4^+ + OH^-$$

The alkyl group pushes electrons slightly towards the nitrogen atom making it more $\delta-$ than it is in ammonia. Therefore, primary amines are stronger bases than ammonia:

K_b of ethylamine $= 5.4 \times 10^{-4}\,\text{mol}\,\text{dm}^{-3}$

K_b of butylamine $= 4.1 \times 10^{-4}\,\text{mol}\,\text{dm}^{-3}$

K_b of ammonia $= 1.8 \times 10^{-5}\,\text{mol}\,\text{dm}^{-3}$

Diethylamine, $(C_2H_5)_2NH$, is a slightly stronger base than ethylamine because it contains two electron-pushing groups attached to the nitrogen atom.

Phenylamine (aminobenzene) is a weaker base than ammonia. This is because the lone pair of p_z electrons overlaps with the π system of the benzene ring. This withdraws electrons from the nitrogen, making it less able to accept an H^+ ion.

The strength of amines as bases is ordered as follows: primary aliphatic amines > ammonia > aromatic amines.

Reaction with acids
When an amine reacts with a strong acid, such as dilute hydrochloric acid, a salt (similar to an ammonium salt) is formed. For example, 1-butylamine and dilute hydrochloric acid produce 1-butylammonium chloride:

$$CH_3CH_2CH_2CH_2NH_2 + HCl \rightarrow CH_3CH_2CH_2CH_2NH_3^+Cl^-$$

or

$$CH_3(CH_2)_3NH_2 + HCl \rightarrow CH_3(CH_2)_3NH_3^+Cl^-$$

With ethylamine the equation is:

$$C_2H_5NH_2 + HCl \rightarrow C_2H_5NH_3^+Cl^-$$

The general equation is:

$$RNH_2 + HCl \rightarrow RNH_3^+Cl^-$$

This reaction can be reversed by adding a strong base, such as sodium hydroxide:

$$CH_3(CH_2)_3NH_3^+ + OH^- \rightarrow CH_3(CH_2)_3NH_2 + H_2O$$

The amine can then be distilled off from the mixture of the amine salt and sodium hydroxide.

Reaction with acyl chlorides
The lone pair of electrons on the nitrogen atom in the amine acts as a nucleophile and attacks the $\delta+$ carbon atom in the acyl chloride in an addition–elimination reaction. For example, when ethanoyl chloride is added to 1-butylamine, a secondary amide, N-ethylbutanamide, and misty fumes of hydrogen chloride are produced:

$$CH_3(CH_2)_3NH_2 + CH_3COCl \rightarrow CH_3CONH(CH_2)_3CH_3 + HCl$$

With ethylamine the product is N-ethylethanamide and the equation is:

$$C_2H_5NH_2 + CH_3COCl \rightarrow CH_3CONHC_2H_5 + HCl$$

> **Tip**
> Ammonia reacts with acids to form ammonium salts such as ammonium chloride:
> $$NH_3 + HCl \rightarrow NH_4^+Cl^-$$

> **Tip**
> Ammonia reacts with acyl chlorides to give amides (p. 220).

Paracetamol can be made by reacting 4-hydroxyphenylamine with ethanoyl chloride (Figure 11.4).

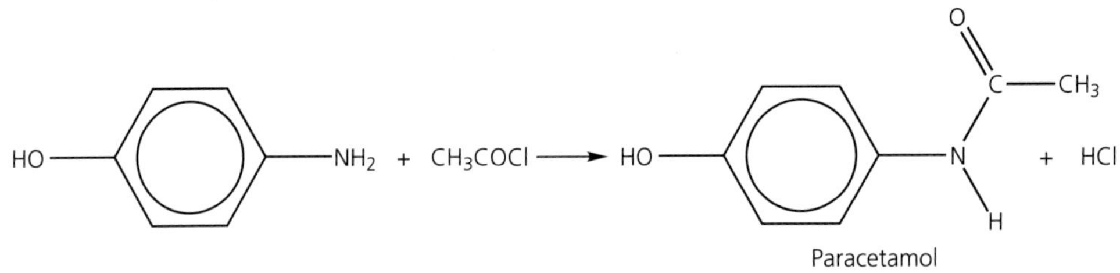

Figure 11.4

Paracetamol is also known as acetaminophen or as Tylenol.

The product is N-4-hydroxyphenylethanamide or paracetamol.

Amines with two $-NH_2$ groups in the molecule form polyamides with acyl chlorides with two $-COCl$ groups (p. 258).

Reaction with halogenoalkanes

A primary amine reacts with a halogenoalkane to produce a mixture of the salts of a secondary and a tertiary amine. Figure 11.5 shows the reaction with 1-butylamine and a limited amount of chloroethane.

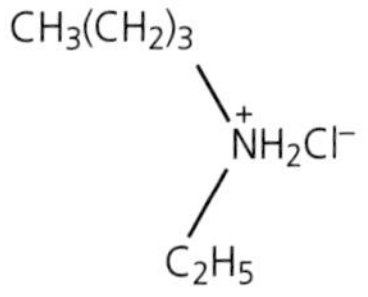

Figure 11.5

With ethylamine and excess chloroethane:

$$C_2H_5NH_2 + C_2H_5Cl \rightarrow (C_2H_5)_2NH_2{}^+Cl^-$$

$$(C_2H_5)_2NH_2{}^+Cl^- + C_2H_5Cl \rightarrow (C_2H_5)_3NH^+Cl^- + HCl$$

The reagents are heated in a solution in ethanol in a sealed tube.

If the free secondary and tertiary amines are required, a strong base is added to the solution and the amines formed are extracted from the reaction mixture and then separated by fractional distillation:

$$(C_2H_5)_2NH_2{}^+Cl^- + OH^- \rightarrow (C_2H_5)_2NH + H_2O + Cl^-$$

$$(C_2H_5)_3NH^+Cl^- + OH^- \rightarrow (C_2H_5)_3N + H_2O + Cl^-$$

Reaction with *d*-block metal ions

Amines can act as ligands with transition metal ions. The lone pair of electrons on the amine group can form a bond with the empty orbital of some *d*-block metal ions. The reaction is similar to the formation of ammines with excess ammonia.

A precipitate of the metal hydroxide is produced first. With Co^{2+}, Ni^{2+}, Cu^+, Cu^{2+}, Zn^{2+} and Ag^+ ions the precipitate dissolves because a complex ion is formed. The colour of the complex is similar to that formed with ammonia solution (p. 147).

The first reaction, forming the precipitate, is an example of a deprotonation reaction. For example, the reaction between hexaaquacopper(II) ions and ethylamine produces a pale blue precipitate:

$$[Cu(H_2O)_6]^{2+}(aq) + 2C_2H_5NH_2(aq) \rightarrow [Cu(H_2O)_4(OH)_2](s) + 2CH_3NH_3{}^+(aq)$$

With excess ethylamine solution, a ligand exchange reaction takes place and a soluble complex ion is formed:

$$[Cu(H_2O)_4(OH)_2](s) + 4C_2H_5NH_2(aq) \rightarrow$$
$$[Cu(NH_2C_2H_5)_4(H_2O)_2]^{2+}(aq) + 2OH^-(aq) + 2H_2O(l)$$

The overall reaction is:

$$[Cu(H_2O)_6]^{2+}(aq) + 4C_2H_5NH_2(aq) \rightarrow$$
$$[Cu(NH_2C_2H_5)_4(H_2O)_2]^{2+}(aq) + 4H_2O(l)$$

This complex is deep blue.

All primary amines including 1-butylamine and phenylamine form complex ions with hydrated copper(II) ions. The equivalent equations with ammonia are:

$$[Cu(H_2O)_6]^{2+}(aq) + 2NH_3(aq) \rightarrow [Cu(H_2O)_4(OH)_2](s) + 2NH_4^+(aq)$$

$$[Cu(H_2O)_4(OH)_2](s) + 4NH_3(aq) \rightarrow$$
$$[Cu(NH_3)_4(H_2O)_2]^{2+}(aq) + 2OH^-(aq) + 2H_2O(l)$$

1,2-diaminoethane is a bidentate ligand and reacts with many *d*-block metal ions to form a complex ion. The driving force is the increase in entropy as four particles produce seven (p. 148). The equation for the reaction between hydrated chromium ions and 1,2-diaminoethane, symbolised as en for simplicity, is

$$[Cr(H_2O)_6]^{3+} + 3en \rightarrow [Cr(en)_3]^{3+} + 6H_2O$$

Test yourself

4 Write equations for the reaction of 2-aminoethanol, $NH_2CH_2CH_2OH$, with:

a) dilute hydrochloric acid

b) ethanoyl chloride

c) iodomethane

Phenylamine, $C_6H_5NH_2$

Figure 11.6 shows the structural formula of phenylamine.

The lone pair of electrons on the nitrogen atom is in the same plane as the delocalised π-electrons of the ring and so, to some extent, becomes part of the delocalised system. This pulling of the electrons into the ring and away from the nitrogen atom has two effects — the ring becomes more susceptible to electrophilic attack and the nitrogen atom becomes less δ− and so less effective as a base.

Physical properties

- Phenylamine is a liquid at room temperature. It boils at 184°C and is slightly denser than water.
- The nitrogen atom is δ− and the hydrogen atoms attached to the nitrogen are δ+. Therefore, phenylamine can form intermolecular hydrogen bonds as well as strong London forces between molecules. It is slightly soluble in water because it forms hydrogen bonds with water molecules. However, the benzene ring inhibits solubility.

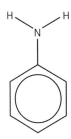

Figure 11.6

Phenylamine used to be called aniline.

- It dissolves readily in many organic solvents such as ether (ethoxyethane) and ethanol.
- It is a toxic substance that can be absorbed through the skin.

Laboratory preparation

The procedure for the laboratory preparation of phenylamine is as follows:

- Nitrobenzene and tin are mixed in a round-bottomed flask fitted with a reflux condenser. Concentrated hydrochloric acid is carefully added and, after the rapid evolution of hydrogen has ceased, the mixture is heated to 100°C in a bath of boiling water for 30 minutes.
- The reaction mixture is cooled to room temperature, the condenser removed and an *excess* of sodium hydroxide is carefully added with cooling.
- The mixture is steam distilled to remove the phenylamine from the sludge of tin hydroxides. This is carried out by blowing steam into the mixture and condensing the phenylamine and steam mixture that comes off.
- The distillate is placed in a separating funnel and some solid sodium chloride is added to reduce the solubility of phenylamine. The phenylamine layer is run off into a flask and some solid anhydrous potassium carbonate added to remove any traces of water.
- The phenylamine is decanted off from the solid potassium carbonate and distilled, using an air condenser. The fraction that boils between 180°C and 185°C is collected.

The overall equation for the process can be represented by:

$$C_6H_5NO_2 + 6[H] \xrightarrow{\text{Sn and conc. HCl}} C_6H_5NH_2 + 2H_2O$$

Chemical reactions

Phenylamine reacts as both an aromatic compound and as a primary amine.

Bromination

In neutral solutions the benzene ring is activated by the lone pair of electrons on the nitrogen atom. Phenylamine reacts with bromine water in an electrophilic substitution reaction to form a white precipitate of 2,4,6-tribromophenylamine and hydrogen bromide. The molecular equation is:

$$C_6H_5NH_2 + 3Br_2 \rightarrow C_6H_2Br_3NH_2 + 3HBr$$

As a base

The pulling of the lone pair of electrons from the nitrogen atom by the benzene ring makes the nitrogen atom less $\delta-$ and, therefore, less effective as a base and as a nucleophile.

Phenylamine is a weak base, so it reacts reversibly with water:

$$C_6H_5NH_2 + H_2O \rightleftharpoons C_6H_5NH_3^+ + OH^-$$

It reacts with strong acids to form phenylammonium salts. For example, the molecular equation for the reaction of phenylamine with hydrochloric acid to form phenylammonium chloride is:

$$C_6H_5NH_2 + HCl \rightarrow C_6H_5NH_3^+Cl^-$$

This is similar to the reaction between phenol and bromine water to form a white precipitate of 2,4,6-tribromophenol.

The ionic equation is:

$$C_6H_5NH_2(l) + H^+(aq) \rightarrow C_6H_5NH_3^+(aq)$$

Liquid phenylamine dissolves in aqueous acids because it forms an ionic salt.

Phenylamine is a weaker base than ammonia, because of the electron-withdrawing effect of the benzene ring.

Test yourself

5 Write equations for the reaction of phenylamine with:

  a) hydrochloric acid

  b) ethanoyl chloride

Amides

Amides contain the group shown in Figure 11.7.

This is usually written as $-CONH_2$.

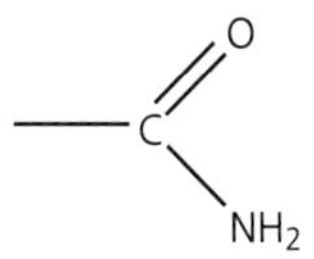

Figure 11.7

Physical properties

An amide molecule contains two $\delta+$ hydrogen atoms, a $\delta-$ oxygen atom and a $\delta-$ nitrogen atom. Therefore, the molecules can form several *inter*molecular hydrogen bonds. This means that amides have higher melting temperatures than acyl chlorides derived from the same acid.

Table 11.2 Some amides

Name	Formula	Melting temperature/°C	Boiling temperature/°C
Ethanamide	CH_3CONH_2	82	222
Propanamide	$CH_3CH_2CONH_2$	79	222
Benzamide	$C_6H_5CONH_2$	132	290

Apart from those with a large hydrophobic group, for example benzamide, amides are water-soluble. This is because the molecules can form several hydrogen bonds with water molecules.

Preparation

Amides can be prepared by the reaction between ammonia and an acyl chloride:

$$CH_3COCl + NH_3 \rightarrow CH_3CONH_2 + HCl$$

Chemical reactions

Hydrolysis

When boiled under reflux with either aqueous acid or aqueous alkali, amides are hydrolysed. For example, ethanamide is hydrolysed in acid solution to ethanoic acid and ammonium ions:

$$CH_3CONH_2 + H^+ + H_2O \rightarrow CH_3COOH + NH_4^+$$

With alkali, the salt of the carboxylic acid is formed and ammonia gas is evolved. For example, when hydrolysed by sodium hydroxide, benzamide gives sodium benzoate:

$$C_6H_5CONH_2 + OH^- \rightarrow C_6H_5COO^- + NH_3$$

If the carboxylic acid is required, the product of alkaline hydrolysis must be acidified with a solution of a strong acid:

$$C_6H_5COO^- + H^+ \rightarrow C_6H_5COOH$$

Benzoic acid is insoluble in cold water and so on cooling it precipitates out.

Test yourself

6 Write the equation for the reaction between 3-bromo-2-methylpropanamide and excess aqueous sodium hydroxide.

Polyamides

The reaction between an acyl chloride and an amine was described above. If a compound that has two COCl groups reacts with a substance with two NH_2 groups a polyamide is formed.

The first commercial polyamide was nylon-6,6. This can be made in the laboratory by the reaction of hexane-1,6-dioyl dichloride, $ClOC(CH_2)_4COCl$, and 1,6-diaminohexane, $NH_2(CH_2)_6NH_2$. The former is soluble in 1,1,2-trichloroethane and the latter in water. If the two solutions are carefully added together so that the aqueous layer floats on top of the organic layer, a thread of nylon can be drawn from the interface of the two liquids.

The equation for the reaction is shown in Figure 11.8.

A thread of nylon being pulled from the interface of the two solutions

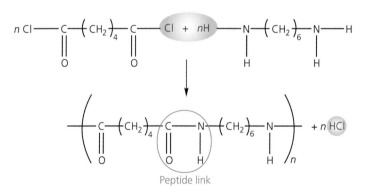

Peptide link

Figure 11.8

Nylon is a condensation polymer — a molecule of hydrogen chloride is eliminated as each acid chloride group reacts with an amino group.

The strength of nylon is increased by cold-drawing. This involves putting the threads under tension. The polymer chains become more aligned. This results in hydrogen bonding between the $\delta-$ oxygen in the C=O groups and the $\delta+$ hydrogen atoms in the NH groups.

Uses of nylon include the following:

- Nylon fibres are used in stockings and carpets.
- Nylon is used to make a number of machine parts such as bearings and rollers. This is because it is a very tough material that has a melting point above 250°C.
- It has a high electrical resistance and so is used to make switches.

Other polyamides

Figure 11.9 shows the general equation for the formation of polyamides.

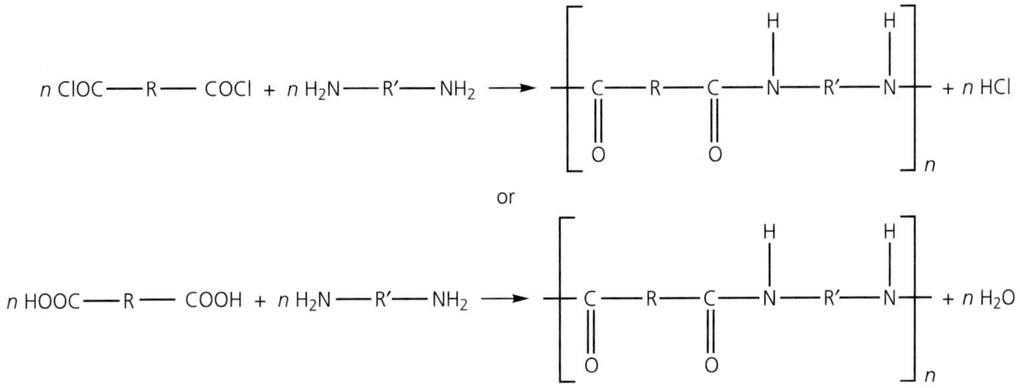

Figure 11.9

Nomex® is a long, straight-chain polymer with flame-resistant properties. The equation for its formation is shown in Figure 11.10.

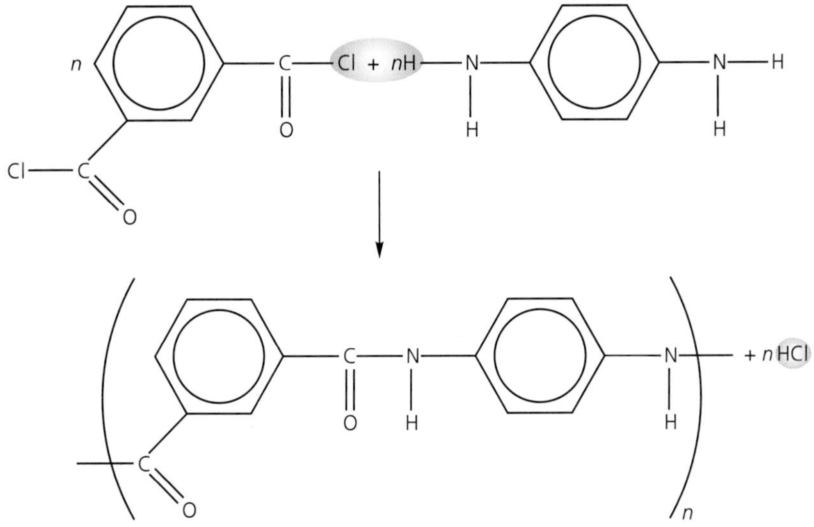

Figure 11.10

Kevlar® is another tough polyamide. It is used in bulletproof vests. The equation for its formation is shown in Figure 11.11.

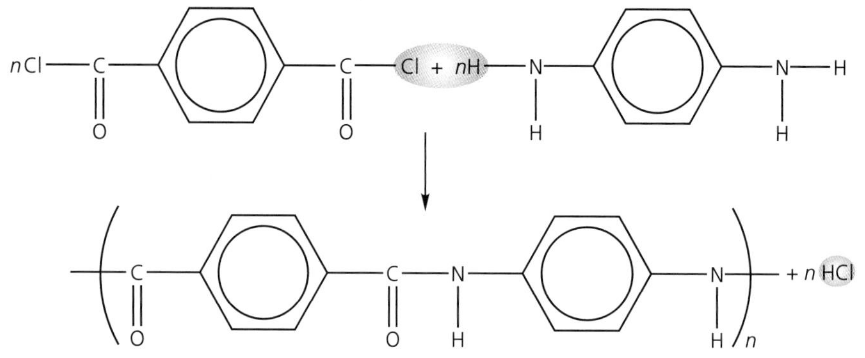

Figure 11.11

All polyamides contain the peptide link. This is the same link that joins α-amino acid residues in proteins. The strands of polyamides are held together by hydrogen bonds between different chains (see below). This gives them considerably greater tensile strength than polyalkenes such as poly(ethene).

Natural polyamides

Silk and wool are made up of polyamides. Silk contains a high proportion of peptide links between serine molecules. Serine is an amino acid of formula $NH_2CH(CH_2OH)COOH$. The $-COOH$ group at one end forms a peptide link with the $-NH_2$ group of another serine molecule and its $-COOH$ group forms a peptide link with an $-NH_2$ group of a third serine molecule and so on.

Figure 11.12 gives the structural formula, showing three repeat units.

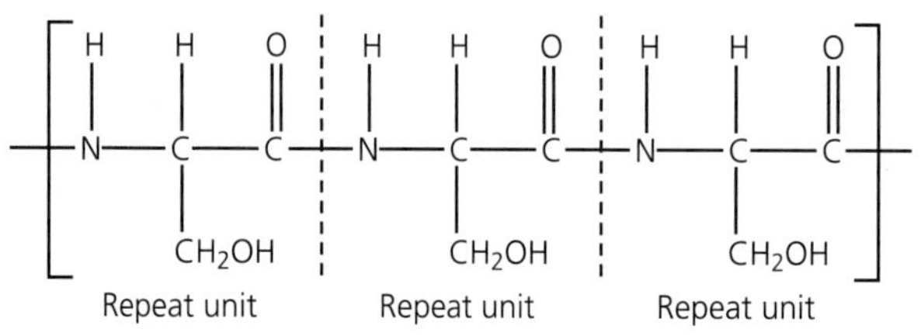

Figure 11.12

Wool has a high proportion of aminoethanoic acid (glycine) NH_2CH_2COOH, residues.

Test yourself

7 Draw two repeat units of poly(aminoethanoic acid).

Physical properties of polyamides

Nylon, silk and wool have a β-pleated sheet structure. The chains are arranged in such a manner that the fibre is like a stack of corrugated cardboard with hydrogen bonds between the δ− oxygen of the >C=O group in one repeat unit and the δ+ hydrogen atom in an >NH group in another repeat unit. This makes the fibres strong.

Condensation polymerisation

The formation of nylon, Nomex and Kevlar are all examples of condensation polymerisation.

In most cases, two different monomers, each having two identical functional groups, react. However, sometimes a polymer is formed in a condensation reaction from a single monomer that has two different functional groups.

An example is the polymerisation of 6-aminohexanoic acid, $NH_2(CH_2)_5COOH$ (Figure 11.13).

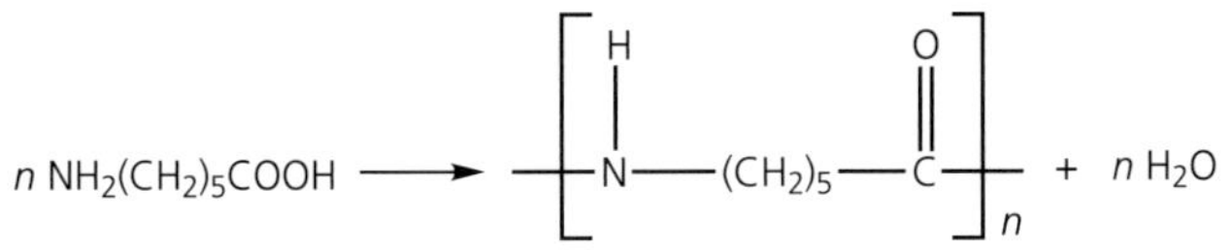

$$n\ NH_2(CH_2)_5COOH \longrightarrow \left[\begin{matrix} H \\ | \\ N \end{matrix} —(CH_2)_5—\begin{matrix} O \\ \| \\ C \end{matrix} \right]_n + n\ H_2O$$

Figure 11.13

Another example of condensation polymerisation is the formation of polyesters such as Terylene (p. 226) from a dicarboxylic acid and a diol.

Addition polymerisation

Addition polymerisation has been covered in the first A-level year. The monomer is a compound with a $>C=C<$ group. The π-bond in a monomer breaks and a new σ-bond forms with another monomer. As a π-bond is weaker than a σ-bond, and as all bond making is exothermic, such polymerisations are exothermic. A simple example is the production of poly(propene) from propene (Figure 11.14).

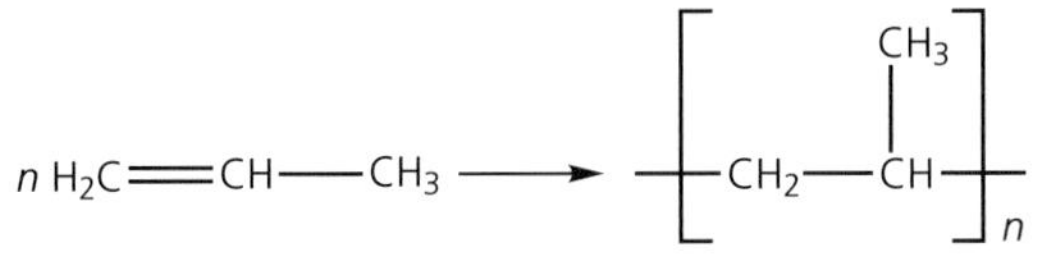

$$n\ H_2C{=}CH—CH_3 \longrightarrow \left[—CH_2—\begin{matrix} CH_3 \\ | \\ CH \end{matrix}— \right]_n$$

Figure 11.14

Some special addition polymers have been invented that show unusual properties in the presence of water.

Poly(propenamide) and poly(propenoic acid)

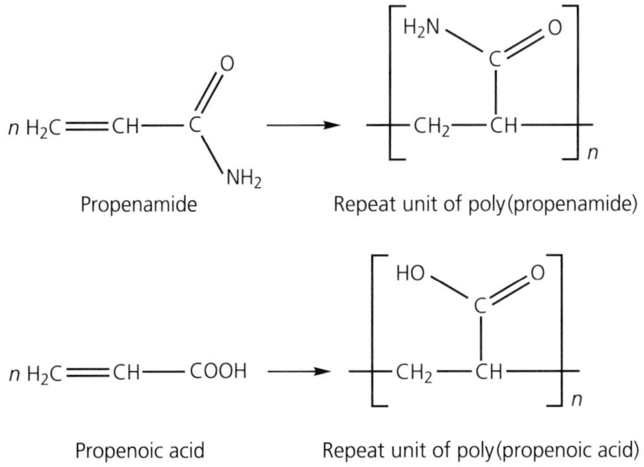

$$n\ H_2C{=}CH—\begin{matrix} O \\ \| \\ C \\ \backslash \\ NH_2 \end{matrix} \longrightarrow \left[—CH_2—CH— \right]_n$$

Propenamide   Repeat unit of poly(propenamide)

$$n\ H_2C{=}CH—COOH \longrightarrow \left[—CH_2—CH— \right]_n$$

Propenoic acid   Repeat unit of poly(propenoic acid)

Figure 11.15

> **Tip**
>
> In all addition polymers the repeat unit consists of a chain of two carbon atoms.

These two polymers, particularly when cross-linked, absorb water through hydrogen bonding. They are used in disposable nappies and as water-holding gels in the soil of pot plants and hanging baskets. As they absorb water, the polymers swell to many times their original volumes.

Some toys make use of this property. For example, there is a toy dinosaur egg in which the shell does not have cross-linking and is, therefore, water-soluble. When the egg is placed in water the shell dissolves. The 'yolk' is cross-linked and as it absorbs water it expands. Therefore, the egg appears to hatch and grow into a toy dinosaur.

Poly(ethenol)

This polymer is also called (polyvinylalcohol). Its repeat unit is shown in Figure 11.16.

Poly(ethenol) has the unusual property of being water-soluble. It is used as the coating in liquitabs, which contain liquid washing detergent, and in soluble bags to hold soiled hospital laundry. The polymer is water-soluble because of the many hydrogen bonds that can form between the $-OH$ groups that occur on alternate carbon atoms and water molecules.

This polymer is also unusual in that its monomer does not exist. Attempts to make ethenol, $CH_2=CHOH$, result in the production of ethanal, CH_3CHO. The polymer is manufactured by reacting the polyester, polyvinylacetate (PVA), with methanol in a transesterification reaction (Figure 11.17).

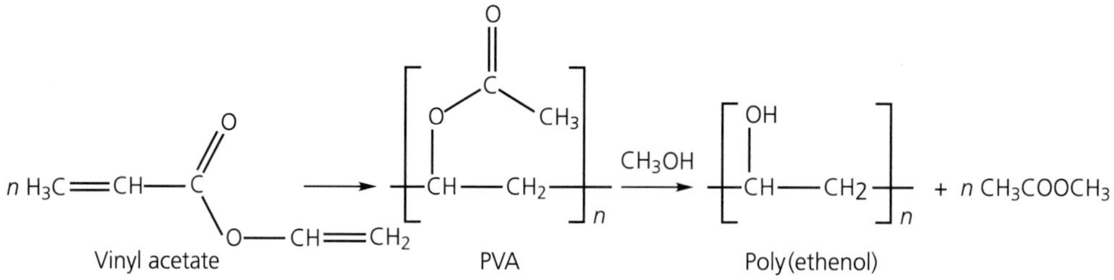

> The prefix vinyl is sometimes used as the name for the $CH_2=CH-$ group.

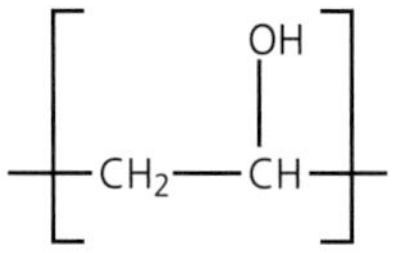

$$\left[\begin{array}{c} OH \\ | \\ CH_2-CH \end{array}\right]$$

Figure 11.16

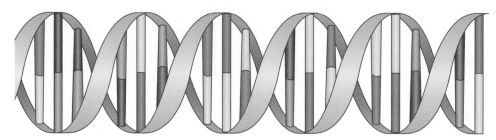

Figure 11.17

Natural products containing the amine group

The bases in DNA and RNA contain a nitrogen atom with a lone pair of electrons. Each base is attached to a carbohydrate (deoxyribose in DNA) in the carbohydrate–phosphate chain and forms hydrogen bonds with a particular base in the opposite DNA strand (Figure 11.18). Adenine (A) always forms hydrogen bonds with thymine (T); guanine (G) always forms hydrogen bonds with cytosine (C).

Figure 11.18 The DNA double helix

Therefore, if one DNA strand in the double helix has the base order ATGGAC, the opposite strand will have the order TACCTG. Hydrogen bonds between strands are shown in red in Figures 11.19 and 11.20. The bond that attaches the base to the carbohydrate is shown in green.

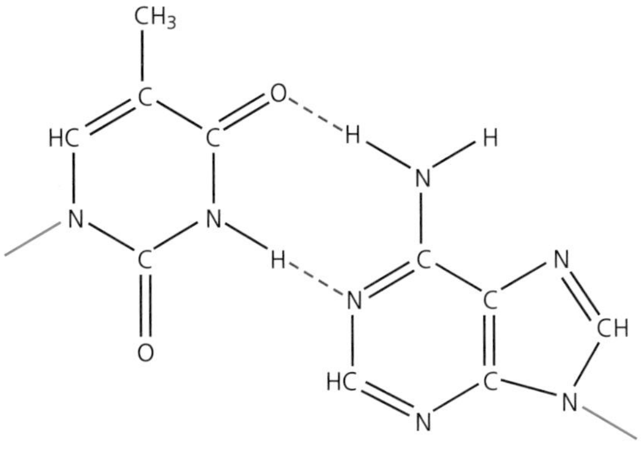

Figure 11.19 The base pair thymine and adenine in DNA

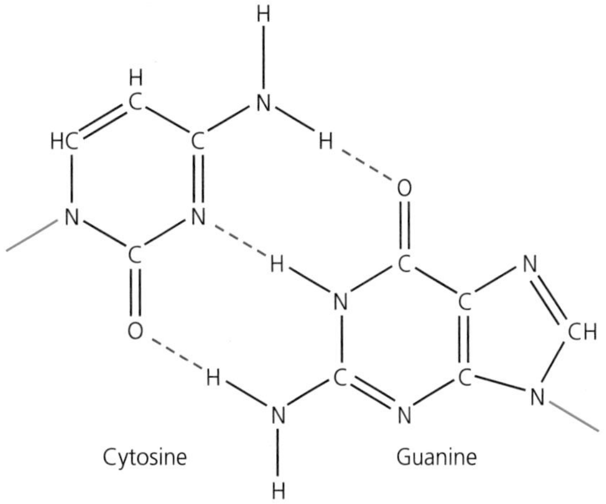

Figure 11.20 The base pair cytosine and guanine in DNA

In RNA, uracil replaces thymine and is found hydrogen-bonded to adenine. Thymine has a CH_3 group on one of the doubly bonded carbon atoms whereas uracil has a hydrogen atom.

Other organic bases that contain an amine group include:

- the alkaloid poison, strychnine
- the painkillers, morphine and codeine
- the stimulants, caffeine and nicotine

Amino acids

Amino acid molecules contain at least one $-NH_2$ group and one $-COOH$ group. Those amino acids that are the building blocks of proteins have the $-NH_2$ group attached to the carbon atom next to the $-COOH$ group. These are called α-amino acids. The simplest is aminoethanoic acid (glycine), NH_2CH_2COOH.

Amino acids have the general formula shown in Figure 11.21, where R is either a hydrogen atom or an organic residue.

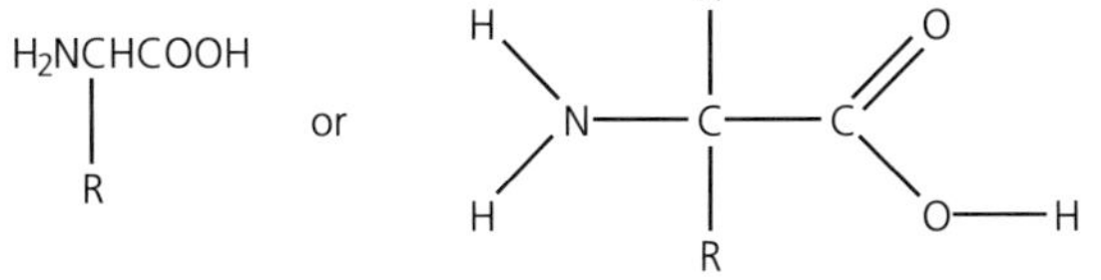

Figure 11.21

There are 20 amino acids that make up the proteins in the human body. Of these, 12 can be synthesised from other amino acids, but eight cannot. The latter are called **essential amino acids** and must be present in the diet. Two examples are valine and lysine.

Amino acids can be divided into three types:

- **neutral amino acids** — a molecule of a neutral amino acid contains only one basic $-NH_2$ group and one acidic $-COOH$ group
- **acidic amino acids** — a molecule of an acidic amino acid contains two $-COOH$ groups and one $-NH_2$ group
- **basic amino acids** — a molecule of a basic amino acid contains two $-NH_2$ groups and one $-COOH$ group

Table 11.3 Some amino acids

Type	Common name	Systematic name	Formula
Neutral	Glycine	Aminoethanoic acid	$CH_2(NH_2)COOH$
	Alanine	2-aminopropanoic acid	$CH_3CH(NH_2)COOH$
	Valine	2-amino-3-methylbutanoic acid	$(CH_3)_2CHCH(NH_2)COOH$
	Leucine	2-amino-4-methylpentanoic acid	$(CH_3)_2CHCH_2CH(NH_2)COOH$
	Cysteine	2-amino-3-sulfanylpropanoic acid	$HSCH_2CH(NH_2)COOH$
Acidic	Aspartic acid	2-aminobutane-1,4-dioic acid	$HOOCCH_2CH(NH_2)COOH$
	Glutamic acid	2-aminopentane-1,5-dioic acid	$HOOC(CH_2)_2CH(NH_2)COOH$
Basic	Lysine	2,6-diaminohexanoic acid	$NH_2CH_2CH_2CH_2CH_2CH(NH_2)COOH$

The salt of glutamic acid in which the hydrogen in one of the COOH groups has been replaced by sodium is monosodium glutamate, the flavour enhancer added to some foods.

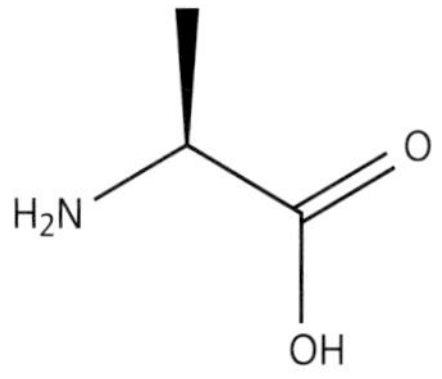

Figure 11.22

Figure 11.22 shows the skeletal formula of alanine.

Physical properties

Amino acids are solids at room temperature. This is because the molecules form **zwitterions**. The $-COOH$ group in one molecule protonates the $-NH_2$ group in another molecule, forming a species that has a positive charge at one end and a negative charge at the other. The positive charge on one zwitterion is strongly attracted to the negative charge of an *adjacent* zwitterion. The $-COOH$ group is weakly acidic and the $-NH_2$ group is weakly basic, so the formation of the zwitterion is reversible. Therefore, both the zwitterion and the neutral molecule are present. This can be represented for aminoethanoic acid (glycine) by the equation:

$$NH_2CH_2COOH \rightleftharpoons {}^+NH_3CH_2COO^-$$

where ${}^+NH_3CH_2COO^-$ is the zwitterion.

> **Tip**
>
> It is common practice to write the formula of an amino acid as an uncharged molecule, rather than as the zwitterion. However, it should be remembered that the position of this equilibrium is well to the right. Equations for reactions of amino acids should have the zwitterion on the left. However, an equation with the molecular species on the left will score full marks at A level.

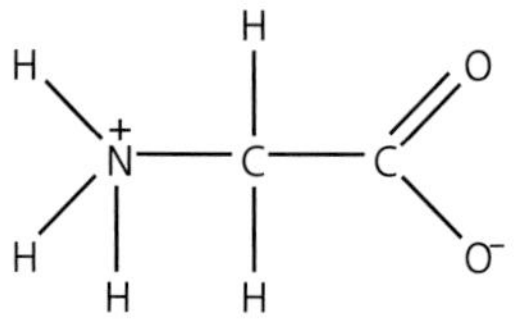

Figure 11.23

Figure 11.23 shows the full structural formula of the zwitterion of glycine.

Chemical reactions

The two most important reactions are those of amino acids with acids and with bases.

Reaction with acids
The COO^- group in the zwitterion acts as a base and accepts an H^+ ion from the acid:

$$^+NH_3CH_2COO^- + H^+ \rightarrow {}^+NH_3CH_2COOH$$

This reaction can also be written with the uncharged molecule as the starting species:

$$NH_2CH_2COOH + H^+ \rightarrow {}^+NH_3CH_2COOH$$

The basic $-NH_2$ group reacts with the H^+ ions in a strong acid.

Reaction with bases
The NH_3^+ group in the zwitterion acts as an acid and protonates the base:

$$^+NH_3CH_2COO^- + OH^- \rightarrow NH_2CH_2COO^- + H_2O$$

The $-NH_3^+$ group, which is the conjugate acid of the weakly basic $-NH_2$ group, gives a proton to the OH^- ion.

The alternative equation shows the acidic $-COOH$ group in the uncharged molecule protonating hydroxide ions:

$$NH_2CH_2COOH + OH^- \rightarrow NH_2CH_2COO^- + H_2O$$

Polymerisation reactions
Amino acids can join to each other by formation of a peptide link in a condensation polymerisation reaction. Enzymes catalyse this reaction and when it happens many times the result is a protein (p. 266).

> The name 'zwitterion' is derived from the German for the word 'mongrel', which is the offspring of two different breeds of dog. In the chemical sense, it is the mongrel of a cation and an anion.

> **Tip**
>
> A base is a species that accepts a proton. An acid is a species that protonates a base.

Test yourself

8 The formula of all naturally occurring amino acids can be written as $NH_2CHRCOOH$.

   a) Rewrite this formula as the zwitterion.

   b) Write ionic equations for the reaction of the zwitterion with i) aqueous acid and ii) aqueous alkali.

Stereoisomerism

All the natural amino acids, except glycine, are optically active. The carbon atom next to the $-COOH$ is a chiral centre because it has four different groups attached to it. Alanine (2-aminopropanoic acid) has two optical isomers (Figure 11.24).

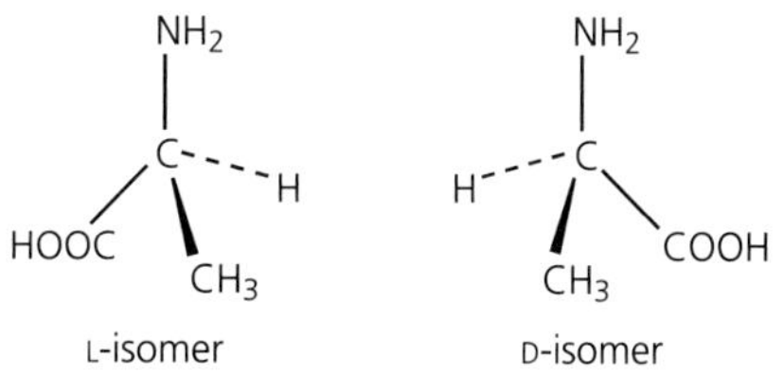

Figure 11.24 The two optical isomers of 2-aminopropanoic acid (alanine)

> **Tip**
>
> Almost all the amino acids in proteins have the same absolute configuration in space. This is the L-configuration, as shown in the diagram of alanine (Figure 11.24).

> **Tip**
>
> The structural formula of an amino acid can also be written as $NH_2CHRCOOH$, where R is a hydrogen atom (in glycine) or an organic group.

The isomers can be written as zwitterions or as uncharged molecules. The latter is more common, especially in biochemistry.

Alanine, which occurs in proteins, is only one of the two optical isomers shown in Figure 11.24. Alanine rotates the plane of polarisation of plane-polarised light clockwise (p. 191).

Glycine (aminoethanoic acid, NH_2CH_2COOH) is optically inactive because it does not have a chiral centre. The carbon atom next to the −COOH group has two hydrogen atoms bonded to it, so it cannot be chiral. Therefore, a solution of glycine has no effect on the plane of polarisation of plane-polarised light.

Separation and identification of amino acids

These processes can be carried out in school laboratories using thin-layer chromatography, TLC. The principles of TLC are the same as for other chromatographic techniques (p. 313). The stationary phase is either silica gel or aluminium oxide immobilised on a flat inert sheet that is made usually from glass or plastic.

- The unknown amino acid or mixture of amino acids is dissolved in a suitable solvent and a spot of the test solution is placed about 2 cm from the bottom of the plate.
- Spots of dissolved known amino acids are placed separately on the same plate at the same level.
- The plate is then dipped in a suitable eluent (the mobile phase) with the spots above the level of the liquid eluent. The plate is placed in a sealed container. The eluent is drawn up the plate by capillary action.
- The plate is left until the eluent has risen to the top of the plate.
- The plate is removed and sprayed with a solution of ninhydrin and then heated. Ninhydrin reacts with amino acids (and amines) producing a blue-purple colour.

The height that the unknown reached is compared with the heights reached by the known amino acids. Spots at the same height are caused by the same amino acid and so the amino acids in the unknown can be identified.

$$R_f \text{ value} = \frac{\text{distance moved by amino acid}}{\text{distance moved by solvent}}$$

The separation works because different amino acids have different R_f values. This is because the interaction with the stationary phase compared with solubility in the eluent differs for different amino acids.

Proteins

Proteins consist of a number of amino acids joined together by peptide links. If two amino acids join together in a condensation reaction, the product is called a **dipeptide**. The artificial sweetener aspartame is a dipeptide formed from phenylalanine and aspartic acid (Figure 11.25). The peptide link is shown in red.

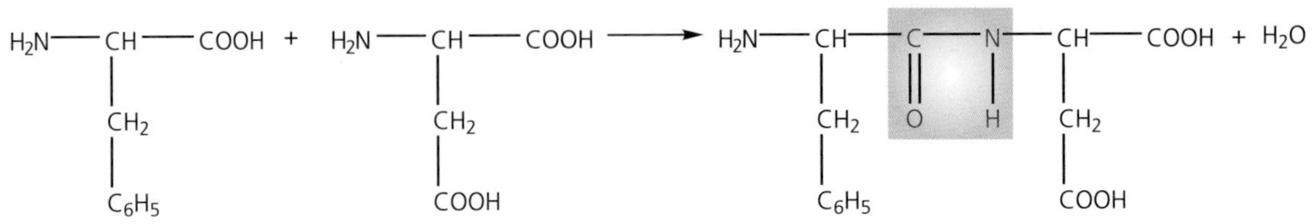

Figure 11.25

An amino acid in a peptide chain is called a **residue**. Thus, aspartame has the residues of phenylalanine and aspartic acid.

Natural proteins are **polypeptides** formed by condensation polymerisation of many amino acids. Bovine insulin has 51 amino acids in one specific sequence. The number of different ways of arranging these 51 amino acids is about the same as there are atoms in the whole of the Milky Way galaxy, but only one way produces insulin.

The peptide bond in proteins and dipeptides can be hydrolysed by heating under reflux with dilute sulfuric acid. The amino acids can then be separated by thin-layer chromatography.

It is remarkable that so few mutations occur to produce rogue polypeptides. However, sickle cell anaemia is a hereditary disease that results when two glutamic acid molecules (one in each β-polypeptide sequence in haemoglobin) are replaced by valine molecules. The resulting haemoglobin molecule is a much poorer oxygen carrier, which tends to shorten the life of the sufferer. However, this mutation does provide protection against malaria, and the gene is passed on from generation to generation, in regions where malaria is endemic.

Structure of proteins

The **primary structure** is the order of the amino acids in the chain. This is specific to the protein. However, the peptide chains are not randomly arranged like a pile of spaghetti. They are organised into a **secondary structure**, of which there are two types:

False-colour scanning electron micrograph of normal red blood cells (rounded) and sickle cells (crescent-shaped)

- **α-helix** — the peptide is coiled in a spiral and the structure held together by *intramolecular* hydrogen bonds between one group in one part of the chain and another group four residues away along the chain. There are also ionic bonds between the residues of basic and acidic amino acids. Myoglobin is an example of a protein with an α-helical structure (Figure 11.26).
- **β-pleated sheet** — the polypeptide chains are almost fully extended and are held by hydrogen bonds to other polypeptide chains (Figure 11.27). The result is rather like a stack of corrugated cardboard. Silk has this structure. A thread of silk is strong because of the many intermolecular hydrogen bonds between its polypeptide chains.

> **Tip**
>
> Nylon is a polyamide in which all the pairs of residues are identical. Its secondary structure is a β-pleated sheet, which is why nylon is so strong.

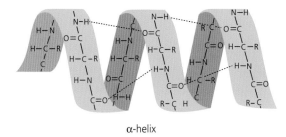

α-helix

Figure 11.26

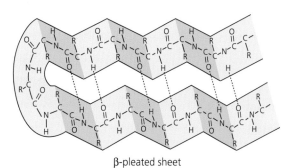

β-pleated sheet

Figure 11.27

Summary tasks

Make sure that you can:

- identify amine and amide functional groups
- write equations for the reactions of any primary amine with water, acids, acyl chlorides, halogenoalkanes and Cu^{2+}(aq) ions
- explain why phenylamine is a weaker base than 1-butylamine which, in turn, is stronger than ammonia

Check that you can describe the preparation of

- a primary aliphatic amine from a halogenoalkane and from a nitrile
- an aromatic amine, such as phenylamine, from a nitro compound

Can you:

- write the equations and name the products for the reactions of ethanoyl chloride with ammonia, amines and also with alcohols?
- draw the repeat units of polyesters and polyamides given the monomers, and vice versa?
- explain why amino acids are solids and are soluble in water?
- write equations for the reaction of amino acids with H^+(aq) and with OH^-(aq) ions?

Make sure you understand that:

- proteins are examples of polyamides
- proteins are hydrolysed by acid into their constituent amino acids

Questions

1 Give the N−C−C bond angle in ethanamide. Justify your answer.

2 Explain why ethylamine is soluble in water but chloroethane and ethane are both insoluble.

3 Explain why ethanoic acid, CH_3COOH, has a higher boiling point than 1-propylamine, $CH_3CH_2CH_2NH_2$, and why both these compounds have a higher boiling point than butane, $CH_3CH_2CH_2CH_3$.

4 Ethylamine, $C_2H_5NH_2$, can be prepared from ethanoic acid by a three-step synthesis. Outline this process.

5 An organic compound contains 39.3% carbon, 11.5% hydrogen, 26.2% oxygen and 23.0% nitrogen by mass.

   a) Calculate its empirical formula.

   b) The molecular formula of this compound is the same as its empirical formula. It reacts with phosphorus pentachloride, giving off misty fumes. Suggest a structural formula for this compound.

6 Explain why methylamine is a stronger base than ammonia, which itself is a stronger base than phenylamine.

7 Explain why aminoethanoic acid is a solid at room temperature and is soluble in water.

8 Ethylamine has a distinctive smell. When some dilute hydrochloric acid is added, the smell disappears. If aqueous sodium hydroxide is now added in excess, the smell returns. Write equations for the reactions involved.

9 State the reagents for the conversion of nitrobenzene to phenylamine.

10 Phenylamine and chlorobenzene are equally polar molecules. Phenylamine boils at 184°C; chlorobenzene boils at 132°C. Phenylamine is slightly soluble in water and forms a clear solution when dilute hydrochloric acid is added. Chlorobenzene is immiscible with both water and dilute hydrochloric acid.

   Explain:

   a) the difference in boiling temperatures of the two substances

   b) why phenylamine is more soluble in hydrochloric acid than in water

   c) why chlorobenzene is insoluble both in water and in hydrochloric acid

11 Explain why ethanamide is soluble in water.

12 Write the equation for the formation of the polymer made from 1,5-pentanedioic acid and diaminoethane.

13 Explain why a polyamide such as Terylene has a higher melting temperature than an addition polymer such as poly(propene).

14 Explain why poly(ethenol) is water soluble.

15 Draw the two optical isomers of amino-butane-1,4-dioic acid. Identify which of the two is aspartic acid.

16 Write the structure of a dipeptide formed from aminoethanoic acid and 2-aminopropanoic acid.

17 RNA contains the base uracil (Figure 11.28).

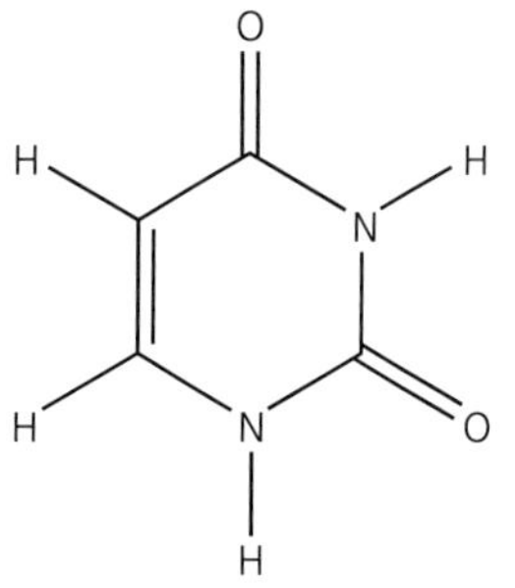

Figure 11.28

Draw a diagram of a uracil molecule in one strand of mRNA when hydrogen-bonded to an adenine molecule in a strand of DNA (see p. 263).

The information needed for questions 18–20 is not found in this textbook. You are advised to do your own research to find answers to these questions. Possible sources are the internet, biology textbooks and other students who are studying biochemistry.

18 Explain the link between a DNA molecule, an mRNA molecule and the polypeptide formed. What is the sequence of bases needed to put a leucine residue in a polypeptide?

19 Use the internet to find out about Chargaff's rule.

20 Write brief notes on the discoveries about DNA structure made by Wilkins and Franklin in London and Crick and Watson in Cambridge.

Exam practice questions

1 Alanine, 2-aminopropanoic acid, and glycine, aminoethanoic acid, are amino acids.

a) Which statement is true about *all* naturally occurring amino acids? (1)

   A They can be prepared by the hydrolysis of DNA.

   B They are formed by the hydrolysis of proteins.

   C They all show optical isomerism.

   D Their aqueous solutions have a pH of about 7.

b) Explain why alanine is a solid which melts above 250°C whereas propanoic acid and 1-propylamine both melt below 0°C. (4)

c) Naturally occurring alanine is one of two enantiomers.

   i) Define the term *enantiomer*. (1)

   ii) State one difference in physical properties that alanine has compared with its enantiomer. (1)

   iii) Draw the two enantiomers of 2-aminopropanoic acid. (1)

d) Write the ionic equations for the reaction of alanine, 2-aminopropanoic acid, with:

   i) dilute hydrochloric acid

   ii) sodium hydroxide solution (2)

e) Alanine can form a dipeptide with glycine. Write the structural formulae of the *two* dipeptides that can be formed from these two amino acids. (2)

(Total 12 marks)

2 **a)** Write equations for the reactions of 1-butylamine with:

   i) water

   ii) 1-chlorobutane

   iii) ethanoyl chloride (3)

b) The order of increasing pH of $0.1 \, mol \, dm^{-3}$ solutions of ammonia, 1-butylamine and phenylamine is:

   A ammonia, 1-buylamine, phenylamine

   B phenylamine, 1-butylamine, ammonia

   C 1-butylamine, ammonia, phenylamine

   D phenylamine, ammonia, 1-butylamine (1)

c) 3-aminopropanoyl chloride, $H_2NCH_2CH_2COCl$, can polymerise.

   i) Draw *two* repeat units of this polymer. (2)

   ii) State the type of polymerisation. (1)

(Total 7 marks)

12 Organic synthesis (Topic 18)

Organic synthesis is the construction of organic molecules using chemical processes. A particular synthesis may involve one or more intermediate compounds. For a complex multi-step synthesis, it may be best to start by considering how the final product can be made and then work backwards to suitable original reactants.

An alternative technique is to determine whether the carbon-chain length has to be altered. If so, then the synthesis will involve one of the reactions below.

Increase in carbon-chain length

There are several ways in which the length of the carbon chain can be increased.

Nucleophilic substitution with KCN

Potassium cyanide reacts with primary, secondary and tertiary halogenoalkanes, RX. The reaction can be represented by:

$$RX + KCN \rightarrow RCN + KX$$

The conditions are heat under reflux in a solution of ethanol and water.

This reaction increases the carbon-chain length by one carbon atom. The product is a nitrile, which can be reduced to a primary amine or hydrolysed to a carboxylic acid:

$$RCN \xrightarrow[\text{2. Hydrolyse with } H_2SO_4(aq)]{\text{1. LiAlH}_4 \text{ in dry ether}} RCH_2NH_2$$

$$RCN \xrightarrow[\text{2. Add dilute acid}]{\text{1. Heat under reflux with NaOH(aq)}} RCOOH$$

> **Tip**
> Alcohols do not react with potassium cyanide. An alcohol must first be converted to a halogenoalkane and then reacted with KCN.

Nucleophilic addition of HCN

Hydrogen cyanide reacts with aldehydes and ketones to form a compound with a $-CN$ group and an $-OH$ group on the same carbon atom:

$$>C=O + HCN \rightarrow >C(OH)CN$$

The conditions are that the reagents are mixed in the presence of a buffer at pH 8. The pH causes some of the hydrogen cyanide to be converted to cyanide ions, which are the catalyst for this reaction. This reaction increases the carbon-chain length by one carbon atom. The product can be hydrolysed to a 2-hydroxycarboxylic acid:

$$>C(OH)CN \rightarrow >C(OH)COOH$$

For example, ethanal, CH_3CHO, can be converted to 2-hydroxypropanoic acid, $CH_3CH(OH)COOH$, by this method.

Friedel–Crafts reaction

A new carbon–carbon single bond can be formed when a halogenoalkane or an acid chloride reacts with an arene, such as methylbenzene. Figure 12.1 show an example.

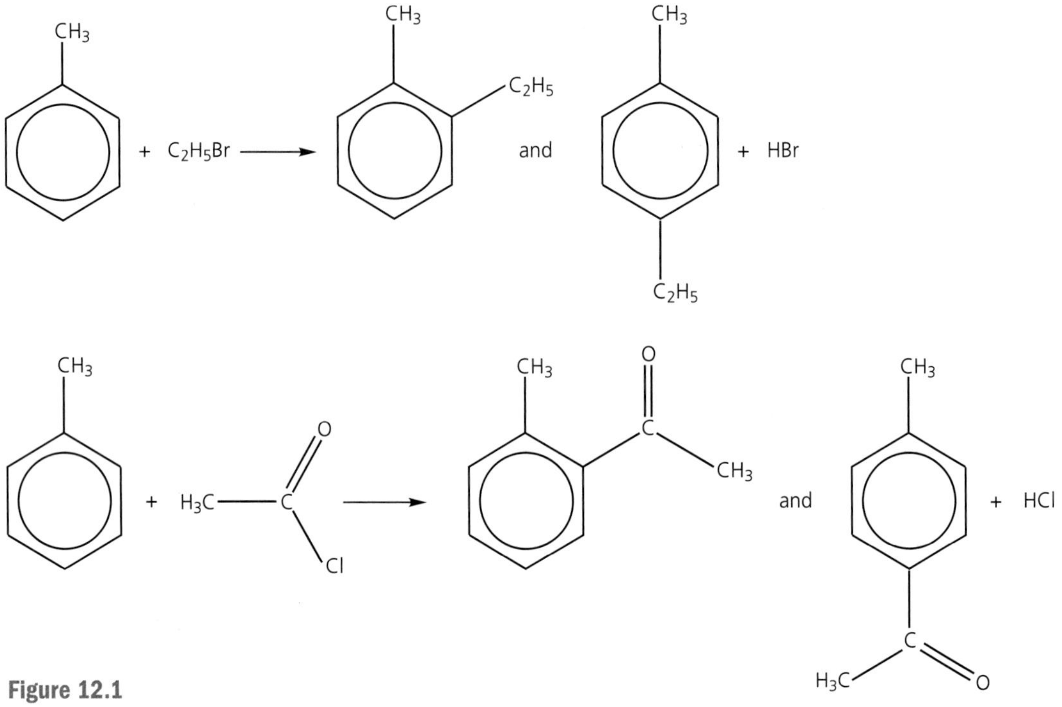

The product will be a mixture of the 1,2- and 1,4- isomers.

Figure 12.1

A catalyst of anhydrous aluminium chloride is needed and the reagents must be dry.

Grignard reagents

Victor Grignard won the Nobel prize for chemistry in 1912 for his discovery of what are now called Grignard reagents. This is a reagent which couples halogenoalkanes with compounds containing the C=O group. He reacted magnesium metal with halogenoalkanes dissolved in dry ether (ethoxyethene).

$$RI + Mg \rightarrow RMgI$$

The result is an alkyl magnesium halide RMgX in which the carbon atom attached to the magnesium is $\delta-$. This makes it an excellent nucleophile and so will attack the $\delta+$ carbon atom in the C=O group, forming a new carbon–carbon σ-bond. The product is then hydrolysed by dilute acid to give a C–OH group.

Reaction with methanal

When methanal and a solution of a Grignard reagent in ether are mixed, and after reaction hydrolysed by dilute acid, a **primary alcohol** is formed:

Step 1: $C_2H_5MgBr + HCHO \rightarrow C_2H_5CH_2OMgBr$

Step 2: $C_2H_5CH_2OMgBr + H^+(aq) \rightarrow C_2H_5CH_2OH + Mg^{2+} + Br^-$

Test yourself

1 Write a three-step reaction sequence for the conversion of propene to 2-methylpropylamine.

Worked example

Outline how ethanol can be converted to propan-1-ol.

Answer

1 Add ethanol to moist red phosphorus and iodine. This converts it to iodoethane.

2 Dissolve the iodoethane in ether and add magnesium turnings. This produces the Grignard reagent C_2H_5MgI.

3 Add the solution of this Grignard reagent to methanal and then hydrolyse the product with dilute sulfuric acid.

The route for the third step of this preparation is:

$$C_2H_5MgI \xrightarrow{\text{HCHO}} C_2H_5CH_2MgI \xrightarrow{\text{H}_2\text{O}} C_2H_5CH_2OH$$

Reaction with other aldehydes

When an aldehyde and a Grignard reagent, dissolved in ether, are mixed and after reaction hydrolysed by dilute acid, a **secondary alcohol** is formed.

Step 1: $C_2H_5MgI + CH_3CHO \rightarrow C_2H_5CH(OMgI)CH_3$

Step 2: $C_2H_5CH(OMgI)CH_3 + H^+ \rightarrow C_2H_5CH(OH)CH_3 + Mg^{2+} + I^-$

Ethylmagnesium iodide is converted to butan-2-ol. A carbon chain of 2 becomes one of 4.

Reaction with ketones

When a ketone and a Grignard reagent, dissolved in ether, are mixed and after reaction hydrolysed by dilute acid, a **tertiary alcohol** is formed:

Step 1: $C_2H_5MgI + CH_3COCH_3 \rightarrow$

Step 2:

The product is the tertiary alcohol 2-methylbutan-2-ol.

Reaction with carbon dioxide

When carbon dioxide is bubbled into a solution of a Grignard reagent in ether, and after reaction hydrolysed by dilute acid, a carboxylic acid with one more carbon atom in the chain is produced.

Step 1: $C_2H_5MgI + CO_2 \rightarrow C_2H_5COOMgI$

Step 2: $C_2H_5COOMgI + H^+ \rightarrow C_2H_5COOH + Mg^{2+} + I^-$

Iodoethane gives ethyl magnesium iodide which then produces propanoic acid.

Summary of the reactions of Grignard reagents

The reactions of Grignard reagents are summarised in Figure 12.2.

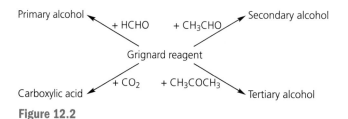

Figure 12.2

Decrease in carbon-chain length

Iodoform reaction

Iodine and sodium hydroxide react with alcohols with a $CH_3CH(OH)$ group and carbonyl compounds with a $CH_3C=O$ group to form iodoform, CHI_3, and the salt of a carboxylic acid with one less carbon atom than the alcohol or carbonyl compound.

Propan-2-ol and propanone each give sodium ethanoate. The general reactions are:

$$RCH(OH)CH_3 \xrightarrow{I_2 + NaOH(aq)} RCOONa$$

$$RCOCH_3 \xrightarrow{I_2 + NaOH(aq)} RCOONa$$

The carboxylic acid can be formed from the salt by adding aqueous sulfuric or hydrochloric acid:

$$RCOONa + HCl \rightarrow RCOOH + NaCl$$

Aromatic ketones, such as $C_6H_5COCH_3$, also undergo the iodoform reaction.

Other common transformations

Alkene to halogenoalkane

$$CH_2=CH_2 + HX \rightarrow CH_3CH_2X$$

Reagent: hydrogen halide, for example hydrogen bromide

Conditions: mix gases at room temperature

Halogenoalkane to alcohol

$$RX + NaOH \rightarrow ROH + NaX$$

Reagent: aqueous sodium hydroxide

Conditions: heat under reflux in aqueous solution

Halogenoalkane to amine

$$RX + 2NH_3 \rightarrow RNH_2 + NH_4X$$

Reagent: ammonia

Conditions: concentrated aqueous solution of ammonia at room temperature or heat in a sealed tube

Alcohol to halogenoalkane

$$ROH + PCl_5 \rightarrow RCl + HCl + POCl_3$$

Reagent: phosphorus pentachloride, PCl_5, for chlorination; KBr and 50% sulfuric acid for bromination; moist red phosphorus and iodine for iodination

Conditions: mix reagents at room temperature

Primary alcohol to aldehyde

$$RCH_2OH + [O] \rightarrow RCHO + H_2O$$

Reagent: acidified potassium dichromate(VI)

Conditions: add oxidising agent to hot alcohol and allow the aldehyde to distil off as it is formed

Primary alcohol to carboxylic acid

$$RCH_2OH + 2[O] \rightarrow RCOOH + H_2O$$

Reagent: acidified potassium dichromate(VI)

Conditions: heat under reflux

Secondary alcohol to ketone

$$RCH(OH)R' + [O] \rightarrow RCOR' + H_2O$$

Reagent: acidified potassium dichromate(VI)

Conditions: heat under reflux

Carboxylic acid to acyl chloride

$$RCOOH + PCl_5 \rightarrow RCOCl + HCl + POCl_3$$

Reagent: phosphorus pentachloride

Conditions: mix dry reagents

Acyl chloride to amide

$$RCOCl + 2NH_3 \rightarrow RCONH_2 + NH_4Cl$$

Reagent: aqueous ammonia

Conditions: mix at room temperature

Test yourself

3 How would you convert:

a) propan-2-ol to 2–chloropropane

b) a secondary alcohol to a ketone

Summary

Figure 12.3 summarises the above transformations.

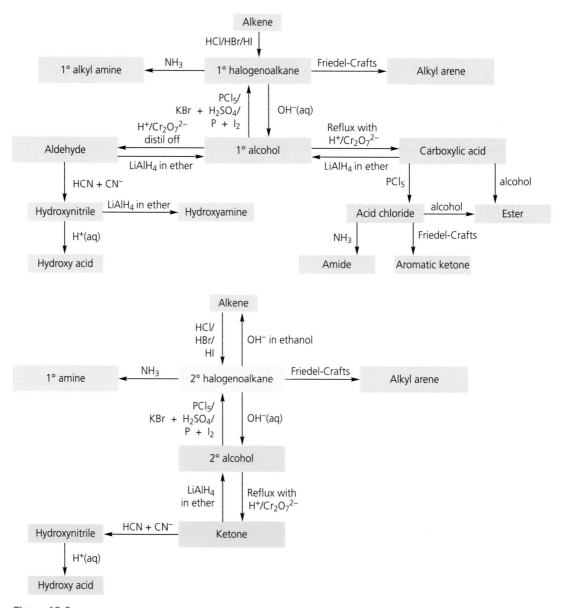

Figure 12.3

Reactions of arenes

Nitration

$$C_6H_6 + HNO_3 \rightarrow C_6H_5NO_2 + H_2O$$

Organic product: nitrobenzene

Reagent: concentrated nitric acid

Conditions: mix with concentrated sulfuric acid at 50°C

Friedel–Crafts alkylation

$$C_6H_6 + C_2H_5Br \rightarrow C_6H_5C_2H_5 + HBr$$

Organic product: ethylbenzene

Reagent: bromoethane

Conditions: dry, in the presence of an anhydrous aluminium chloride catalyst

Friedel–Crafts acylation

$$C_6H_6 + CH_3COCl \rightarrow C_6H_5COCH_3 + HCl$$

Organic product: phenylethanone

Reagent: ethanoyl chloride

Conditions: dry, in the presence of an anhydrous aluminium chloride catalyst

Halogenation

$$C_6H_6 + Br_2 \rightarrow C_6H_5Br + HBr$$

Organic product: bromobenzene

Reagent: liquid bromine

Conditions: dry with iron to form $FeBr_3$, which is the catalyst

Reactions of compounds with two functional groups

At A level, the assumption is made that functional groups behave independently. The exception to this is amino acids (p. 264), where a zwitterion is formed, so there is no $-NH_2$ group to act as a nucleophile in the reaction with an acyl chloride.

The assumption means that a compound such as 2-bromoethanol, CH_2BrCH_2OH, can be hydrolysed by aqueous alkali to a diol and can also be oxidised to a halogenoacid:

$$CH_2OHCH_2OH \xleftarrow[\text{with } OH^-]{\text{heat under reflux}} CH_2BrCH_2OH \xrightarrow[\text{with } Cr_2O_7{}^{2-}/H^+]{\text{heat under reflux}} CH_2BrCOOH$$

Multi-step syntheses

There are two distinct types of question on this topic. The first type is when you are asked for an outline of a multi-step synthesis. In this case, what is required is a route that shows all the intermediate compounds and the reagents and conditions for each step. There are several ways of tackling this type of question:

- Look to see if the carbon chain length has been increased or decreased.
- Start from the final product and work towards the starting substance.
- Start from the starting substance and think of the types of reaction that it can undergo.

Worked example 1

Deduce the necessary reagents and conditions and the intermediates in the conversion of benzene into the compound shown in Figure 12.4.

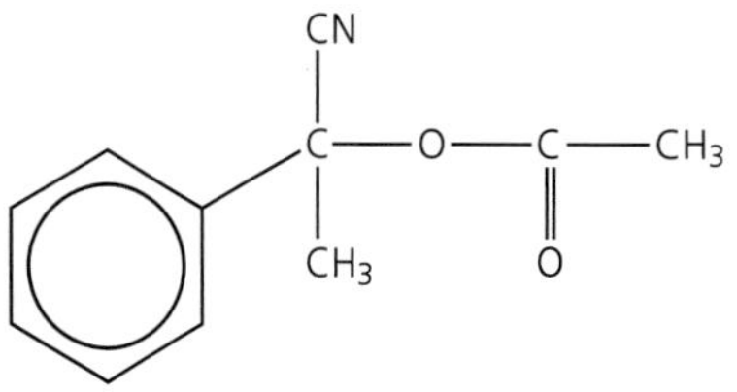

Figure 12.4

Answer

Working backwards:

The final product is an ester of ethanoic acid and so can be made by the reaction between an alcohol and ethanoic acid or ethanoyl chloride.

The −CN and −OH groups on the same carbon atom come from the reaction of a ketone with HCN.

Working forwards:

A side chain has to be introduced into the benzene ring. This implies a Friedel–Crafts reaction. Since a ketone is required, the reaction is between benzene and ethanoyl chloride.

Step 1: reaction between benzene and ethanoyl chloride in the presence of anhydrous $AlCl_3$

$$C_6H_6 + CH_3COCl \rightarrow C_6H_5COCH_3 + HCl$$

Step 2: requires pH 8

$$C_6H_5COCH_3 + HCN \rightarrow C_6H_5C(OH)(CN)CH_3$$

Step 3:

See Figure 12.5.

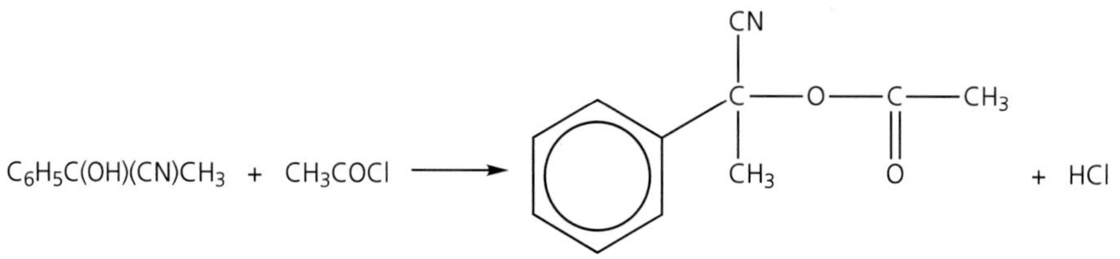

Figure 12.5

Worked example 2

Deduce the necessary reagents and conditions and the intermediates in the conversion of ethene into 2-aminoethanoic acid (glycine), NH_2CH_2COOH.

Answer

Working backwards:

An acid group can be made by oxidising a primary alcohol. An amine group can be made from a halogenoalkane, so a compound with a –Br and a –CH_2OH group is likely to be an intermediate.

Working forwards:

An alkene will react with a halogen to form a dihalogenoalkane or with a halogen dissolved in water to form a halogenoalcohol. Therefore, the first step is to bubble ethene into bromine water:

$$CH_2\text{=}CH_2 + H_2O + Br_2 \rightarrow BrCH_2CH_2OH + HBr$$

The second step is to react the product with excess concentrated ammonia:

$$BrCH_2CH_2OH + 2NH_3 \rightarrow NH_2CH_2CH_2OH + NH_4Br$$

Finally, the aminoalcohol is oxidised by heating under reflux with acidified potassium dichromate(VI) solution:

$$NH_2CH_2CH_2OH + 2[O] \rightarrow NH_2CH_2COOH + H_2O$$

Test yourself

4 Outline how ethene could be converted to butan-2-ol.

The second type of question is where an intermediate has to be isolated before a subsequent step. The answer will include the reactants and conditions for each step, how the intermediate is isolated and how the final product is purified.

Worked example

Describe how benzoic acid, C_6H_5COOH, can be converted in a two-step synthesis into methyl 3-nitrobenzoate (Figure 12.6). Show how the intermediate is isolated and a pure sample of the product obtained.

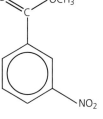

Figure 12.6

Answer

Step 1 is the conversion of benzoic acid into the ester, methyl benzoate, $C_6H_5COOCH_3$:

- Reflux together 10 g of benzoic acid, 20 cm^3 of methanol and 3 cm^3 of concentrated sulfuric acid for about 30 minutes.
- Allow the mixture to cool. Transfer it to a large separating funnel and add 40 cm^3 of water and 20 cm^3 of hexane.
- Shake the funnel, releasing the pressure from time to time.
- Allow the two layers to settle. Run off and discard the lower aqueous layer.
- Wash the organic layer with about 20 cm^3 of dilute aqueous sodium carbonate, releasing the pressure created by the production of carbon dioxide by the reaction of any remaining acid with the sodium carbonate.
- Discard the lower aqueous layer and wash the organic layer with about 20 cm^3 water. This removes salts and any excess methanol.

- Discard the lower aqueous layer and add some anhydrous calcium chloride to the organic layer.
- When the liquid clears, decant it into a flask and carefully distil off all the hexane (boiling temperature 69°C) leaving the methyl benzoate (boiling temperature 196°C) in the flask.

Step 2 is the nitration of methyl benzoate:

- Carefully add $10\,cm^3$ of concentrated sulfuric acid to the methyl benzoate and cool in an icebath to 5°C. Then add $10\,cm^3$ of a mixture of equal parts concentrated nitric and concentrated sulfuric acids dropwise, making sure that the temperature of the reaction mixture does not rise above 15°C.
- Leave the reaction mixture at room temperature for at least 20 minutes.
- Pour the reaction mixture onto some crushed ice and stir. Methyl 3-nitrobenzene is a solid and will crystallise out.
- Once the ice has melted, filter the mixture using a Buchner funnel.
- Collect the solid methyl 3-nitrobenzene and recrystallise it using the minimum amount of hot ethanol as the solvent.

This would be a suitable experiment for assessment of practical skills. It requires four 1-hour periods.

Test yourself

5 Outline how 2-chloropropan-1-ol could be converted to 3-amino-2-methylpropanoic acid, $NH_2CH_2CH(CH_3)COOH$.

Risk and hazard

Safety issues

Hazard is a property of the substances involved in the procedure. For example, some substances are toxic, others can be absorbed through the skin, and some are corrosive.

Risk is about how these hazards are dealt with. For example, for a flammable liquid being heated, the risk is reduced by using an electric heater rather than a Bunsen flame.

It is assumed in A level questions that the following safety precautions are always taken:

- Safety glasses and laboratory coats are worn at all times in all practical classes.
- Hands are washed before leaving the laboratory, particularly if toxic substances have been used.
- Food and drink are never consumed in the laboratory.

Special care must be taken with certain chemicals and marks will be awarded for identifying the hazard and relevant ways to reduce risk.

- Almost all organic chemicals are flammable (hazard). Flasks and test tubes containing them should not be heated directly with a Bunsen flame. A water bath or an electric heater should be used (reduces risk).
- If a chemical can be absorbed through the skin, gloves must be worn.
- If a chemical has a harmful, irritating or poisonous vapour, the experiment must be carried out in a fume cupboard.

Hazard symbols

- If a chemical is corrosive, harmful, irritating or poisonous (toxic), gloves must be worn and extra care must be taken.
- Any substance suspected of being a carcinogen must not be used in a school laboratory.

Tip

You are expected to be able to relate safety aspects to the specific hazards of the reaction or chemicals being handled.

Worked example

When methyl 3-nitrobenzoate is recrystallised, the solvent used is ethanol. This is a flammable liquid with a boiling temperature of 78°C. What specific safety precautions should you take when dissolving methyl 3-nitrobenzoate in the minimum amount of hot ethanol and filtering the solution?

Answer

The solid should be placed in a round-bottomed flask fitted with a reflux condenser. Some ethanol is added and the flask warmed until the ethanol is just boiling. Heating should be carried out using either an electric heater or a water bath. Extra ethanol is added down the condenser until all the solid dissolves. The heater is removed, followed by the condenser, and the hot solution is filtered using a warm stemless glass funnel.

Danger can be avoided by careful reading of hazard labels and appropriate precautions taken. The risk can be further reduced by using small quantities. If there is still doubt as to the safety of the experiment, it should be abandoned or replaced using safer materials.

Test yourself

6 State the main hazard of using ethanoyl chloride when preparing ethylethanoate from ethanoic acid.

Methods of preparation and purification

For spectral analysis and for the measurement of melting and boiling temperatures, substances need to be very pure.

The result of any organic reaction will be a mixture of substances. The required product must be separated from the reaction mixture and then purified.

Heating under reflux

Slow reactions involving volatile and toxic or flammable substances are carried out using the technique of heating under reflux. The reactants and solvent are placed in a round-bottomed flask fitted with a vertical condenser (Figure 12.7).

When the reaction has finished, the condenser is altered to the normal distillation position and the wanted product distilled off, collecting it at the correct boiling temperature (Figure 12.8).

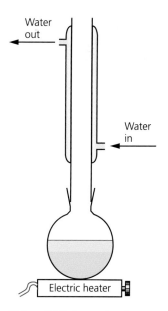

Figure 12.7 Apparatus for heating under reflux

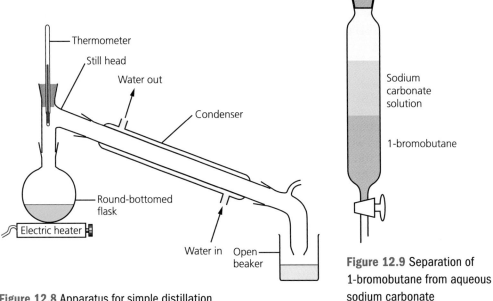

Figure 12.8 Apparatus for simple distillation

Figure 12.9 Separation of 1-bromobutane from aqueous sodium carbonate

The distillate will still be impure so, if it is insoluble in water, it is purified as follows:

- The distillate is washed with sodium carbonate solution in a separating funnel (Figure 12.9). Washing removes any acidic impurities that may be present. The pressure due to the carbon dioxide produced must be released from time to time. Washing is repeated until no more gas is produced.
- The aqueous layer is discarded and the organic layer is washed with water. This removes any unreacted sodium salts and any soluble organic substances, such as ethanol.
- This new aqueous layer is discarded and the organic layer dried, usually with anhydrous calcium chloride.
- The dried organic liquid is decanted off from the solid calcium chloride and distilled, collecting the liquid that boils off at ±2°C of the boiling temperature of the substance.

Simple distillation can also be used to:

- remove a volatile liquid from non–volatile substances
- separate two volatile liquids that form a homogeneous solution

The latter works only if there is a small amount of one of the two liquids present as an impurity. The neck of the flask and the still head act as a mini–fractionating column. Larger amounts of an impurity require fractional distillation for separation.

> Other drying agents that can be used are anhydrous sodium sulfate, potassium hydroxide and calcium oxide. Calcium chloride must not be used for drying amines or alcohols because it reacts with them.

Worked example

1-bromobutane can be prepared from butan-1-ol by reaction with a 50% solution of sulfuric acid and potassium bromide in a flask fitted with a reflux condenser. At first, steamy fumes of hydrogen bromide (HBr) are produced. Subsequently, bromine (brown) and sulfur dioxide (colourless) are produced. After reaction, 1-bromobutane and unreacted butan-1-ol are distilled out of the flask together with some acidic impurities.

The organic liquid is washed with sodium carbonate solution and then with water. Anhydrous calcium chloride is added and left for 1 hour. The liquid is decanted off and distilled.

	Boiling temperature/°C	Density/g cm^{-3}
Butan-1-ol	117	0.8
1-bromobutane	102	1.3

a) What impurities are removed by washing with sodium carbonate solution?

b) Why does the lower layer contain the 1-bromobutane?

c) What impurities are removed by washing with water?

d) Why is anhydrous calcium chloride added?

e) Over what temperature range should the purified 1-bromobutane be collected?

Answer

a) Sulfur dioxide, hydrogen bromide and bromine

b) Because it is denser than water

c) Some of the butan-1-ol and sodium salts such as sodium bromide from the reaction of acidic impurities with the sodium carbonate

d) To remove any water dissolved in the organic layer

e) Between 100°C and 104°C

Solvent extraction

An organic product that is sparingly soluble in water can be separated from the reaction mixture by solvent extraction. The reaction mixture is shaken in a separating funnel (Figure 12.9) with a solvent such as ether or cyclohexane. The organic layer is washed and dried and then the solvent distilled off.

For example, 1-chloropentane can be prepared by adding excess phosphorus pentachloride to pentan-1-ol:

$$CH_3(CH_2)_3CH_2OH(l) + PCl_5(s) \rightarrow CH_3(CH_2)_3CH_2Cl(l) + HCl(g) + POCl_3(l)$$

Phosphorus oxychloride, POCl$_3$, has a boiling temperature of 105°C, which is very similar to that of 1-chloropentane (108°C). Therefore, it is not possible to separate the two by distillation of the reaction mixture.

The organic compound is separated by adding ethoxyethane (ether). This solvent dissolves 1-chloropentane but not phosphorus oxychloride. The solution of 1-chloropentane in ether is washed first with aqueous sodium carbonate (to remove acid) and then with water. It is dried with anhydrous calcium chloride and the ether is distilled off by gentle warming, leaving pure 1-chloropentane in the flask.

If necessary, the product can be further purified by distillation, collecting the liquid that boils off at ±2° of the substance's boiling temperature.

Ether is highly flammable. It is distilled off in a fume cupboard by warming the flask with hot water in a beaker, previously heated in the open laboratory.

Solid product: recrystallisation

A solid product is removed from the reaction mixture by filtration. It is then purified by recrystallisation. A solvent has to be found in which the substance is soluble when the solvent is hot, but insoluble (or very much less soluble) when it is cold.

The method is as follows:

- Dissolve the impure solid in the *minimum* of hot solvent.
- Filter the hot solution through a fluted filter paper, using a *warmed* stemless funnel, into a conical flask. This removes insoluble impurities.
- Allow the solution to cool.
- Filter the mixture of the pure solid and the solvent under *reduced pressure*, using a Buchner funnel (Figure 12.10). Collect the solid on the filter paper and discard the liquid. This removes soluble impurities.
- Wash the solid on the filter paper with a little ice-cold solvent and leave the solid to dry.
- Carefully remove the pure solid from the filter paper.

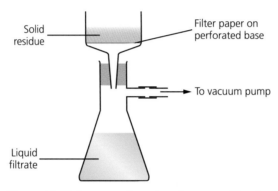

Figure 12.10 Apparatus for reduced pressure filtration

Benzoic acid is very soluble in hot water, but almost insoluble in cold water. Therefore, it can be purified by recrystallisation from hot water.

The compound formed by the reaction between an aldehyde or a ketone and 2,4-dinitrophenylhydrazine can be recrystallised from hot ethanol.

Test yourself

7 How would you purify the liquid 1-chlorobutane from the reaction mixture when phosphorus(V) chloride is added to butan-1-ol?

Steam distillation

Steam distillation (Figure 12.11) is used to extract a volatile liquid that is immiscible with water, from a complex mixture. It is particularly useful for obtaining a substance that would decompose at its boiling point. It is used to extract perfumes from fruits and flowers.

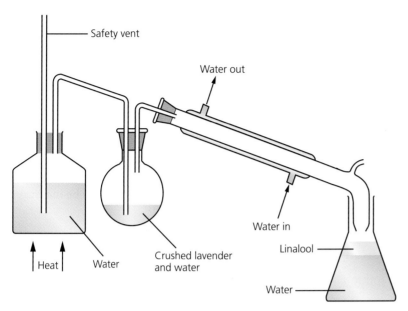

Safety vent

Water out

Water in

Linalool

Crushed lavender and water

Heat   Water

Water

Figure 12.11 Apparatus for steam distillation

For example, lavender oil contains the compound linalool. Linalool can be obtained by crushing lavender flowers and stalks with water and then subjecting the mixture to steam distillation. The liquid boils below the boiling temperature of both water and linalool, so no decomposition of the product takes place. The procedure is as follows:

- Crush lavender flowers and stems in water and place the mixture in a flask.
- Steam distil and collect the distillate until pure water, with no oily droplets, distils over.
- Pour the mixture into a separating funnel and run off the aqueous layer.
- Add lumps of anhydrous potassium carbonate to the organic layer and leave until the product becomes clear.

Steam distillation is used to extract phenylamine from the reaction mixture after the reduction of nitrobenzene with tin and concentrated hydrochloric acid.

The nitrobenzene is warmed with a mixture of tin and concentrated hydrochloric acid. The tin is oxidised to tin(IV) chloride and the nitrobenzene is reduced to phenylamine. This reacts with the hydrochloric acid to form a solution of the salt $C_6H_5NH_3Cl$:

$$C_6H_5NO_2 + 6[H] + HCl \rightarrow C_6H_5NH_3Cl + 2H_2O$$

When alkali is added, phenylamine and a precipitate of tin hydroxide are produced:

$$C_6H_5NH_3Cl(aq) + NaOH(aq) \rightarrow C_6H_5NH_2(l) + H_2O(l) + NaCl(aq)$$

$$SnCl_4(aq) + 4NaOH(aq) \rightarrow Sn(OH)_4(s) + 4NaCl(aq)$$

The volatile phenylamine is removed from the suspension of tin hydroxide in alkali by steam distillation. Salt is added to the distillate to reduce the solubility of the phenylamine in water. The organic layer is separated from the aqueous layer using a separating funnel and then dried with solid potassium hydroxide.

A higher yield is obtained if the phenylamine is separated from the aqueous layer by solvent extraction.

Testing for identity

The identity of a liquid can be found by measuring its boiling temperature (or the melting temperature of its solid derivative). The identity of a solid can be determined by measuring its melting temperature.

Boiling temperature determination

The boiling temperature of an organic liquid can be determined and the value compared with those in a database.

The apparatus for measuring the boiling temperature is shown in Figure 12.12. If large amounts are available, the boiling temperature can be measured using standard distillation apparatus.

A test for purity is that a pure substance will boil over a very small range of temperature, whereas an impure substance will boil over a considerable range.

The method is as follows:

- Place a small amount of the test liquid in the ignition tube and, using a rubber band, attach it to the thermometer.
- Place the capillary tube in the liquid, with its open end below the surface.
- Clamp the thermometer in the beaker of water.
- Slowly heat the water, stirring all the time. When the stream of bubbles coming out of the capillary tube is rapid and continuous, note the temperature and stop heating.
- Allow the beaker of water to cool, stirring continuously. Note the temperature when bubbles stop coming out of the capillary tube and the liquid begins to suck back into the capillary tube.

The average of these two temperatures is the boiling temperature of the liquid.

As the beaker of water is heated, the air in the capillary tube expands and bubbles of air slowly come out of the tube. These act as nuclei on which the bubbles of boiling liquid can form. This prevents superheating, which is when the temperature of the liquid rises above its boiling temperature.

The temperature measured on cooling is when the liquid stops boiling.

Both temperatures are slightly inaccurate because there is a time lag before the thermometer can register the boiling temperature. Averaging the two readings cancels out this error.

There are two problems with this method:

- The boiling points of similar substances are often quite close together and can differ by less than the experimental error.
- Impurities, and variation in atmospheric pressure, alter the boiling point.

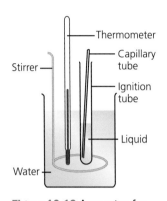

Figure 12.12 Apparatus for the determination of boiling point

Table 12.1 Boiling temperatures of some esters and alcohols

Esters	Boiling temperature/°C	Alcohols	Boiling temperature/°C
Ethyl ethanoate	77.1	Ethanol	78.5
Methyl propanoate	78.7	Propan-2-ol	82.4
1-propyl methanoate	81.3	2-methylpropan-2-ol	82.5

Melting temperature determination

The measurement of boiling temperature is not very reliable. Therefore, it is common practice for a liquid to be converted to a solid derivative. For example, a carbonyl compound can be converted to a 2,4–dinitrophenylhydrazine derivative. The derivative is then purified by recrystallisation and its melting temperature determined.

One method of determining melting temperature is as follows:

- Insert some of the pure solid into a capillary tube and then attach the tube open end upwards to a thermometer with a rubber band.
- Place the thermometer into a bath of liquid. The liquid must boil at a higher temperature than the melting temperature of the solid being tested.
- Slowly heat the liquid bath, with constant stirring, and observe the solid in the capillary tube. Note the temperature when the solid melts.

Another method is as follows:

- Place the solid in a boiling tube.
- Heat the boiling tube in a beaker of hot liquid (water if the solid melts below 100°C).
- When the solid melts, put a thermometer and stirrer in the molten solid and remove the boiling tube from the liquid bath.
- Allow the molten substance to cool, stirring the whole time, and read the temperature when the first crystals of solid appear.

Figure 12.13 show the apparatus used for both methods.

> **Tip**
> The terms 'boiling point' and 'boiling temperature' are interchangeable.

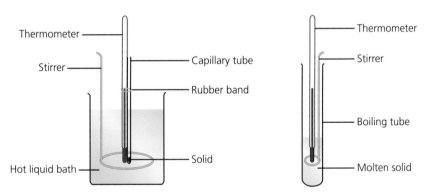

Figure 12.13 Apparatus for the two methods of melting point determination

> **Tip**
> A test for purity is that a solid has a sharp melting temperature rather than melting over a range of temperatures.

Yields

Organic reactions rarely go to completion and there are usually competing side reactions. The yield is often as low as 60%. Purification processes also lower the yield. For instance, some solid will remain in solution during recrystallisation and a distillation apparatus will retain some vapour, so not all will be turned to liquid in the condenser.

If a synthesis requires three steps, each of which has a yield of 70%, the yield will be $0.7 \times 0.7 \times 0.7 = 0.34 = 34\%$. If the purification of the final product is 80% efficient, the final yield will be $0.80 \times 34 = 27\%$.

Worked example

Benzene (molar mass 78.0 g mol^{-1}) can be converted into benzoic acid (molar mass 122.0 g mol^{-1}), which then has to be recrystallised. If 9.3 g of pure benzoic acid was made from 10.0 g of benzene, calculate the percentage yield.

Answer

$$\text{amount of benzene used} = \frac{\text{mass}}{\text{molar mass}} = \frac{10.0\,\text{g}}{78.0\,\text{g mol}^{-1}} = 0.128\,\text{mol}$$

theoretical yield of benzoic acid = 0.128 mol × 122.0 g mol^{-1} = 15.6 g

actual yield of pure benzoic acid = 9.3 g

$$\text{percentage yield} = \frac{9.3 \times 100}{15.6} = 59.6 = 60\%\ (\text{to 2 s.f.})$$

Tip

A common error is to work out the yield as mass of product × 100 divided by the mass of reactant. Making this mistake in this example would give the incorrect answer of 93%.

Test yourself

8 3.86 g of 2-hydroxypropanenitrile, $CH_3CH(OH)CN$, was made in a two-step synthesis from 3.93 g of ethanol. Calculate the percentage yield.

Stereochemistry of reactions

Many drugs are stereospecific. This means that only one stereoisomer has a therapeutic effect. If possible, a reaction pathway that produces only the desired stereoisomer is used because this increases the atom economy of the manufacture.

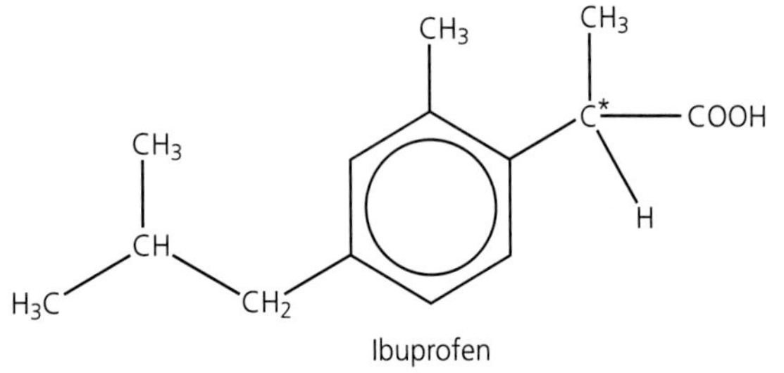

Figure 12.14

Ibuprofen (Figure 12.14) has a chiral carbon atom (marked with ⋆).

Only one isomer is effective as a pain-reliever and as an anti-inflammatory drug. The chemical reactions that produce it are non-stereospecific and so the drug is sold as the racemic mixture. In the body, an **isomerase** enzyme slowly converts the inert enantiomer into the active form. Therefore, there is no point in attempting to devise a stereospecific manufacturing process.

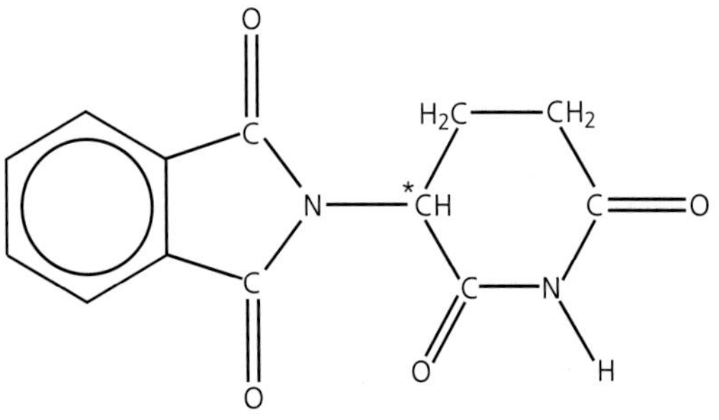

Figure 12.15

In the 1950s, thalidomide (Figure 12.15) was used as a drug to relieve morning sickness in pregnant women. The molecule contains a chiral carbon atom (marked with ⋆).

It was later found that while one optical isomer relieved morning sickness the other isomer caused horrific birth defects. Unfortunately, the body spontaneously converts one optical isomer into the other. This means that even if a method were developed to produce the beneficial isomer only, the drug would still not be suitable for pregnant women. It is used today to relieve vomiting in patients undergoing chemotherapy.

Some reactions are stereospecific. Knowledge of the mechanism of a reaction allows chemists to predict whether the product will be a single isomer or a 50:50 mixture of the two stereoisomers.

Addition across a C=C bond

When bromine adds on across a double bond, the addition is *trans*. The reaction of bromine with cyclopentene gives the *trans* isomer only (Figure 12.16).

Figure 12.16

Reactions that take place on the surface of a heterogeneous catalyst are often stereospecific, as are most biochemical reactions.

A simplified explanation is that the first step is the addition of Br^+ to one of the carbon atoms. In the second step, the bromine atom in the carbocation intermediate sterically hinders the approach of the Br^- ion. It must therefore attack from the other side and so the *trans* geometric isomer is produced.

Hydrogen, in the presence of a platinum catalyst, adds on the same side. This is called *cis* addition. This is because the alkene is held onto the catalyst surface and hydrogen diffuses through the metal and adds across the C=C bond.

Summary tasks

Check that you know how to increase the carbon chain:

- with halogenoalkanes and KCN
- with carbonyl compounds and HCN
- using Grignard reagents and aldehydes, ketones and carbon dioxide

Make sure that you know the reagents and conditions for converting:

- alkenes to halogenoalkanes and vice versa
- halogenoalkanes to alcohols and vice versa
- alcohols to aldehydes, ketones and carboxylic acids

Can you:

- plan a synthesis of up to four steps
- differentiate between hazard and risk

Make sure that you can describe (including drawing relevant diagrams):

- heating under reflux
- distillation and fractional distillation
- solvent extraction
- washing and drying
- recrystallisation
- determination of melting and boiling temperatures

Questions

1 An organic compound X is thought to contain chlorine and iodine bonded to carbon atoms. Describe the tests that you would carry out to prove this.

2 Linalool is the major component of lavender oil. Its formula is

$$(CH_3)_2C=CHCH_2CH_2C(CH_3)(OH)CH=CH_2$$

Describe the tests that would prove the presence of the functional groups in this molecule.

3 Spearmint oil contains the compound carvone. Use the results of the following tests that were carried out on carvone to deduce the functional groups present in the molecule. Justify your deductions from each test.

a) It turned brown bromine water colourless.

b) On warming with acidified potassium dichromate(vi), the solution remained orange.

c) It gave a yellow precipitate with Brady's reagent.

4 This question concerns citral, $C_{10}H_{16}O$ (found in lemon grass oil), and geraniol, $C_{10}H_{18}O$ (found in rose oil).

a) Describe a test to show that citral is an aldehyde.

b) Describe a test to show that geraniol is an alcohol.

c) Describe a test to show that both compounds contain a C=C group.

d) In what way would the infrared spectra of citral and geraniol differ?

e) Outline how citral could be converted to geraniol.

5 Compound Z has the following composition by mass: carbon, 55.8%; hydrogen, 7.0%; oxygen, 37.2%.

a) Calculate the empirical formula of compound Z.

b) Use the information below to deduce the structural formula of compound Z:

- The largest m/z value in the mass spectrum of compound Z was 86.
- Bromine water remained brown on the addition of compound Z.
- No steamy fumes formed when phosphorus pentachloride was added to compound Z.

- Addition of 2,4-dinitrophenylhydrazine to compound Z gave a yellow precipitate.
- When Tollens' reagent was added to compound Z and the mixture warmed, a silver mirror formed.
- When warmed with a solution of iodine in sodium hydroxide, compound Z gave a yellow precipitate.

6 When phenylamine reacts with ethanoyl chloride, a solid is formed that is soluble in hot water but insoluble in cold water. Describe how you could purify this solid.

7 Cyclohexanol (boiling point 161°C) can be converted into cyclohexanone (boiling point 156°C).

a) State the reagents and conditions for this reaction.

b) State how you would obtain a pure sample of cyclohexanone from a mixture containing it and 2% cyclohexanol.

c) State how you would obtain a pure sample of cyclohexanone from a mixture containing it and 25% cyclohexanol.

8 Before cyclohexanone and cyclohexanol (produced as in question 9) can be separated, the organic substances, which are insoluble in water, have to be extracted from the reaction mixture.

a) Describe how this would be achieved.

b) How are traces of water removed from the organic substances?

c) How would you know when the water removal was complete?

9 An organic compound Z contains carbon, hydrogen and oxygen only. When 4.85 g of Z was burnt in excess oxygen 11.9 g of carbon dioxide and 4.85 g of water were produced.

The mass spectrum of Z had a peak due to its molecular ion at a mass/charge ratio of 72. Compound Z gave a yellow precipitate with Brady's solution but no precipitate with iodine and sodium hydroxide solution. Its NMR spectrum had four peaks in the ratio 3:2:2:1.

Showing all your working and using all the data provided, deduce the structural formula of Z.

10 a) Give the reagents, conditions and intermediates in the conversion of but-2-ene to 3-aminobutan-2-one, $CH_3COCH(NH_2)CH_3$.

   b) Explain what effect the product would have on the plane of polarisation of plane-polarised light.

11 Write the structural formulae of the organic products of the reaction of the substance in Figure 12.17 with the following (you may assume that the functional groups behave independently):

   a) phosphorus pentachloride

   b) sodium hydrogencarbonate

   c) iodine dissolved in sodium hydroxide

   d) 2,4-dinitrophenylhydrazine

   e) lithium aluminium hydride, $LiAlH_4$, in ether followed by hydrolysis of the product.

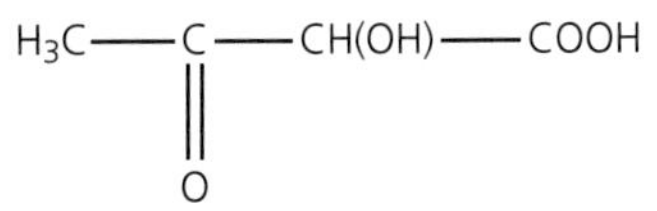

$$H_3C—C—CH(OH)—COOH$$
$$\|$$
$$O$$

Figure 12.17

12 Give the reagents, conditions and intermediates in the conversion of ethanol to ethanoyl chloride.

13 A compound $C_4H_8O_2$ was tested as follows:

   • It did not give a precipitate with Brady's reagent.
   • It turned bromine water from brown to colourless.
   • When excess PCl_5 was added, 2 mol of HCl was given off per mol of the organic compound.
   • The compound had three peaks in its NMR spectrum and a peak at $m/z = 57$ in its mass spectrum.

   Suggest a formula for the compound. Justify your answer.

14 Outline how 1-phenylethanol, $C_6H_5CH(OH)CH_3$, could be prepared in a two-step synthesis from benzene and one other organic reagent.

15 a) Outline how you would convert $C_6H_5CH=CHCH_3$ into compound M (Figure 12.18).

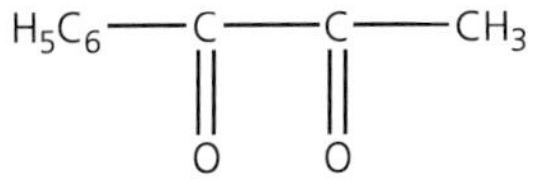

$$H_5C_6—C—C—CH_3$$
$$\|\quad\|$$
$$O\quad O$$

Figure 12.18

   b) Identify the product formed by reacting compound M with iodine and sodium hydroxide.

16 12.6 g of benzene was nitrated and the nitrobenzene produced was reduced with tin and concentrated hydrochloric acid. After addition of sodium hydroxide, the phenylamine was steam-distilled out of the reaction mixture, washed, dried and redistilled. The mass of pure phenylamine produced was 6.75 g. Calculate the percentage yield.

17 It was required to prepare the compound $(CH_3)_2C(OH)CONH_2$ from propanone. A student suggested the outline synthesis shown in Figure 12.19.

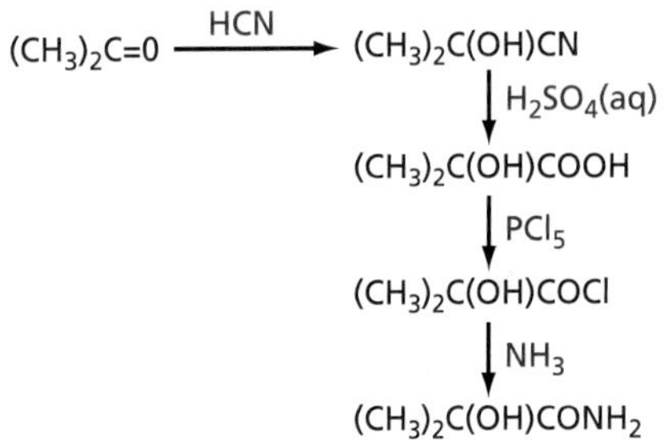

$$(CH_3)_2C=0 \xrightarrow{HCN} (CH_3)_2C(OH)CN$$
$$\downarrow H_2SO_4(aq)$$
$$(CH_3)_2C(OH)COOH$$
$$\downarrow PCl_5$$
$$(CH_3)_2C(OH)COCl$$
$$\downarrow NH_3$$
$$(CH_3)_2C(OH)CONH_2$$

Figure 12.19

Explain why this sequence would *not* give the required product.

18 Explain why the addition of hydrogen cyanide, HCN, to butanone, $CH_3COC_2H_5$, gives a racemic mixture, rather than a single optical isomer.

Exam practice questions

1 a) Outline a three-step synthesis for the conversion of propan-1-ol into propanamide. Include reagents, conditions and formulae of all intermediates in your answer. (6)

b) Propanamide is a solid at room temperature and is soluble in water. Outline how a sample of propanamide obtained in (a) could be purified. State what types of impurities are removed at each stage. (6)

(Total 12 marks)

2 a) Explain why a Grignard reagent is able to form new C−C single bonds with carbonyl compounds. (2)

b) i) Outline a four-step synthesis to convert iodoethane to 1-propylbenzene, $CH_3CH_2CH_2C_6H_5$. Give the reagents and conditions necessary for each step and the formulae of all intermediate compounds. (8)

ii) 1-propylbenzene is a liquid with a boiling temperature of 160°C. Describe how the product could be extracted from the reaction mixture and then purified. (3)

(Total 13 marks)

3 An ester E has the molecular formula $C_7H_{14}O_2$. When heated under reflux with aqueous sodium hydroxide, followed by the addition of excess acid, it was converted into two compounds F and G:

- Compound F has the following composition by mass: carbon, 54.5%; oxygen, 36.4%; hydrogen, 9.1%.
- Compound F gives off carbon dioxide when added to a solution of sodium hydrogencarbonate.
- Compound F has three peaks in its ^1H NMR spectrum.
- Compound G does not give a precipitate with iodine and sodium hydroxide.
- Deduce the structural formula of the ester E and write the equation for its reaction with sodium hydroxide.

(Total 10 marks)

4 A student wished to convert propan-1-ol into 1-bromopropane. Two different methods were suggested:

1 Heat the alcohol under reflux with a mixture of solid potassium bromide and concentrated sulfuric acid.

2 Heat the alcohol under reflux with a mixture of solid potassium bromide and concentrated phosphoric acid.

Both methods initially produce gaseous hydrogen bromide. This then reacts with the alcohol to form the bromoalkane, which is distilled off and condensed.

The hazards were identified as:
- concentrated sulfuric acid: corrosive and an oxidising agent
- concentrated phosphoric acid: corrosive
- hydrogen bromide vapour: irritant and a reducing agent
- propan-1-ol and 1-bromopropane: volatile and flammable
- bromine: volatile and irritant vapour

a) Explain which method should be used to minimise the risk. (2)

b) For the method selected in (a), suggest and explain suitable special safety precautions that should be taken to minimise the risk. (3)

(Total 5 marks)

5 Tests on compound Y, $C_3H_4O_3$, gave the following results:

a) When phosphorus pentachloride was added, steamy fumes that turned damp litmus red were observed.

b) When a solution of sodium carbonate was added, a gas was evolved that turned limewater cloudy.

c) A yellow precipitate was obtained when a solution of 2,4-dinitrophenylhydrazine was added.

d) Orange acidified potassium dichromate(vi) solution turned green when warmed with Y.

Explain the observations in a)–d) and hence deduce the structural formula of compound Y.

(Total 5 marks)

13 Analytical techniques (Topic 19)

Organic analysis

The traditional method is to find the empirical formula, followed by the molecular formulae and then the functional groups present.

To find the molecular formula

Percentage composition

This is normally carried out by combustion analysis. A known mass of the substance is burned in excess dry oxygen and the masses of water and carbon dioxide produced are measured. The mass of water is found by adsorbing the water vapour on either silica gel or anhydrous calcium chloride; the mass of carbon dioxide is found by reacting it with calcium oxide.

The route is:

- mass of carbon dioxide → mass of carbon → % carbon
- mass of water → mass of hydrogen → % hydrogen
- % oxygen = 100 − (% of carbon + % hydrogen)

Worked example

2.90 g of an organic compound X, containing hydrogen, carbon and oxygen only, was burnt in excess oxygen. 6.60 g of carbon dioxide and 2.70 g of water were produced. Calculate the percentage composition of compound X.

Answer

Method 1: using moles

$$\text{moles of } CO_2 = \frac{\text{mass}}{M_r} = \frac{6.60}{44.0} = 0.150 = \text{moles carbon}$$

$$\text{mass carbon} = \text{moles} \times A_r = 12.0 \times 0.150 = 1.80\,\text{g}$$

$$\%\ \text{carbon} = \frac{1.80}{2.90} \times 100 = 62.1\%$$

$$\text{moles of } H_2O = \frac{\text{mass}}{M_r} = \frac{2.70}{18.0} = 0.150$$

$$\text{moles of H} = 2 \times 0.150 = 0.300$$

$$\text{mass of hydrogen} = \text{moles} \times A_r = 0.300 \times 1.0 = 0.300\,\text{g}$$

$$\%\ \text{hydrogen} = \frac{0.300}{2.90} \times 100 = 10.3\%$$

$$\%\ \text{oxygen} = 100 - (62.1 + 10.3) = 27.6\%$$

Method 2: by mass ratio

44.0 g of CO_2 contains 12.0 g of carbon

6.60 g of CO_2 contains $12 \times \dfrac{6.60}{44.0} = 1.80$ g of carbon

% carbon $= \dfrac{1.80}{2.90} \times 100 = 62.1\%$

18.0 g of H_2O contains 2.0 g of hydrogen

2.70 g of H_2O contain $2.0 \times \dfrac{2.70}{18.0} = 0.300$ g of hydrogen

% hydrogen $= \dfrac{0.300}{2.90} \times 100 = 10.3\%$

% oxygen $= 100 - (62.1 + 10.3) = 27.6\%$

The percentage composition by mass of compound X is: carbon 62.1%, hydrogen 10.3%, oxygen 27.6%.

Empirical formula

The empirical formula of a compound is obtained by dividing the percentage composition of each element by its atomic mass and then dividing through by the smallest.

> **Tip**
>
> Remember:
>
> - Do not round up the %/A_r values.
> - Round the final column to 1 decimal place.
> - If the numbers in the final column are not whole numbers, try multiplying by 2 or 3 to obtain integers.

Worked example

Find the empirical formula of compound X, which has the following percentage composition by mass: carbon 62.1%, hydrogen 10.3%, oxygen 27.6%.

Answer

	%	Divide by A_r	Divide by smallest
Carbon	62.1	62.1/12.0 = 5.175	3.0
Hydrogen	10.3	10.3/1.0 = 10.3	5.97 ≈ 6.0
Oxygen	27.6	27.6/16.0 = 1.725	1.0

The empirical formula of compound X is C_3H_6O.

Test yourself

1 The ratio obtained by dividing the % by the atomic numbers of carbon, hydrogen and oxygen and then by the smallest was 1.5:4:1. What is its empirical formula?

Molecular formula

The empirical formula can be converted to the molecular formula if the molar mass is known.

$$\frac{\text{molar mass}}{\text{mass of empirical formula}} = x \,(\text{an integer})$$

Then:

molecular formula = x times the empirical formula

Worked example

An alkene has the empirical formula CH_2 and molar mass $56.0\,g\,mol^{-1}$. What is its molecular formula?

Answer

$$\frac{\text{molar mass}}{\text{mass of empirical formula}} = \frac{56.0}{14.0} = 4$$

molecular formula $= 4 \times CH_2 = C_4H_8$

Finding the molar mass

- Molar mass can be found from the m/z value of the molecular ion (the largest) in the mass spectrum.
- If the unknown can be titrated, the number of moles of a given mass can be estimated. Then, molar mass = mass/moles.
- If the unknown is a gas, molar mass = volume/molar volume, where the molar volume is $24\,dm^3$ under normal laboratory conditions.

Tip

Normal laboratory conditions are 25°C and 100 kPa pressure.

Test yourself

2 $0.126\,g$ of a volatile liquid was vaporised at a temperature of 100°C and at a pressure of 106 kPa. It occupied a volume of $63.4\,cm^3$. Calculate its molar mass.

Specific identification of the unknown

This is carried out in two stages. First, the functional groups are identified and then the exact formula is derived.

Tests for functional groups

In organic analysis, care must be taken to follow the logic of the tests. For example, a positive test with Brady's reagent (2,4-dinitrophenylhydrazine) indicates that the unknown is a carbonyl compound but does not distinguish between an aldehyde and a ketone. If the unknown does not react with acidified potassium dichromate(VI) but gives a positive result with Brady's reagent then it must be a ketone. Aldehydes are oxidised by acidified potassium dichromate(VI), so a positive result in both these tests shows that the unknown is an aldehyde.

C=C group

The test for the C=C group is to add bromine water. Compounds that contain a C=C group quickly decolorise the brown bromine water and do not give a precipitate.

Alkenes rapidly turn neutral potassium manganate(VII) from a purple solution to a brown precipitate at room temperature. However, aldehydes also do this.

Tip

Phenols also decolorise bromine water, but they give a white precipitate of a polybrominated phenol.

Halogenoalkanes

Halogenoalkanes contain a halogen atom, which, on warming with aqueous sodium hydroxide, is removed by hydrolysis. *Excess* dilute nitric acid is added to this solution to neutralise the sodium hydroxide. On addition of a solution of silver nitrate a precipitate is obtained. The equations for the reactions of a chloroalkane are:

$$RCl + OH^- \rightarrow ROH + Cl^-$$

$$Cl^-(aq) + Ag^+(aq) \rightarrow AgCl(s)$$

- A white precipitate soluble in dilute ammonia solution proves the presence of chlorine in the organic compound:

$$AgCl(s) + 2NH_3(aq) \rightarrow [Ag(NH_3)_2]^+(aq) + Cl^-(aq)$$

- A cream precipitate, insoluble in dilute ammonia but soluble in concentrated ammonia, shows the presence of bromine in the organic compound:

$$AgBr(s) + 2NH_3(aq) \rightarrow [Ag(NH_3)_2]^+(aq) + Br^-(aq)$$

- A pale yellow precipitate, insoluble in both dilute and concentrated ammonia, proves the presence of iodine in the original organic compound:

$$AgI(s) + 2NH_3(aq) \rightarrow \text{no reaction}$$

The distinction between primary, secondary and tertiary halogenoalkanes cannot be made by a simple chemical test. Analysis by mass spectrometry or spin coupling in NMR spectroscopy can be conclusive (pp. 301 and 306).

Alcohols

- Apart from phenols, compounds with an −OH group give steamy fumes of hydrogen chloride on the addition of solid phosphorus pentachloride:

$$ROH + PCl_5 \rightarrow HCl + RCl + POCl_3$$

$$RCOOH + PCl_5 \rightarrow HCl + RCOCl + POCl_3$$

Therefore, all alcohols and all carboxylic acids give a positive result. However, alcohols (unlike carboxylic acids) do not give bubbles of carbon dioxide on the addition of either sodium hydrogencarbonate or sodium carbonate.

- On warming with ethanoic acid in the presence of a few drops of concentrated sulfuric acid, all alcohols form esters:

$$ROH + CH_3COOH \rightleftharpoons CH_3COOR + H_2O$$

If the product is poured into a beaker of dilute sodium hydrogencarbonate solution, the characteristic odour of an ester (like nail varnish, glue or fruit) will be detected.

- Primary and secondary alcohols turn orange acidified potassium dichromate(VI) solution to a green solution of $Cr^{3+}(aq)$ ions. Tertiary alcohols are not oxidised by acidified dichromate(VI) ions, so the solution remains orange.
  - This test can be modified to distinguish between primary and secondary alcohols, by distilling off the oxidised organic product as it is formed. If this is mixed with Tollens' reagent, only the oxidised product of the primary alcohol (an aldehyde) reduces the silver ion complex to give a silver mirror.
  - The oxidised product of the secondary alcohol (a ketone) has no reaction with Tollens' reagent, but (like all carbonyl compounds) gives a yellow-orange precipitate with Brady's reagent (2,4-dinitrophenylhydrazine).

- Alcohols, as well as carboxylic acids, have a broad band in the IR spectrum at approximately $3000\,cm^{-1}$. Carboxylic acids, but not alcohols, also have a peak at approximately $1700\,cm^{-1}$ (p. 300).

Tip

Do not state that the appearance of steamy fumes of HCl with PCl_5 is a test for alcohols, because carboxylic acids (and water) also give the same result.

Tip

When a colour change indicates a positive result to a test, always give the colour of the solution *before* the test as well as after.

Aldehydes and ketones

Both aldehydes and ketones give a yellow or orange precipitate when a few drops of 2,4-dinitrophenylhydrazine (Brady's reagent) are added. The equation for the reaction with ethanal is shown in Figure 13.1.

Figure 13.1

The infrared spectra of aldehydes and ketones have peaks at about $1700\,cm^{-1}$, as do the IR spectra of all other compounds with a C=O group. This includes carboxylic acids, esters, amides and acid chlorides.

There are several simple chemical tests to differentiate between aldehydes and ketones:

- The carbonyl compound is warmed with Fehling's or Benedict's solution. Aldehydes give a red precipitate of copper(I) oxide. Ketones do not react. Therefore, the copper(II) complex in the test solution is not reduced and the solution remains blue.
- On warming with potassium dichromate(VI), dissolved in dilute sulfuric acid, aldehydes turn the orange solution green. Ketones do not react, so the solution stays orange.

Aldehydes can be distinguished from ketones by examination of ^1H NMR spectra. The NMR spectrum of an aldehyde has a peak at $\delta = 9.0-10.0$, caused by the hydrogen atom in the aldehyde group, CHO. This is absent in ketones.

The iodoform reaction

The formula of iodoform is CHI_3. It is a pale yellow solid that is insoluble in water and has an antiseptic smell. Iodoform is produced when an organic compound containing the $CH_3C=O$ or $CH_3CH(OH)$ group is gently warmed with iodine mixed with sodium hydroxide solution.

Distinguishing between an aldehyde and a ketone: left, Fehling's solution; centre, Fehling's solution that has been reduced by an aldehyde; right, ketones do not react with Fehling's solution

Silver mirror test for the presence of an aldehyde; ketones do not react and the solution remains colourless

In these tests an aldehyde is oxidised to the salt of a carboxylic acid:

$$RCHO + [O] + OH^- \rightarrow RCOO^- + H_2O$$

The unstable Tollens' reagent is made by adding a few drops of sodium hydroxide to silver nitrate solution and dissolving the precipitate formed in dilute ammonia solution. If the carbonyl compound is gently warmed with Tollens' reagent, aldehydes give a silver mirror but ketones do not.

Tip

Primary and secondary alcohols also give a positive result with acidified dichromate(VI) ions. Therefore, their absence must first be shown by a lack of steamy fumes with phosphorus pentachloride.

- The only aldehyde that performs the iodoform reaction is ethanal.
- All methyl ketones give a yellow precipitate. The equation for the reaction of butanone is:

$$CH_3COC_2H_5 + 3I_2 + 4NaOH \rightarrow CHI_3 + C_2H_5COONa + 3NaI + 3H_2O$$

The products are a precipitate of iodoform and a solution of sodium propanoate and sodium iodide.

- Alcohols undergo this reaction if they can be oxidised to give rise to a $CH_3C=O$ group. Ethanol is the only primary alcohol that gives a precipitate of iodoform. The alkaline solution of iodine oxidises it to ethanal, which then reacts to give the precipitate:

$$CH_3CH_2OH + [O] \rightarrow CH_3CHO + H_2O$$

$$CH_3CHO + 3I_2 + 4NaOH \rightarrow CHI_3 + HCOONa + 3NaI + 3H_2O$$

The sequence is:

*ethan*ol $\rightarrow$ ethanal $\rightarrow$ iodoform + sodium *methan*oate

Methyl secondary alcohols are oxidised to methyl ketones and, therefore, give a positive iodoform test. For example, propan-2-ol gives a yellow precipitate with an alkaline solution of iodine:

$$CH_3CH(OH)CH_3 + [O] \rightarrow CH_3COCH_3 + H_2O$$

$$CH_3COCH_3 + 3I_2 + 4NaOH \rightarrow CHI_3 + CH_3COONa + 3NaI + 3H_2O$$

The sequence is:

propan-2-ol $\rightarrow$ propanone $\rightarrow$ iodoform + sodium *ethan*oate

Propan-1-ol does not undergo the iodoform reaction.

$$CH_3CH_2CH_2OH + [O] \rightarrow CH_3CH_2CHO + H_2O$$

$$CH_3CH_2CHO + I_2 + NaOH \rightarrow \text{no precipitate of iodoform}$$

Carboxylic acids
- Carboxylic acids as well as alcohols give steamy fumes of hydrogen chloride when phosphorus pentachloride is added:

$$RCOOH + PCl_5 \rightarrow RCOCl + HCl + POCl_3$$

- An acid can be distinguished from an alcohol by the addition of a solution of either sodium hydrogencarbonate or sodium carbonate. With a carboxylic acid, bubbles of gas are seen:

$$RCOOH + NaHCO_3 \rightarrow RCOONa + H_2O + CO_2$$

$$2RCOOH + Na_2CO_3 \rightarrow 2RCOONa + H_2O + CO_2$$

The gas turns limewater cloudy.

$$CO_2 + Ca(OH)_2 \rightarrow CaCO_3 + H_2O$$

- If a carboxylic acid is warmed with ethanol in the presence of a few drops of concentrated sulfuric acid, an ester is produced. If the reaction mixture is poured into a dilute solution of sodium hydrogencarbonate, the characteristic smell of the ester can be detected.
- The infrared spectra of carboxylic acids have a broad band at approximately $3000 \, cm^{-1}$ and a sharp band at approximately $1700 \, cm^{-1}$.

Aromatic compounds

- Aromatic compounds burn with a smoky flame.
- Phenol and phenylamine rapidly turn bromine water from brown to colourless, with the formation of a white precipitate (Figure 13.2).

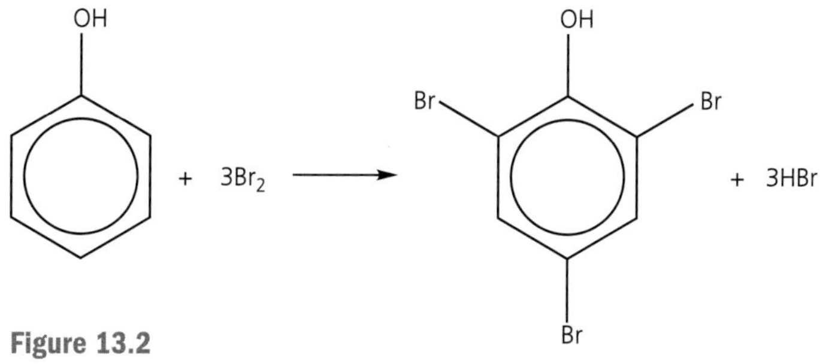

Figure 13.2

Test yourself

3 A compound X has a molecular formula of C_5H_8O. It decolorised bromine water, gave an orange precipitate with 2,4-dinitrophenylhydrazine and a pale yellow precipitate with iodine in alkali. State the functional groups in X and draw a skeletal formula that fits the data.

Modern analytic techniques

Infrared spectra

Absorption of infrared radiation causes a bond to stretch or bend, thus gaining vibrational energy. A particular bend or stretch is only infrared active if it is accompanied by a change in dipole moment. Thus, oxygen and nitrogen, along with all other diatomic elements, do not absorb infrared radiation. This means that they are not greenhouse gases.

Linear carbon dioxide and tetrahedral methane are non-polar, even though they have polar bonds. This is because the individual bond dipoles cancel out due to the molecules being symmetrical. Any asymmetrical bending or stretching will cause the dipole moment to change from zero and so the molecule will then be infrared active. All vibrations in polar molecules such as water and nitric oxide result in changes in their dipole moments and so they absorb infrared radiation. This means that carbon dioxide, methane, water and nitric oxide are greenhouse gases.

Different bonds in a covalent molecule absorb radiation of different frequencies, which are normally measured as wavenumbers. An infrared spectrum usually has a range from $4000\,cm^{-1}$ to $600\,cm^{-1}$.

The frequency of the infrared radiation absorbed depends on the energy required to cause the bond to bend or stretch. Thus particular bonds have specific frequencies at which they absorb. The remainder of the molecule also has some effect, so the absorption due to the stretching of a particular bond occurs over a range of frequencies. For example, the stretching of the C–H bond in alkanes absorbs over the range 2853–$2962\,cm^{-1}$, depending on the exact molecular environment of the C–H bond.

The C=O bond absorbs at around $1700\,cm^{-1}$, but the actual value depends on the other atoms attached to the C=O group. This is shown in Table 13.1.

Other types of bond absorb at different frequencies, but the actual value again depends on the neighbouring atoms and groups. For example the ketonic C=O group in $CH_3CH_2COCH=CH_2$ absorbs below $1700\,cm^{-1}$.

Table 13.1 Absorption frequencies of different C=O groups

Type of compound	Wavenumber/cm^{-1}
Aliphatic aldehyde	1720–1740
Aliphatic ketone	1700–1730
Aromatic aldehyde	1690–1715
Aromatic ketone	1680–1700
Carboxylic acid	1700–1725
Ester	1735–1750
Acyl chloride	1815–1825
Amide	1640–1680

Table 13.2 Absorption frequencies of some common groups

Bond	Functional group	Wavenumber/cm^{-1}
O–H	Alcohols (hydrogen bonded)*	3200–3600
	Alcohols (not hydrogen bonded)	3600–3700
	Carboxylic acids	2500–3300
N–H	Amines (hydrogen bonded)*	3300–3500
C–H	Alkanes	2850–3000
	Alkenes and arenes	3000–3100
C–C	Alkanes	1360–1490
C=O	See Table 13.1	
C=C	Aromatic	1450–1650
	Alkenes	1650–1700

*These peaks are very broad due to intermolecular hydrogen bonding.

The region below about $1500\,cm^{-1}$ is known as the **fingerprint region**. It shows a complex series of peaks that depends on the exact compound being analysed. Just as human fingerprints can be matched by computer to give a unique identification, so computer analysis of the fingerprint region can be used to identify a pure unknown organic substance.

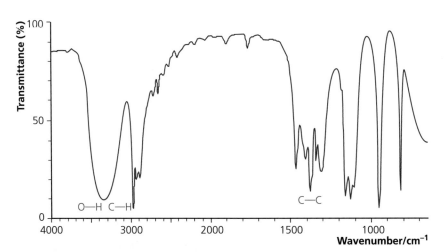

Figure 13.3 Infrared spectrum of propan-2-ol

In the infrared spectrum of propan-2-ol shown in Figure 13.3:

- the broad peak at around $3330\,cm^{-1}$ is due to hydrogen-bonded O–H
- the peak at $2970\,cm^{-1}$ is due to the C–H bond
- the peak at $1380\,cm^{-1}$ is due to the C–C bond

Identification of an organic compound

The infrared spectrum of a pure compound is compared with spectra in a database. The fingerprint region is specific and so can be used to identify an unknown. For example, all aliphatic alcohols absorb around $3600\,cm^{-1}$ (O−H stretch), $2900\,cm^{-1}$ (C−H stretch) and $1400\,cm^{-1}$ (C−H bend), but the absorption patterns of their fingerprint regions differ. Therefore, in the infrared breathalyser, the absorption detected must be in the fingerprint region of ethanol and not at higher frequencies.

Test of purity

The infrared spectrum of a pure compound should match that in the database. Any stray peaks will be due to impurities. For example, a peak at around $1700\,cm^{-1}$ in the spectrum of an alcohol would probably be due to a carbonyl or acid impurity.

Mass spectroscopy

When a molecule, M, is bombarded by high-energy electrons, it becomes ionised:

$$M(g) + e^- \rightarrow M^+(g) + 2e^-$$

The molecular ions produced have high energy and some may then break up into a smaller positive ion, X^+, and a radical, $Y\bullet$:

$$M^+(g) \rightarrow X^+(g) + Y\bullet$$

In a **mass spectrometer**, these positive ions are then accelerated by an electric field and deflected by a magnetic field. The lighter ions are deflected more than the heavier ions and so a spectrum of ions of different masses is produced.

The peak with the largest mass/charge ratio, m/z, is caused by the **molecular ion**. The peaks at lower m/z values arise from fragments of that ion. A small peak at $M +$ 1, where M is the molecular ion value, may be observed. This is due to the presence of ^{13}C atoms in the molecule. Natural carbon contains 1.1% ^{13}C.

Fragmentation of the molecular ion

The fragments give clues to the groups that are present in the molecule. A CH_3 group has a mass of 15 units and so an ion of $m/z = (M − 15)$ indicates that the substance has a CH_3 group:

$$(RCH_3)^+ \rightarrow R^+ + CH_3\bullet$$

Table 13.3 Common fragments lost

m/z	Group
15	CH$_3$
29	C$_2$H$_5$ or CHO
31	CH$_2$OH
45	COOH or CH$_2$CH$_2$OH
77	C$_6$H$_5$

The masses of some common fragments that are often lost are given in Table 13.3.

....

Structure II exists as two optical isomers.

Worked example 1

Compound X does not react with bromine water or with sodium hydrogencarbonate. When excess PCl$_5$ is added it produces, 1 mol of hydrogen chloride gas per mole of X. It has a molecular formula of C$_3$H$_6$O$_2$.

a) Write down the structural formulae of four possible isomers of X. Justify your answer.

b) Its mass spectrum also has peaks at m/z values of 29 and 59. Deduce the identity of X.

Answer

a) It does not react with bromine water, so it does not have a C=C group.

It does not react with sodium hydrogencarbonate, so it does not contain a COOH group.

It only contains one OH group as 1 mol HCl is produced, so the other oxygen must be in a C=O group.

Possible structures are:

      CH$_3$COCH$_2$OH   CH$_3$CHOHCHO   CH$_2$OHCH$_2$CHO
            I   II   III

b) Its molar mass is 74 g mol^{-1}.

An m/z value of 29 implies a C$_2$H$_5$ or a CHO group, so it cannot be I.

An m/z value of 59 (74 − 15) implies a CH$_3$ group, so it cannot be III.

X is CH$_3$CHOHCHO.

Worked example 2

Study the mass spectrum of propanoic acid, CH$_3$CH$_2$COOH (Figure 13.4). Identify the species responsible for the peaks at m/z values of 74, 73, 45 and 29 and state how they are formed.

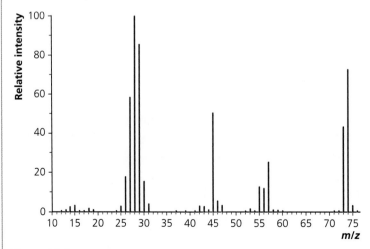

Figure 13.4

The molar mass of propanoic acid is $74\,g\,mol^{-1}$ and so the peak at 74 was caused by the molecular ion, $(CH_3CH_2COOH)^+$, produced by the removal of an electron from the gaseous molecule:

$$CH_3CH_2COOH(g) + e^- \rightarrow (CH_3CH_2COOH)^+(g) + 2e^-$$

The peak at 73 is caused by the molecular ion losing one of its hydrogen atoms.

$$(CH_3CH_2COOH)^+ \rightarrow (CH_3CH_2COO)^+ + H\bullet$$

The peak at 45 is 29 less than the molecular peak. It results from the loss of a C_2H_5 group and so is caused by the $(COOH)^+$ ion:

$$(CH_3CH_2COOH)^+ \rightarrow (COOH)^+ + C_2H_5\bullet$$

The peak at 29 is due to the $(C_2H_5)^+$ ion:

$$(CH_3CH_2COOH)^+ \rightarrow (C_2H_5)^+ + COOH\bullet$$

Tip

Do not forget to put the positive charge on the formulae of the ions that produce the peaks in a mass spectrum.

Test yourself

6 A compound Z with a molecular formula $C_4H_{10}O$ had peaks in its mass spectrum at m/z values of 74, 43 and 15 but none at 29. Identify the species causing these peaks and suggest a formula for Z.

Determination of identity using accurate mass spectrometry

Modern mass spectrometers can determine the relative molecular mass of a compound to an accuracy of four decimal places. Molecules with the same molar mass, measured by conventional means to the nearest whole number, can be distinguished using mass spectra data to four decimal places.

Relative atomic masses are known to considerable accuracy and so the small variations in relative molecular masses can be used to identify a compound's molecular formula. In practice, the four decimal place data are fed into a computer and the only molecular formula of the compound that fits the data is automatically worked out and displayed.

Worked example

An organic compound X had a molar mass of $84\,g\,mol^{-1}$, and could be either C_6H_{12} or C_5H_8O.

a) Its molecular ion had a m/z value of 84.0573. Use the data below to show that it is C_5H_8O and not C_6H_{12}. Relative atomic masses: $^{12}C = 12.0000$; $^1H = 1.0078$; $^{16}O = 15.9949$.

b) Its infrared spectrum is shown in Figure 13.5. Identify the group that caused the peak at $1704\,cm^{-1}$.

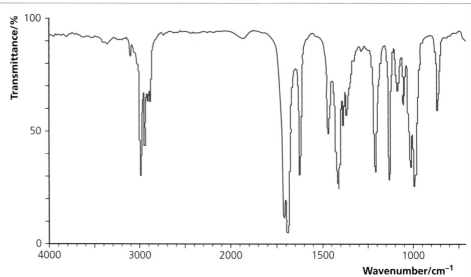

Figure 13.5

c) Compound X decolorises bromine water. It does not react with Tollens' reagent, but does give a pale yellow precipitate when mixed with iodine in sodium hydroxide solution. It exhibits geometric (*cis/trans*) isomerism.

   Draw the skeletal formulae of the *E*- and *Z*- isomers of compound X.

Answer

a) The m/z value for $C_5H_8O = (5 \times 12.0000) + (8 \times 1.0078) + 15.9949 = 84.0573$. The m/z value for C_6H_{12} is 84.0936, so compound X has the molecular formula C_5H_8O and not C_6H_{12}.

b) The group that caused the peak at about $1700\,cm^{-1}$ is the C=O group (in aliphatic aldehydes or ketones).

c) The decolorisation of bromine water shows that it must contain a C=C group.

   As it does not react with Tollens' reagent it is not an aldehyde. The precipitate is that of iodoform, CHI_3, so X must be a methyl ketone. Possible structural formulae are:

   $CH_3COCH{=}CHCH_3$ $CH_3COCH_2CH{=}CH_2$ $CH_3COC(CH_3){=}CH_2$

   Only the first exhibits geometric isomerism, so the skeletal formulae of the geometric isomers of X are shown in Figure 13.6.

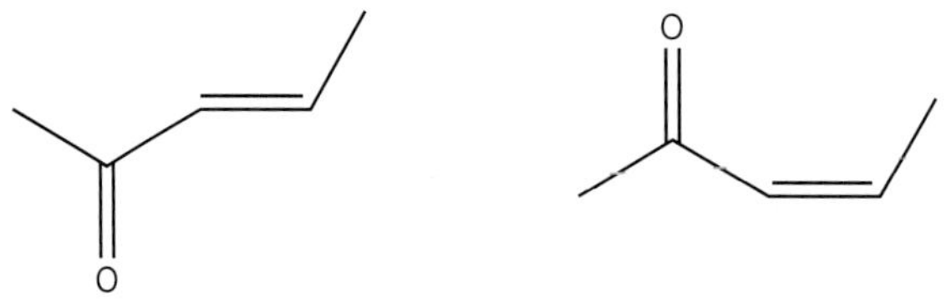

   E-isomer   *Z*-isomer

Figure 13.6

Nuclear magnetic resonance

Most materials are transparent to radio waves, which is why it is possible to have indoor television and radio aerials.

All nuclei in atoms are spinning and in some cases there is a resultant magnetic field. If the nucleus is exposed to a strong external magnetic field, the spinning nucleus aligns itself so that its own magnetic field is parallel with, or antiparallel to, the external field. There is a slight energy difference between these two states. Its magnitude depends on the molecular environment of the nucleus and the strength of the external magnetic field.

If a nucleus has an odd number of protons or an odd number of neutrons *and* an odd mass number, its spin will produce a slight magnetic field. Two nuclei that fit these conditions are that of ^{1}H (1 proton and 0 neutrons) and ^{13}C (6 protons and 7 neutrons). Deuterium, ^{2}H, which is often written as D, has an even number of protons + neutrons, and ^{12}C has an even number of protons and of neutrons and so their nuclei will not produce a magnetic field.

^{13}C is a stable isotope; normal carbon contains 1.1% of ^{13}C.

The nuclei of hydrogen atoms, ^{1}H, and those of ^{13}C produce a measurable magnetic field and the effect on it of an applied external magnetic field can be studied.

If an external magnetic field is applied, the magnetic moment caused by the spinning nucleus will either be aligned with the applied field or be opposed to it. The former state is of lower energy. This is shown in Figure 13.7.

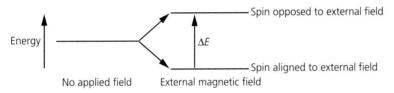

Figure 13.7 Nuclear-spin energy levels split by an external magnetic field

Electromagnetic radiation is absorbed as the spin of the nucleus flips from the lower-energy aligned orientation to the higher-energy opposed orientation. The frequency of the radiation, v, that causes this is given by $v = \Delta E/h$, where h is the Planck constant.

If a magnetic field of over 20 kilogauss is applied, the splitting is such that radio waves of a frequency up to 400 MHz are absorbed. The actual frequency depends on the environment of the nucleus and the strength of the applied magnetic field. Nuclei with spins that are aligned with the applied field will absorb the energy of the radiation and flip over to the spin–opposed state.

After a short time, normally of the order of a second, the nucleus spontaneously changes its spin and reverts to the lower-energy spin-aligned state, giving off a particular radio frequency as it drops. The average time for this process is called the **relaxation time**.

Obtaining an NMR spectrum

The sample of the material, dissolved in a suitable solvent, is placed between the poles of a powerful electromagnet. Between the poles of the magnet there is also a radio-frequency coil that is then activated with oscillating radio waves. The absorption of these waves by the sample followed by the re-emission of the radio waves is detected and the results fed to a computer that shows the results as a trace.

The experiment can be carried out by:

- steadily altering the strength of the magnetic field and keeping the frequency of the radio waves constant
- keeping the magnetic field constant and sending pulses of radio waves of gradually increasing frequency through the sample

The extent of the splitting depends on the strength of the magnetic field. Therefore, the ΔE value of the nuclei being investigated must be compared with that of a standard. The standard always used is the hydrogen nuclei in TMS, tetramethylsilane, $(CH_3)_4Si$.

The sample is dissolved in a solvent that does not contain any protons. Deuterated trichloromethane, $CDCl_3$, or D_2O are the usual choices. A small amount of TMS is added to provide the zero line for comparison and the sample is placed in the spectrometer.

Under these conditions, nuclei in different chemical environments have different ΔE values. The extent to which they differ from the ΔE of the TMS protons is called the **chemical shift**, δ, which is the same for all machines and all external magnetic fields.

Proton NMR (^{1}H NMR)

Low-resolution ^{1}H NMR

Low-resolution NMR investigates the value of the chemical shift and the area under the absorption peak (the peak height). The chemical shift indicates the environment of the hydrogen atom in the molecule and the peak height indicates the number of hydrogen atoms in that environment.

Chemical shift

The chemical shift, relative to the protons in TMS, depends mainly on the chemical environment of the hydrogen atom in the molecule.

The hydrogen nuclei are shielded from the external magnetic field by the electrons in orbit around it. The chemical shift is caused by the extent to which the electrons in orbit around the hydrogen nucleus are pulled away from the hydrogen — a process called deshielding. Carbon is more electronegative than hydrogen so it pulls the bonding electrons towards it. In the CH_3 group, the carbon is pulling electrons away from three hydrogen atoms, so the chemical shift in a CH_3 group is less than that in a CH_2 group. Oxygen is even more electronegative, so the hydrogen nucleus in the COOH and CHO groups is much more deshielded, causing the chemical shift to be much greater.

Some typical δ values are given in Table 13.4.

Table 13.4 Chemical shifts of common groups containing hydrogen

Group	δ/ppm	Group	δ/ppm
C–**CH$_3$**	0.8–1.2	**CH$_2$**OH	3.3–4.0
C–**CH$_2$**–C	1.1–1.5	C——C(**H**)——OH (with C below)	3.2–4.1
C——C(**H**)——C (with C below)	1.5	——C(**H**)——C(=O) in aldehydes, ketones, acids, esters and amides	2.0–3.0
C–**H** on benzene ring	6.8–8.2	C**HO**	9.0–10.0
C=C–**H** in alkenes	4.5–6.5	COO**H**	10.0–12.0
C≡C–**H**	1.8–2.0	C–O**H**	1.0–6.0*

* The value of the shift for hydroxyl hydrogen atoms depends on the solvent and the extent of hydrogen bonding and, therefore, it might be difficult to identify such compounds using NMR spectra alone.

Peak height

The peak height (more properly called integral area) is often indicated by a number above the peak. It can also be estimated by looking at the spectrum. Some high-resolution spectra have an integration trace superimposed on the NMR spectrum. The ^{1}H NMR spectrum of ethoxyethane, $CH_3CH_2-O-CH_2CH_3$, with the integration trace added is shown in Figure 13.8.

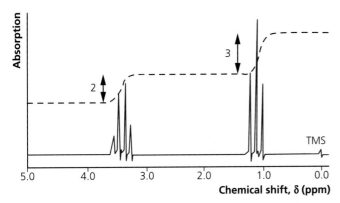

Figure 13.8 NMR spectrum of ethoxyethane with integrated trace

There are two different chemical environments for the hydrogen atoms — the CH_2 hydrogens and the CH_3 hydrogens. There are four CH_2 hydrogen atoms and six CH_3 hydrogen atoms, so the peaks heights are in the ratio 4:6 or 2:3.

The peak at $\delta = 1.0$ is caused by the hydrogen atoms in the CH_3 group; the peak at $\delta = 3.4$ is caused by the CH_2 hydrogen atoms. The high value for the CH_2 hydrogen nuclei is the result of deshielding caused by the neighbouring electronegative oxygen atom.

The NMR spectrum of propanal is shown in Figure 13.9.

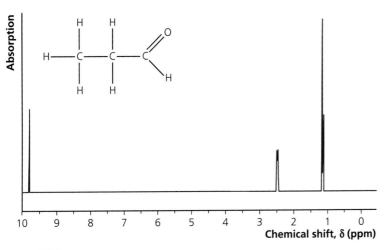

Figure 13.9

There are three peaks:

- The peak at $\delta = 9.8$ is caused by the hydrogen atom on the CHO group.
- The peak at $\delta = 2.4$ is caused by the two hydrogen atoms in the CH_2 group that is next to the CHO group.
- The peak at $\delta = 1.1$ is caused by the hydrogen atoms in the CH_3 group.

The areas under the peaks have not been calculated.

Tip

Do not state that the chemical shift is caused by a group. It is caused by the protons in the nuclei of the hydrogen atoms in that group.

Worked example

Examine the NMR spectrum of propan-2-ol, $CH_3CH(OH)CH_3$, in Figure 13.10 and identify the peaks.

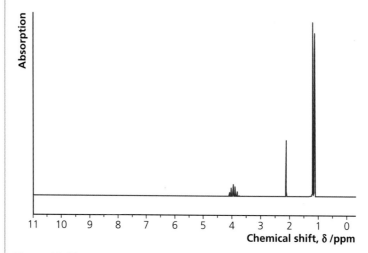

Figure 13.10

Note the splitting of the peaks in the spectrum of propan-2-ol.

Answer

The tall peak at $\delta = 1.1$ is due to the six hydrogen atoms in the CH_3 groups.

The peak at $\delta = 4.0$ is due to the CH hydrogen on the CH(OH) group.

The unsplit peak (see below) at $\delta = 2.2$ is caused by the hydrogen atom in the OH group.

Test yourself

7 How many peaks are there in the low-resolution NMR spectrum of butanone, $CH_3CH_2COCH_3$? What is the ratio of their heights?

High-resolution ^{1}H NMR spectra

If the spectrum is investigated with a high-resolution spectrometer, the peaks are seen to be split. Splitting occurs because the magnetic environment of a proton in one group is affected by the magnetic field of protons on a neighbouring carbon atom. If the field caused by a hydrogen atom is aligned with the applied field it is reinforced and increases the field on the neighbouring hydrogen atom.

Consider the effect of a proton in a CH group on the hydrogen atoms in the neighbouring CH_2 group:

- The CH hydrogen atom can have its spin aligned ↑ or opposed ↓.
- This results in two different fields affecting the CH_2 hydrogen atoms, so their peaks are split into two.
- The CH_2 hydrogen atoms affect the field on the CH hydrogen atom. Here, the situation is more complex because there are two neighbouring hydrogen atoms and there are four ways in which their spins can be aligned — ↑↑, ↑↓, ↓↑ or ↓↓. The effect of ↑↓ is the same as that of ↓↑ so they produce one peak, twice as high as the others. This results in the CH peak splitting into three, in a 1:2:1 ratio.

This process is called spin coupling or **spin–spin splitting**.

If the proton of a hydrogen atom has *n* hydrogen atoms on neighbouring carbon atoms, its peak will be split into (*n* + 1) sub-peaks.

The relative heights and the numbers that a peak is split into can be told by Pascal's triangle (Figure 13.11).

Tip

This is called the (*n* + 1) rule and is crucial to the interpretation of ^{1}H NMR spectra.

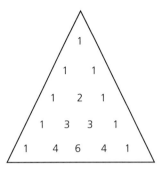

No H atom on neighbouring C atom

1 H atom on neighbouring C atom

2 H atoms on neighbouring C atom

3 H atoms on neighbouring C atoms

4 H atoms on neighbouring C atoms

Figure 13.11

The hydrogen atoms on a CH_2 group next to a CH_3 group will be split into four peaks of relative heights 1:3:3:1. The only exception to this rule is that the hydrogen atom on an OH or on an NH_2 group does not normally cause splitting, particularly if it is hydrogen-bonded. This is shown by the high-resolution NMR spectrum of propan-1-ol, $CH_3CH_2CH_2OH$ (Figure 13.12).

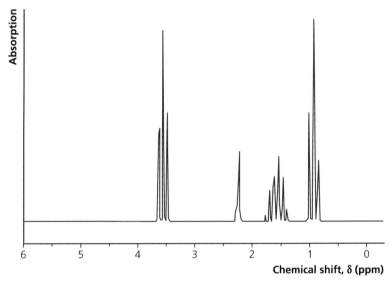

Chemical shift, δ (ppm)

Figure 13.12

- The peak at 0.9 is due to the hydrogen atoms in the CH_3 group. It is split into three by the neighbouring two CH_2 hydrogen atoms.
- The peak at 1.5 is due to the hydrogen atoms in the middle CH_2 group. It is split into six by the five neighbouring hydrogen atoms.
- The peak at 3.5 is split into three. The peak is caused by the two hydrogen atoms in the CH_2OH group. It is split into three by the two neighbouring hydrogen atoms.
- The peak at 2.4 is caused by the OH hydrogen. It neither causes splitting nor is split.

Examination of the splitting indicates the number of hydrogen atoms on the neighbouring carbon atoms. If a peak is split into 2, the neighbouring carbon atom has one H atom attached. If the peak is split into 5, there are four neighbouring hydrogen atoms. This means that there is either a CH_3 group plus a CH group, or two CH_2 groups, as neighbours.

Tip

Look back at Figure 13.8 and try to explain the splitting in the NMR spectrum of ethoxyethane.

Worked example

Look at the ^{1}H NMR spectrum in Figure 13.13 and Table 13.4 on p. 306 and decide whether it is that of butanone, $CH_3CH_2COCH_3$, or methylpropanal, $(CH_3)_2CHCHO$. Identify which hydrogen nuclei cause each peak by consideration of the number of peaks, and their splitting patterns.

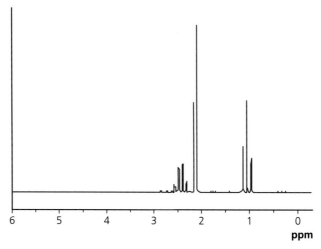

Figure 13.13

Answer

Both will have three peaks (the two CH_3 groups in methylpropanal are in identical chemical environments).

It must be butanone because:

- there is a singlet caused by the CH_3 group next to the C=O (δ = 2.1)
- the hydrogen atoms in the CH_2 group will be split into four by the neighbouring CH_3 (δ = 2.5)
- the hydrogen atoms in the CH_3 next to the CH_2 will be split into three. (δ = 1.0)
- methylpropanal will have a singlet peak (CHO) — one split into seven and one doublet

The CHO peak in the aldehyde will be a singlet with δ of 9–10 ppm.

Test yourself

8 A particular peak in a high-resolution proton NMR spectrum is split into six peaks. Give the formulae of the neighbouring groups. Is this consistent with the compound being butan-1-ol?

Carbon 13 NMR (^{13}C NMR)

The ^{13}C spectra are much simpler as there will be no splitting. The chance of two ^{13}C atoms being next to each other in the carbon chain is about one in a thousand.

Unlike ^{1}H NMR, the peak heights are not proportional to the number of carbon atoms in that environment.

The number of peaks is equal to the number of carbon atoms in different environments. So butane, $CH_3CH_2CH_2CH_3$, will have two peaks in its ^{13}C NMR spectrum, one due to both CH_3 carbon atoms and the other due to the carbon atoms in both CH_2 groups.

Table 13.5 Typical chemical shifts in ^{13}C NMR spectroscopy

	Chemical shift/ppm
C of C–H or C–C in –CH$_3$, >CH$_2$ and ≥CH	5–50 (CH$_3$ < CH$_2$ < CH)
C of arenes	110–160
C of C–X in halogenoalkanes	30–75
C of C–N in amines	30–60
C of CON in amides	160–180
C of C–OH in alcohols	50–90
C of C next to C–OH in alcohols	25–70
C of C=C in alkenes	120–140
C of COO in carboxylic acids and esters	165–180
C=O in aldehydes and ketones	200–220
C of C next to C=O in aldehydes, ketones and acids	20–50

The ^{13}C NMR spectra of propanoic acid and propan-1-ol are shown in Figures 13.14 and 13.15.

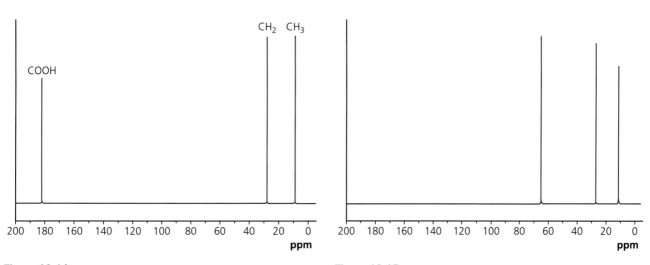

Figure 13.14

Figure 13.15

The peak at δ = 64 in the spectrum of propan-1-ol is caused by the C of CH$_2$OH, that at δ = 20 by the C of CH$_2$ and that at δ = 10 due to the C in the CH$_3$ group.

Worked example

Assign the peaks in the ^{13}C NMR spectrum of butanal (Figure 13.16) to its carbon atoms.

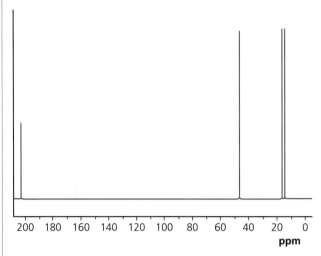

Figure 13.16

Answer

The peak at 205 ppm is caused by the carbon in CHO.

The peak at 46 ppm is caused by the carbon atom in the CH_2 next to the CHO.

The peak at 17 ppm is caused by the carbon atom in the CH_2 next to the CH_3.

The peak at 14 ppm is caused by the carbon atom in CH_3.

The chemical shift of carbon atoms that are *trans-* to each other (e.g. in *trans*-but-2-ene) is slightly larger than that in the *cis-* isomer. In ^1H NMR, it is the hydrogen atoms that are *cis-* to each other that have the larger chemical shift.

Test yourself

9 A compound had three peaks in its ^{12}C NMR spectrum. These were at δ values of 27, 72 and 85 ppm. Suggest a formula for this compound.

MRI

Magnetic resonance imaging is used as a diagnostic tool for medical problems in soft tissue and in collagen in bones. The technique is slightly different and requires extremely powerful electromagnets. This is achieved by cooling the metal core of the magnet to a temperature of 4K with liquid helium. The metal then becomes a superconductor and high electric currents can be made to flow through it without any heat being produced. This results in an extremely powerful magnetic field of 10 kilogauss. Pulses of radio waves at around 40 MHz are then radiated through the patient.

The hydrogen nuclei in soft tissue have a different chemical shift from those in harder tissue. Computers can generate pictures of slices through the part of the body being investigated and, therefore, problems can be detected. The patient suffers no ill effects because the procedure is non-invasive.

Chromatography

Chromatography of all types works on the same principle. The sample is dissolved in a solvent and washed through a stationary phase by a mobile phase called the eluent. The competition between the sample molecules adsorbed by the stationary phase and dissolved by the eluent results in separation. Substances that are more soluble in the eluent and less adsorbed by the stationary phase move faster through the apparatus.

The speed at which a specific substance passes through depends on the nature of the stationary phase and of the eluent. For a given stationary phase and eluent, this is measured by the R_f value of the substance:

$$R_f \text{ value} = \frac{\text{distance moved by substance}}{\text{distance moved by eluent}}$$

All students will be aware of paper chromatography, but the resolution obtained by this method is poor. There are three main advanced techniques that are used.

Thin-layer chromatography, TLC

This is described in detail in Chapter 11, p. 266, where the separation of amino acids is explained.

High-performance liquid chromatography, HPLC

This technique uses a column packed with a solid of uniform particle size — the stationary phase. The sample to be separated is dissolved in a suitable solvent and added to the top of the column. The liquid eluent — the mobile phase — is then forced through the column under high pressure.

This technique used to be called high-pressure liquid chromatography.

The principle is the same as for other chromatographic techniques. Different substances have different strengths of interaction between the stationary phase and the mobile phase. The time taken for a component in the sample mixture to pass through the column is called the **retention time** and is a unique characteristic of the substance, the composition of the eluent, the nature of the stationary phase and the pressure. This means that different components will pass through one after the other, with gaps between each.

The use of high pressure increases the speed at which the eluent passes through the column and so reduces the extent to which the band of a component spreads out due to diffusion. This means that HPLC has a much higher resolution than paper or thin-layer chromatography. The column can be connected to an infrared spectrometer, which can be used to identify each component in the mixture.

The early columns used a polar stationary phase and a non-polar eluent. However, this has been superseded by a non-polar stationary phase and a polar eluent. This technique is called reversed-phase high-performance liquid chromatography, RPHPLC. It is used in the pharmaceutical industry to separate a drug from a mixture and to check the purity of its products.

Gas chromatography, GC

Gas chromatography is sometimes called gas liquid chromatography (GLC). It involves a sample being injected into a chromatography column in a thermostatically controlled oven (Figure 13.17). The sample evaporates and is forced through the column by the flow of an inert, gaseous mobile phase, called the carrier gas. The column itself contains a liquid stationary phase that is adsorbed onto the surface of an inert solid.

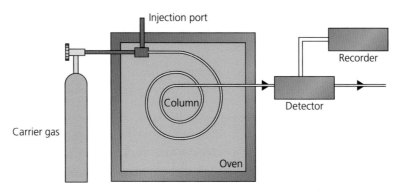

Figure 13.17 A representation of GLC

The carrier gas can be hydrogen, argon, oxygen, nitrogen or air. The rate at which a substance passes through the column depends on the extent to which it interacts with the liquid stationary phase.

A detector measures the thermal conductivity of the gas exiting the column. When one of the components of the original mixture is mixed with the carrier gas, the thermal conductivity changes. The time that a particular component of the mixture takes to pass through the column is called the retention time.

This method is suitable for separating mixtures of gases or volatile liquids. The identity of the components in the mixture can be found by removing samples leaving the column and measuring their mass, NMR or infrared spectra. These are then compared with spectra in a database. This technique is especially valuable in forensic work and in the detection of drugs or their metabolites in an athlete's blood or urine sample.

Summary tasks

Make sure that you understand how to calculate:

- empirical formulae from combustion data
- molecular formulae from empirical formula and *m/z* data
- molecular formulae from mass spectra data to four decimal places

Check that you know the tests for:

- the C=C, C−halogen and C−OH groups
- the C=O and COOH groups

Ensure that you understand:

- how IR, mass and NMR spectra are obtained
- that IR spectra give information about the groups present in a molecule
- that the number of peaks and their δ values in a ^{1}H NMR spectrum depend on the number of different chemical environments and that the areas depend on the number of H atoms in that environment

- that the splitting of the peaks = $n + 1$, where n is the number of neighbouring hydrogen atoms
- that the number of peaks and their δ values in a ^{13}C NMR spectrum depend on the number of different chemical environments, and that the peaks are not split
- the energy per photon decreases X-rays > infrared > radiowaves
- the energy changes in emission spectra (flame tests)
- the energy changes when a substance adsorbs UV or visible light and the changes that this may cause
- that absorption of infrared causes bonds to stretch or bend due to a change in dipole moment

Check that you:

- can interpret mass, IR, ^{13}C NMR and ^{1}H NMR spectra and use them to deduce the identity of an unknown
- can interpret splitting patterns in ^{1}H NMR spectra
- understand that the chemical shift depends on the extent of deshielding
- realise that the lines in a mass spectrum are caused by positive ions
- know that the distance moved by a substance in chromatography depends on its relative solubility between the stationary phase and the eluent
- can describe TLC, HPLC and GC and can deduce identities from chromatograms

Questions

1 Which substance would not react with $NH_2CH_2CH=CHCH_2OH$?

   A dilute hydrochloric acid

   B lithium aluminium hydride in dry ether

   C bromine water

   D ethanoic acid in the presence of concentrated sulfuric acid

2 Ethyl 3-aminobenzoate, $NH_2C_6H_4COOC_2H_5$, can be prepared from benzoic acid in three steps.

$$C_6H_5COOH \xrightarrow{\text{step 1}} C_6H_5COOC_2H_5 \xrightarrow{\text{step 2}} NO_2C_6H_4COOC_2H_5 \xrightarrow{\text{step 3}}$$
$$NH_2C_6H_4COOC_2H_5$$

The correct reagents and conditions for each step are:

	Step 1	Step 2	Step 3
A	Ethanol and concentrated sulfuric acid	Dilute nitric and sulfuric acids at 50°C	Tin and concentrated hydrochloric acid
B	Ethanol and concentrated sulfuric acid	Concentrated nitric and sulfuric acids at 50°C	Tin and concentrated hydrochloric acid
C	Ethanol and concentrated sulfuric acid	Dilute nitric and sulfuric acids at 50°C	Tin and dilute hydrochloric acid
D	Ethanoyl chloride	Concentrated nitric and sulfuric acids at 50°C	Tin and dilute hydrochloric acid

3 The correct sequence for recrystallisation is to dissolve in the minimum amount of hot solvent, then:

A cool, filter, wash the residue with the minimum amount of cold solvent

B cool, filter, wash the residue with the minimum amount of solvent

C filter, wash the residue with the minimum amount of cold solvent

D filter, cool the filtrate, filter, wash the residue with the minimum amount of cold solvent

4 Which drying agent could be used to dry a solution of phenylamine in ether?

A anhydrous calcium chloride

B anhydrous copper sulfate

C potassium hydroxide

D concentrated sulfuric acid

5 A student planned to prepare a small quantity of ethyl ethanoate by heating under reflux ethanol, ethanoic acid and some concentrated sulfuric acid as a catalyst. Some data for possible hazards of these substances are listed below.

- concentrated sulfuric acid: an oily corrosive liquid that boils with decomposition at 340°C and reacts exothermically with compounds containing an −OH group
- ethanol, ethanoic acid and ethyl ethanoate: flammable, volatile liquids

Which would not be necessary for reducing the risk when performing this experiment?

A use a water bath to heat the mixture

B add the concentrated sulfuric acid dropwise to the reaction mixture

C wear gloves

D carry out the reaction in a fume cupboard

6 Which reaction would not give a single stereoisomer?

A the addition of hydrogen cyanide, HCN, to ethanal, CH_3CHO

B the S_N2 substitution of OH^- into a single enantiomer of a halogenoalkane

C the addition of hydrogen, using a platinum catalyst, to cis-3,4-dimethylhex-3-ene, $C_2H_5C(CH_3)=C(CH_3)$ C_2H_5

D the addition of bromine to cyclohexene

7 The ester methyl benzoate can be hydrolysed to benzoic acid and methanol by heating under reflux with dilute hydrochloric acid. The solid benzoic acid is filtered off and solid sodium hydrogencarbonate is added to the solution. The purpose of the sodium hydrogencarbonate is to:

A remove any organic impurities

B remove any inorganic salts

C remove any acidic impurities

D dry the methanol

8 State the effect on a water molecule of it absorbing:

a) infrared radiation

b) microwaves

9 Explain why water vapour is a powerful greenhouse gas.

10 Examine the infrared spectra, A and B, in Figure 13.18. One spectrum is that of propanal; the other is that of propanoic acid.

Identify the peaks in A at $1715\,cm^{-1}$ and $1421\,cm^{-1}$ and the peaks in B at $2986\,cm^{-1}$, $1716\,cm^{-1}$ and $1416\,cm^{-1}$. Hence, decide which spectrum is that of propanoic acid.

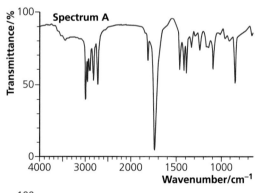

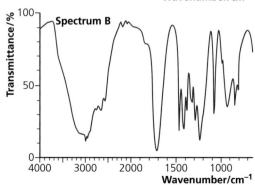

Figure 13.18

Exam practice questions

1 a) 4.50 g of a compound X, which contains carbon, hydrogen and oxygen only, was burnt in excess oxygen and 8.80 g of carbon dioxide and 4.50 g of water were produced.

    i) Calculate its empirical formula. (4)

    ii) Its mass spectrum has a molecular ion peak at $m/z = 90$. State its molecular formula. (1)

b) i) Other data about compound X are:
- 1 mol of X gave 2 mol of hydrogen chloride gas when excess PCl_5 was added.
- The ^{13}C NMR spectrum of X had two peaks.

    Suggest *two* structural formulae for X. Justify your answers. (3)

    ii) The mass spectrum of X had a peak at m/z of 45 but *not* one at m/z of 31. Deduce which of the two structures that you drew in (i) is X and write the equation for the process that gave rise to a peak at m/z of 45. (3)

    (Total 11 marks)

2 a) A compound Y could be either $C_4H_8O_2$ or $C_5H_{12}O$. It has a molecular ion peak at $m/z = 88.0522$. Use the data below to calculate its molecular formula. (2)
[$^1H = 1.0078$; $^{12}C = 12.0000$; $^{16}O = 15.9949$]

b) Compound Y does not react with either 2,4-dinitrophenylhydrazine or sodium carbonate. It decolorises bromine water and gives off steamy fumes of HCl when some PCl_5 is added. Its ^{13}C NMR spectrum is shown in Figure 13.20.

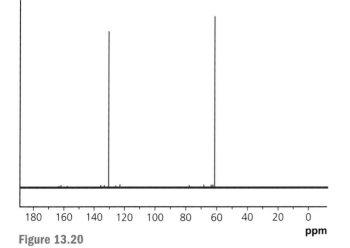

Figure 13.20

State what you can deduce from these tests. Identify the groups that cause the two peaks in the ^{13}C NMR spectrum and hence write the structural formula of compound Y. (7)

c) Another compound Z has a molecular formula of $C_4H_8O_2$ and is a carboxylic acid.

    i) Draw two structural formulae that could be compound Z. (2)

    ii) Its ^1H NMR spectrum has three peaks: a singlet at $\delta = 11.9$, a doublet at $\delta = 1.2$ and a peak split into 7 at $\delta = 2.6$. Use these data to identify compound Z, explaining your reasoning. (4)

    (Total 15 marks)

3 a) i) Compound X contained 58.8% carbon, 9.8% hydrogen and 31.4% oxygen. Show that these data are consistent with X having an empirical formula of $C_5H_{10}O_2$. (2)

    ii) The mass spectrum of X had a peak at $m/z = 102$. Write down its molecular formula. (1)

b) Compound X was heated under reflux with aqueous sodium hydroxide and then compound Y was distilled out. The remaining solution was acidified with dilute sulfuric acid and compound Z was distilled out. Compound Y gave a pale yellow precipitate when warmed with iodine in alkali. The ^{13}C NMR spectrum of compound Z had two peaks.

    i) Use the information above to deduce the structural formulae of Z and Y and hence that of X. Justify your answers. (5)

    ii) Why was it necessary to add acid before distilling out compound Z? (2)

    iii) Write the equation for the reaction of compound X with aqueous sodium hydroxide. (1)

c) W is an isomer of X and was treated in the same way and gave a product similar to Z that had only one peak in its ^{13}C NMR spectrum. W has two optical isomers. Draw the structural formula of W and circle the chiral centre. (2)

    (Total 13 marks)

Index

The periodic table

Group

Key:

Relative atomic mass
Atomic symbol
name
Atomic (proton) number

Period	1	2												3	4	5	6	7	0
1	1.0￼H￼hydrogen￼1																		4.0￼He￼helium￼2
2	6.9￼Li￼lithium￼3	9.0￼Be￼beryllium￼4												10.8￼B￼boron￼5	12.0￼C￼carbon￼6	14.0￼N￼nitrogen￼7	16.0￼O￼oxygen￼8	19.0￼F￼fluorine￼9	20.2￼Ne￼neon￼10
3	23.0￼Na￼sodium￼11	24.3￼Mg￼magnesium￼12												27.0￼Al￼aluminium￼13	28.1￼Si￼silicon￼14	31.0￼P￼phosphorus￼15	32.1￼S￼sulfur￼16	35.5￼Cl￼chlorine￼17	39.9￼Ar￼argon￼18
4	39.1￼K￼potassium￼19	40.1￼Ca￼calcium￼20	45.0￼Sc￼scandium￼21	47.9￼Ti￼titanium￼22	50.9￼V￼vanadium￼23	52.0￼Cr￼chromium￼24	54.9￼Mn￼manganese￼25	55.8￼Fe￼iron￼26	58.9￼Co￼cobalt￼27	58.7￼Ni￼nickel￼28	63.5￼Cu￼copper￼29	65.4￼Zn￼zinc￼30		69.7￼Ga￼gallium￼31	72.6￼Ge￼germanium￼32	74.9￼As￼arsenic￼33	79.0￼Se￼selenium￼34	79.9￼Br￼bromine￼35	83.8￼Kr￼krypton￼36
5	85.5￼Rb￼rubidium￼37	87.6￼Sr￼strontium￼38	88.9￼Y￼yttrium￼39	91.2￼Zr￼zirconium￼40	92.9￼Nb￼niobium￼41	95.9￼Mo￼molybdenum￼42	[98]￼Tc￼technetium￼43	101.1￼Ru￼ruthenium￼44	102.9￼Rh￼rhodium￼45	106.4￼Pd￼palladium￼46	107.9￼Ag￼silver￼47	112.4￼Cd￼cadmium￼48		114.8￼In￼indium￼49	118.7￼Sn￼tin￼50	121.8￼Sb￼antimony￼51	127.6￼Te￼tellurium￼52	126.9￼I￼iodine￼53	131.3￼Xe￼xenon￼54
6	132.9￼Cs￼caesium￼55	137.3￼Ba￼barium￼56	138.9￼La￼lanthanum￼57	178.5￼Hf￼hafnium￼72	180.9￼Ta￼tantalum￼73	183.8￼W￼tungsten￼74	186.2￼Re￼rhenium￼75	190.2￼Os￼osmium￼76	192.2￼Ir￼iridium￼77	195.1￼Pt￼platinum￼78	197.0￼Au￼gold￼79	200.6￼Hg￼mercury￼80		204.4￼Tl￼thallium￼81	207.2￼Pb￼lead￼82	209.0￼Bi￼bismuth￼83	[209]￼Po￼polonium￼84	[210]￼At￼astatine￼85	[222]￼Rn￼radon￼86
7	[223]￼Fr￼francium￼87	[226]￼Ra￼radium￼88	[227]￼Ac￼actinium￼89	[261]￼Rf￼rutherfordium￼104	[262]￼Db￼dubnium￼105	[266]￼Sg￼seaborgium￼106	[264]￼Bh￼bohrium￼107	[277]￼Hs￼hassium￼108	[268]￼Mt￼meitnerium￼109	[271]￼Ds￼darmstadtium￼110	[272]￼Rg￼roentgenium￼111								

Elements with atomic numbers 112–116 have been reported but not fully authenticated

140.1￼Ce￼cerium￼58	140.9￼Pr￼praseodymium￼59	144.2￼Nd￼neodymium￼60	144.9￼Pm￼promethium￼61	150.4￼Sm￼samarium￼62	152.0￼Eu￼europium￼63	157.2￼Gd￼gadolinium￼64	158.9￼Tb￼terbium￼65	162.5￼Dy￼dysprosium￼66	164.9￼Ho￼holmium￼67	167.3￼Er￼erbium￼68	168.9￼Tm￼thulium￼69	173.0￼Yb￼ytterbium￼70	175.0￼Lu￼lutetium￼71
232￼Th￼thorium￼90	[231]￼Pa￼protactinium￼91	238.1￼U￼uranium￼92	[237]￼Np￼neptunium￼93	[242]￼Pu￼plutonium￼94	[243]￼Am￼americium￼95	[247]￼Cm￼curium￼96	[245]￼Bk￼berkelium￼97	[251]￼Cf￼californium￼98	[254]￼Es￼einsteinium￼99	[253]￼Fm￼fermium￼100	[256]￼Md￼mendelevium￼101	[254]￼No￼nodelium￼102	[257]￼Lr￼lawrencium￼103